MOSQUITO

PHILIP J. BIRTLES

SUTTON PUBLISHING

First published in the United Kingdom in 1998 by
Sutton Publishing Limited · Phoenix Mill
Thrupp · Stroud · Gloucestershire · GL5 2BU

Paperback edition first published in 1999

Reprinted 2001

British Library Cataloguing in Publication Data
A catalogue record for this book is available from the British Library.

ISBN 0 7509 2327 X

Typeset in 10/13pt Sabon.
Typesetting and origination by
Sutton Publishing Limited.
Printed and bound in England by
J.H. Haynes & Co. Ltd, Sparkford.

CONTENTS

The Hatfield factory and aerodrome during the Second World War with the grass surface disguised to represent fields. (de Havilland photo)

FOREWORD

BY JOHN CUNNINGHAM

CBE, DSO, DFC, AE, HON FRAES

It gives me great pleasure to commend this history of the de Havilland Mosquito which was the most outstanding aircraft developed during the Second World War.

Its high speed and weight-carrying ability allowed it to be used in a wide variety of roles which are well covered in this very thorough description of its operations.

I had the good fortune to command a Mosquito Night Fighter Squadron and am eternally grateful for the skill and determination of the design team at Hatfield who produced such an outstanding, high performance and delightful to fly aircraft in the face of very considerable opposition from the Establishment Authorities.

ABBREVIATIONS

A&AEE	Aeroplane & Armament Experimental Establishment		IFF	Identification Friend or Foe
AI	airborne interception		LNSF	Light Night Striking Force
AID	Aeronautical Inspection Directorate		MRO	Mosquito Repair Organisation
			MU	Maintenance Unit
AFDU	Air Fighting Development Unit		OCU	Operational Conversion Unit
AFS	Advanced Flying School		OTU	Operational Training Unit
AOC	Air Officer Commanding		PR	photo-reconnaissance
APC	Armament Practice Camp		RAAF	Royal Australian Air Force
ATA	Air Transport Auxiliary		RCAF	Royal Canadian Air Force
BATDU	Blind Approach Training and Development Unit		RNZAF	Royal New Zealand Air Force
			RP	rocket projectile
BEA	British European Airways		RRE	Royal Radar Establishment
CAACU	Civil Anti-Aircraft Co-operation Unit		SAAF	South African Air Force
C of A	Certificate of Airworthiness		SASO	Senior Air Staff Officer
ECM	Electronic Counter Measures		SBAC	Society of British Aerospace Companies
FAA	Fleet Air Arm		TAF	Tactical Air Force
FIU	Fighter Interception Unit		THUM	Temperature and Humidity (Unit)
FRU	Fleet Requirements Unit		USAAF	United States Army Air Force
GCI	Ground Controlled Interception		WIDU	Wireless Intelligence Development Unit
GRU	Gust Research Unit			

INTRODUCTION

The Mosquito was probably the most versatile combat aircraft produced during the Second World War, and was unique because of its high speed and wooden construction. Out of the 7,781 produced in three continents about 30 survive in one form or another, but since the loss of the British Aerospace T.III RR299 none is currently airworthy, although a number are possible candidates for flight one day. This number of survivors is remarkable considering the relatively fragile construction of the fuselage, although some of the restorations or stored remains are little more than a collection of metal parts and some pieces of rotting wood.

The Mosquito design was probably influenced by four earlier de Havilland aircraft with widely contrasting features. The first was the DH.88 Comet Racer of 1934, three of which were produced as a sponsored design by de Havilland for Britain's entry in the Melbourne Centenary Air Race from Mildenhall to Melbourne. The winner of the race was Comet Racer G-ACSS 'Grosvenor House' which is preserved at the Shuttleworth Trust at Old Warden. This aircraft will have influenced the Mosquito with its all-wooden construction, one-piece wing and high performance, achieving over 200 mph at ranges of in excess of 2,000 miles. It was the first de Havilland aircraft to use the stressed wooden monocoque fuselage shell and the first British aircraft to be fitted with a retractable undercarriage, flaps and variable pitch propellers. It was also the first de Havilland aircraft to have the airframe, engines and propellers all designed and produced by one company.

The next influential design was the DH.91 Albatross airliner, which was an all-wood long-range airliner which first flew in May 1937. Using the experience of the Comet Racer, the entire fuselage was made as a moulded wooden monocoque structural shell and once again the wing was made in one piece using a central box spar structure with a double-layer stressed ply skin covering. Designed by a team led by Arthur Hagg, great attention was paid to detail and the very streamlined design gave minimum drag and the greatest efficiency from the power of the four 525 hp Gipsy 12 engines, achieving a maximum speed of 225 mph and a range of over 1,000 miles. A total of up to 23 passengers could be carried at a high level of comfort.

The DH.93 Don is perhaps the furthest from the Mosquito principle, but there is still an influence. Designed as an aircrew trainer and communications aircraft it staggered into the air for the first time in June 1937. The reason for its reluctance to fly was that the Air Ministry Specification T.6/36 called for so much capability that the aircraft was underpowered with its single 525 hp Gipsy King engine, and achieved none of the too many tasks desired of it. Most of the aircraft ended up for ground instruction straight from the production line, before being scrapped. Its structure was similar to that of the Albatross and the later Mosquito, but de Havillands, having learnt from experience from the Don, would have been very reluctant for the Air Ministry to interfere with the Mosquito specification, particularly in connection with defensive armament.

Finally the last de Havilland member of the

The triumphant arrival of Comet Racer G-ACSS at Melbourne in October 1934, crewed by C.W.A. Scott and T. Campbell Black after a flight of 71 hours, taking first place ahead of a KLM entered Douglas DC-2 airliner. (de Havilland photo)

The first DH.91 Albatross airliner G-AEVV designed initially as a long-range mail carrier. Only seven Albatross were built as the start of the Second World War ended the prospects of any further sales. (de Havilland photo)

Out of a total production order for 250 Dons, only 50 were built, and of these only 30 were delivered to the RAF for communications duties with No. 24 Squadron at Hendon and several RAF station flights. Don L2391 was delivered to the A&AEE at Martlesham Heath for acceptance trials and was written off there in a crash on 22 September 1938. (de Havilland photo)

The DH.94 Moth Minor was flown for the first time by Captain Geoffrey de Havilland on 22 June 1937, the last new prototype in which he made the maiden flight. The aircraft stands outside what was known as the '94' Shop after the Moth Minor, and inside, hanging from the roof, is the second DH.71 Tiger Moth Racer monoplane which was destroyed by enemy action when the 94 Shop was bombed in October 1940. (de Havilland photo)

Moth family, the DH.94 Moth Minor had its influence, not only because many of the young designers who produced this modest training and touring aircraft were to join the Mosquito team, but also because it demonstrated clearly that a self-contained dedicated project team could produce the best results without continued interference from external sources. Many of the team of young engineers who produced the Moth Minor had just graduated from the de Havilland Aeronautical Technical School. This practical training exercise, which was closely monitored by Captain Geoffrey de Havilland, gave the engineers the experience of managing a relatively simple project, before becoming involved in something much more complex.

The first memory of a Mosquito by the author was during a visit to Hornchurch in the mid-1950s to the Aircrew Medical Centre as a possible candidate for a flying scholarship. A Mosquito TT.Mk35 was operating from the airfield, but photos were definitely not permitted for security reasons.

When I joined the de Havilland Aeronautical Technical School at Hatfield in September 1957 as an engineering apprentice, the most prominent aircraft was the re-emerging Comet 4, but it was not long before the Mosquito also started to create an interest. While PA to John Cunningham, then Director and chief test pilot, I made my first visits to Salisbury Hall where the prototype was preserved on the site of its conception and Pat Fillingham collected T.III RR299 from Shawbury and delivered it to Chester. I made sure I booked a ride on the regular Dove flight to Chester to see this aircraft soon after its arrival. The Mosquito was always a popular airshow performer and in the early days the flying was shared by Pat Fillingham, John Cunningham, Ron Clear and Chris Capper. The aircraft was kept at Chester where it was less likely to be seen by senior people from Hawker Siddeley, who may not have had the

same enthusiasm for this historic aircraft and ordered its disposal on economic grounds. It was with Ron Clear as pilot that I had my only flight in the Mosquito from Hatfield to the Dunsfold Family Day in June 1970.

On being appointed deputy public relations manager at Hatfield, I was told that one of my duties would be to serve on the Mosquito Appeal Committee. Although it met quarterly at Salisbury Hall, the meetings always seemed to take place in the depths of winter with a charred log in the fireplace which occasionally had a wisp of smoke coming from it, but no apparent heat.

While serving on the committee it soon became apparent that an expansion of the existing collection would attract more visitors, and gain some independence from just the overflow visitors to the historic moated manor house of Salisbury Hall. The committee agreed to the principle of the acquisition of more aircraft, leading away from the Mosquito image alone, to a broader de Havilland Heritage. The museum formed itself into a charitable company with proceeds in aid of the RAF Benevolent Fund, bought the freehold of the land on which it is located, and formed the voluntary supporters' society on Cup Final Day in May 1974.

Although the collection was to encompass the de Havilland Heritage, the Mosquito was still a major attraction, with the original prototype housed tightly in a Robin hangar and the Mk35 TA634 displayed outside and suffering from the British climate. It became obvious that a hangar would have to be built to house the Mosquito B.35 as it was becoming a losing battle to try and do restoration work outside with large areas of the protective fabric covering deteriorating and cracking, and letting in the damp. Much of the labouring work of site preparation and foundations was done by the volunteers and the Mosquito was finally moved under cover in November 1980, even though the new hangar still needed enclosing walls and doors fitted. A ten-year programme of restoration then commenced with the aircraft stripped down to its basic woodwork and almost everything dismantled except the wing to fuselage joint. The metal parts including engines and undercarriage were taken off and all corrosion removed before restoration and protection with paint ready for reassembly. The configuration of the aircraft was changed from what was left of a TT.Mk35 to a B.MkXVI of the Light Night Striking Force and the final paint scheme included the markings of 571 Squadron. Although externally complete for the Mosquito fiftieth anniversary, detailed work continues on the interior and the structural integrity is also being checked, and so far appears in good shape despite that long period in the open.

The factories at Hatfield and Leavesden where so many Mosquitos were built are now empty and soon to be demolished and the airfields are no longer operational. However plans are in hand for a move of the de Havilland Heritage from its existing congested site by Salisbury Hall to be part of the development of what was Hatfield Aerodrome, where it will be possible for the historic prototype to be brought out into the open air for special events for the first time since it was shown at the SBAC displays at Radlett in 1946 and 1947. It will also be possible to complete the restoration of the FB.VI TA122 and its assembly to commemorate the heroism of Gp Capt. Pickard on the Amiens prison raid in February 1944.

This book is in memory to all those Mosquito aircrew who failed to return, including Kevin Moorhouse and Steve Watson who lost their lives in the crash of RR299 on 21 July 1996 at Barton while keeping the spirit of the Mosquito in front of the public. Not for a long time, if ever, will we once more hear the unique sound of the two Merlin engines in a wooden airframe.

In a book of this nature the historical facts are recorded as accurately as possible, but it is the contribution of the Mosquito people, from designers to builders, maintainers, aircrew and restorers that brings the history alive. My thanks to all those who are mentioned in the text, including those who have passed away in recent years. Norman Malayney helped me with details of the 25th BG Mosquitos. What also brings a history to life are the illustrations, and my thanks go to those who are mentioned in the credits, as well as Ken Delve, editor of *Flypast*, the librarians at the Imperial War Museum, Jerry Shaw, the FAA Museum photo archivist, Ian Thirsk, Mikael Forslund and Chaz Bowyer, all of whom have given me access to their photo collections to make this book more attractive. Thanks are also due to my wife Martha for being very supportive during the writing of it, and for helping with the setting up of the PC.

Stevenage, February 1998

Bibliography

Among the many sources of information for this history, including individual accounts, the files of the Public Record Office and much other documentation, were the following books:

Mosquito at War by Chaz Bowyer (Ian Allan, 1973)
Mosquito Squadrons of the RAF by Chaz Bowyer (Ian Allan, 1984)
Wings on my Sleeve by Capt. E.M. Brown (Airlife, 1978)
DH Aircraft by A.J. Jackson (Putnam, 1962)
Mosquito by C.M. Sharp and M.J.F. Bowyer (Crecy, 1995)
Squadrons of the FAA by Ray Sturtivant (Air Britain, 1984)
Mosquito, a Pictorial History by Philip Birtles (Janes, 1980)

The Mosquito prototype during final assembly in the specially built hangar at Salisbury Hall. The cut-out for the dinghy stowage is on the top of the fuselage behind the cockpit. (de Havilland photo)

The Mosquito fighter prototype W4052 in final assembly at Salisbury Hall. The one-piece machine-gun access door was later split into two sections. This aircraft was flown out of the adjacent fields on 15 May 1941. (de Havilland photo)

1. Design and Development

When Geoffrey de Havilland and his team were considering what they could achieve creatively to contribute to the defence of Great Britain at the start of the Second World War, they began looking at the concept of a high-speed unarmed bomber. The factory was busy with the building of Tiger Moth and Airspeed Oxford trainers, and also the repair of Hurricanes damaged during the dark days of the Battle of Britain.

The design team looked at the current specifications for the four-engine all-metal heavy bombers, which were loaded down with defensive armament. However, these guns were only effective against defending enemy fighters, the aircraft still being vulnerable to anti-aircraft fire from the ground. Therefore de Havilland reasoned that if the bomber could fly faster than the defending fighters, there would be no need for the defensive armament. If the defensive armament was removed, drag, weight and crew numbers would be reduced, increasing the speed. The aircraft would only need two engines instead of four, reducing cost, and only two crew – a pilot and a navigator – would be required to operate the aircraft.

Although de Havilland had used metal structure for aircraft, it had a great deal of experience with wooden construction, and therefore considered building the new bomber from wood, which would use non-strategic material and labour, be easy to repair and give a high standard of finish, keeping drag to a minimum. The new bomber, named Mosquito, proved to be 20 mph faster than the Spitfire and remained the fastest aircraft in

operation during the Second World War, until the introduction of jet-powered aircraft. It could carry up to a 4,000 lb bomb, known as the 'Cookie' in later marks when fitted with enlarged bomb-bay doors, which was the same load as the famous B-17 Flying Fortress. However, the B-17 could not carry the load in one bomb, due to bomb-bay size restrictions. The Mosquito could fly two sorties in one night to Berlin, and, while the loss rate was in the order of 2 to 3 per cent, the heavy bomber loss rate sometimes approached 20 per cent, with almost entire squadrons being wiped out in a single night.

The origins of the Mosquito can be traced back to Specification P.13/36, which was issued by the Air Ministry on 24 August 1936. This outlined a twin-engine medium bomber for world-wide service, which could combine the often diametrically opposite requirements of long range with a heavy bomb load by using catapult-assisted take-off when fully loaded. The maximum bomb load was to be 4,000 lb (1,814 kg) over a range of 3,000 miles (4,828 km), and to keep time to a minimum over hostile territory, the cruising speed was to be 275 mph (442.5 km/hr) at 15,000 ft (4,572 m). Consideration was given to combining the roles of medium bomber, reconnaissance and general-purpose aircraft, the latter task being guaranteed to turn it into a 'Christmas tree', which would not be able to perform any of its tasks well. In addition to the bomb load carried internally, two 18 in (45.7 cm) torpedoes could be carried and defensive armament consisted of gun turrets fitted in the nose and tail.

Sir Geoffrey de Havilland, aviation pioneer and leader of the organisation that not only produced the Mosquito, but also the world's first jet airliner, supersonic all-weather jet fighters; piston, jet and rocket engines; propellers, guided missiles and space rockets. (de Havilland photo)

From experience with the Albatross four-engine airliner, de Havilland realised that attention to the external shape, keeping drag to a minimum, was just as important and effective with a bomber as with a fighter. The company even considered adapting the Albatross and powering it with two Rolls-Royce engines, to meet the specification. In an effort to promote the wooden construction of the proposed bomber, de Havilland sent a letter dated 7 July 1938 to Sir Wilfred Freeman, Air Council Member for Research and Development, who was to become the major official supporter of what became the concept of the Mosquito. The letter suggested that, should war break out without warning, the adequate supplies of suitable timber available could assist in having the new aircraft in service rapidly. As far as strength was concerned, timber had similar structural properties as aluminium and steel for a similar weight, except in tension. The labour employed to build the aircraft would come from the furniture, coach building, exhibition construction and other woodworking trades, which would otherwise be unable to make any direct contribution to the Allied war effort. Unlike metal, wood does not suffer from fatigue, although most of the combat aircraft were considered to have only a short operational life, owing to the risks of combat and training. However, a wooden structure was more resilient and easier to repair.

Using its previous experience, de Havilland proposed to build the fuselage in the form of a moulded wooden stressed skin shell, consisting of a birch ply sandwich filled with lightweight balsa wood to stabilise the structure and provide strength. This would take the form of the modern composite honeycomb filling of structures to give a lightweight but strong construction. The major challenge with this is that, over long periods left in the open, this form of construction is subject to deterioration due to water soakage, particularly in warm, humid climates – but no Mosquito was expected to be a long-life aircraft. The wings were to be made from overlapping laminated planks of spruce, glued together to form a very strong structure without the need for long lengths of timber. The joins used scarfing tapers of 15:1 to give the required strength, which also allowed for easy repair if damage was caused by combat or accident. The spruce used in the wing structure was much more resilient than the fuselage shell, which had limitations on the number of repairs, and the wings have often significantly outlasted the fuselage over long periods of exposure to the elements.

De Havilland had little confidence in Spec. P.13/36 as it was too large for the two specified early Rolls-Royce Merlin engines. His doubts were probably justified, as no aircraft appeared which had been produced to this requirement. However, a good bomber could be produced using two Merlin engines, but without the restrictions of the current specification.

In September 1938 the Munich crisis brought greater urgency to the preparation for hostilities, and de Havilland began to consider a new smaller aircraft with a crew of two, sacrificing armament for speed and using two Merlin engines for power. The use of wooden construction was estimated to save a year in the prototype stage, with consequent savings in subsequent production.

Although the British Government was preoccupied with the urgent task of rearmament, based on the existing programmes, the de Havilland proposals were not taken seriously, so the company was being forced to look at alternative approaches. The defensive armament of a conventional bomber, with the extra crew, structural weight, ammunition and fuel required to carry the additional weight, could be as much as one-sixth of the total weight of the aircraft. The larger structure took more man-hours and materials to produce, maintain and operate, as well as being more vulnerable, owing to the drag of the armament slowing the aircraft down. There was no doubt at de Havilland that the answer was to build a high-speed unarmed bomber, with only two crew, which would be exposed to less risk for a shorter time by outflying the defending fighters and avoiding the anti-aircraft fire. Such an aircraft would be able to make more sorties and thus deliver more bombs.

The official view was that defensive armament was still necessary, as it was believed that the performance estimates were pessimistic, and it was also feared that the enemy might produce faster defending fighters, making the unarmed bomber dangerously vulnerable. In addition there was concern that the wooden structure would not stand up to the stresses of being driven along at high speed by two powerful Merlin engines, although, in practice, wood was found to be more resilient than metal. It was felt that the crew of two might be overworked, especially over long endurance flights, where the pilot would not have any relief. In addition to guiding the aircraft to the target and back, the navigator would also be responsible for the

The de Havilland Aircraft Company main administration building at Hatfield, camouflage painted during the Second World War. (de Havilland photo)

radio and bomb aiming. In practice it was found that the crew were able to work well as a team – being located close together – and therefore share the duties as required. With defensive armament the aircraft would lose all of the speed advantage, with the speed reduced by about 20 mph (32 km/h). However, without the defensive armament, the aircraft began to show potential as a long-range escort fighter, high-speed photo-reconnaissance and unarmed bomber.

The proposal by de Havilland was for a two-crew twin Merlin-powered wooden bomber, capable of carrying a bomb load of 1,000 lb (453.5 kg) over a range of up to 1,500 miles (2,414 km). Although the aircraft

had twice the wetted area and twice the power of the Spitfire, as a result of careful attention to design, plus the smooth surface finish of the wooden construction, it was expected to be 20 mph (32 km/h) faster, thus achieving the desired advantage.

Fortunately de Havilland had an ally in Sir Wilfred Freeman, who was convinced by the company's proposals. Through his influence, Air Ministry Specification B.1/40 was issued, covering the unarmed reconnaissance prototype, to keep the project alive, leaving the options open for later development of the fighter and bomber versions. As a result of Sir Wilfred's support, the new project gained the name 'Freeman's Folly', although this was

The three sons of Geoffrey de Havilland, founder of the organisation: Peter, John who was killed in the Mosquito crash following the collision of HX849 and HX850 on 23 August 1943 and Geoffrey Jnr, the chief test pilot, who eventually lost his life in the DH.108 when penetrating the sound barrier on 26 September 1946. (de Havilland photo)

soon forgotten when the aircraft began to prove itself in flight tests.

The key members of the design team of what was to become the Mosquito were moved on 5 October 1939 from the Hatfield design offices to the remote moated manor house of Salisbury Hall, about 6 miles from Hatfield, and 4 miles south of St Albans. The reason for this move was mainly security – not just from a prying enemy, but also from the British Government, Air Ministry and RAF, which would have stopped the project had it been found out,

even though it was still a de Havilland-funded private venture.

It was also hoped that such a remote site would not attract enemy bombing. However, with the notorious inaccuracy and the nearby location of the de Havilland airfield at Hatfield and Handley Page at Radlett, there were some close calls. On one occasion a new German magnetic land-mine was dropped by parachute in the area and drifted, undetected, towards the secret site at Salisbury Hall. Had it landed, it was close enough to level the entire site, but luckily the parachute became caught in a tree

The wartime entrance to Salisbury Hall, the design offices for the Mosquito, was over a bridge across the moat which surrounds the historic house. (de Havilland photo)

and left the land-mine suspended just above the ground. At least it could then be dismantled under controlled conditions to allow safe inspection and discovery of its secrets.

The design team was led by R.E. Bishop. As well as including some well-established members of the de Havilland staff, it also involved some young engineers who had learned in a very practical way how to project manage as a team the design of an aircraft, using the pre-war DH.94 Moth Minor as an example. Among the more established engineers on the Mosquito team was Ralph Hare, who moved to Salisbury Hall as one of the initial nine designers under the guidance of Mr D.R. Evans. Ralph, in particular, was responsible for the stress calculations of the wing structure, with an interest in the overall stressing of the entire airframe in conjunction with the aerodynamicists. Ralph believes that, although a direct comparison was not made, the wooden construction resulted in a lighter

and stronger structure than if metal had been used. To achieve the required strength, the overall loading for the bomber was factored at times eight, with higher margins for the fighter. By January 1940 the overall general arrangement of the Mosquito was established and preliminary design had commenced. Ralph and the remainder of the design team returned to Hatfield in April 1942. Ralph began with de Havilland at Stag Lane, before the move to Hatfield in 1934. He eventually completed more than 50 years of service, retiring in 1979 as Head of Structures, and still using his 10 inch slide rule for calculations, just as the era of the microchip was about to dawn.

One of the comparatively new members of the team, who had gained his initial experience with the Moth Minor, was the late J.P. (Phil) Smith, who remembered the long hours worked over a six-and a-half-day week, although the atmosphere was very challenging and exciting. To complete the drawings for the first aircraft to commence manufacture, a normal working day was from 08.00 hrs to 19.00 hrs, with a finish at midday on Sunday. It was not unusual to start at 07.00 hrs, one of the duties being fire watching. Under the guidance of Reg Hutchinson, and assisting Alan Peters, who was in charge of the control surfaces, Phil Smith worked on the design of the metal elevators. These were originally a metal structure covered with fabric. However, as a result of early flight testing, it was found that they buffeted in the powerful slipstream of the engines, so they had to became metal skinned, like the ailerons. The rudder, however, remained of fabric-covered metal construction. During his time at Salisbury Hall, Phil Smith participated in the design of the urgent high-altitude pressurised Mosquito MkXV to combat the high-flying Junkers Ju.86p raiders, which could fly at 40,000 ft (12,192 m). He later became Divisional Deputy Managing Director of British Aerospace.

Brian Hunter-Steen was one of the youngest members of the design team and, when he was sent to Salisbury Hall in April 1940, work was continuing at an urgent pace. By that time accommodation in the house was becoming scarce, and Hunter-Steen worked on the hydraulic installation design with Phil Smith, Frank Marking and David Raynes in a wooden office beside the house. The initial hydraulics on the prototype, which were very basic and consisted of the actuation of the bomb doors, undercarriage and flaps, were schemed to determine the best fit, before being drawn for production.

With the design team located in the house, there was also a need for somewhere to build the prototype, so a hangar disguised as a barn was built on the western side of the moat surrounding the house. The building was reached by a rather unstable rope bridge, which was known to cause people to topple off and end up in the mud below. To maintain secrecy from aerial reconnaissance, the workers' cars were camouflaged with netting. As the whole site was fairly compact, everyone shared the same canteen, which helped communication between the designers and builders. Although the site was secure, there were no passes issued, as everyone knew everyone else.

Visitors to Salisbury Hall were fairly frequent, especially Sir Geoffrey de Havilland, and his chief engineer, C.C. Walker. Once the project became more accepted, visits were made by Winston Churchill, who remembered Salisbury Hall from when he used to visit his mother there. King George VI visited with Queen Elizabeth, now HRH The Queen Mother, who returned in May 1984, when she was escorted by John Cunningham for the twenty-fifth anniversary celebrations of the opening of the Mosquito Aircraft Museum.

Although no enemy bombs fell at Salisbury Hall, one was dropped on the Hatfield factory by a Ju.88 during the day on 3 October 1940, just as the Mosquito prototype was being prepared for its move to the aerodrome for its first flight. As well as killing twenty-one people and injuring a further seventy, a great deal of the work in progress on the early Mosquitos was also destroyed. This resulted in the subsequent production of the Mosquito being widely dispersed, to avoid further disruption from enemy action. The bombs fell mainly on the 94 Shop, destroying the Technical School offices, and the Airspeed Horsa design office. By this time de Havilland owned the Airspeed Company and had moved the design team from the more vulnerable south coast areas of Portsmouth and Christchurch. As a result of the Horsa design team being made homeless, it was moved to Salisbury Hall to complete the design of the troop-carrying glider, the first two of which were built in a specially constructed hangar behind the moated manor house. The Ju.88 was damaged by the anti-aircraft guns at the factory, and crashed at nearby Hertingfordbury.

Another excitement near Salisbury Hall

The original 'barn' at Salisbury Hall where the Mosquito prototype was built in June 1940, in the shadow of a large lime tree. The site was camouflaged to look as much as possible like agricultural buildings from the air, but the fleet of cars must have suggested affluent farm workers. (de Havilland photo)

was the landing by parachute, during the darkness on 13 May 1941, of a German courier called Karl Richter. Richter was bringing funds for another German agent located near Colchester, but he had been dropped well beyond his target. Not being very expert, he hid in a wood near Tyttenhanger for the first 24 hours. When he emerged, however, he raised the suspicions of a local lorry driver, who reported him to the police. The buried parachute and equipment were discovered, and Richter was taken to Wandsworth Prison on 21 October, ready for

his trial. He was found guilty 4 days later and hanged at the prison on 10 December. Many German agents were captured and, after interrogation, were turned to the advantage of the Allies. However, not only was Richter captured rather publicly, but he was also uncooperative. His landing so close to Salisbury Hall, two days before the Night Fighter prototype was flown out of an adjacent field, was pure coincidence.

In parallel with the design of the Mosquito, the first prototype was constructed in the nearby hangar by dint of staff working both

Salisbury Hall from the air shows the house with the bridge across the moat bottom right. Just beyond the house and across the moat is the two-bay barn-like hangars used for the construction of the early Mosquitos, the second bay being erected after the prototype was completed, and three further Mosquitos were built on the site. Behind the hall is the hangar erected for the construction of the two Airspeed Horsa troop-carrying glider prototypes. (de Havilland photo)

day and night shifts. It was possible that security could have been compromised, as it was not normal for farm workers to get off the bus at the entrance to Salisbury Hall, ready to start work on the night shift. One of the workers was the late Bob Sneddon, more commonly known as Jock owing to his Scottish origins. He was a skilled pattern maker and retained vivid memories of his time at Salisbury Hall. Despite the need for a blackout, the barn-like hangar housing the prototype had so many holes in it that not only did it let out the light,

but it also let in the rain. As a result, the interior was not very warm in the winter, except when the wood glue was needing to harden and cure. Although the main wing spars were made up from short laminated lengths of spruce, Bob Sneddon used a long smoothing plane to give the correct finish and great accuracy of straightness required along the full span of the one-piece wing.

During the time at Salisbury Hall, work had to cease from time to time owing to air-raid warnings, although it was only the most

Although the hangar at Salisbury Hall was constructed for the building of the Mosquito prototype, there was not much room to spare, and a second bay was added when it was decided to build three more Mosquitos at Salisbury Hall. (de Havilland photo)

imminent ones that were taken seriously. An anti-aircraft gun was mounted on a wagon, and towed up and down the railway line from St Albans through Radlett, to help to deter raiders. There were a number of conveniently placed air-raid shelters at Salisbury Hall, and at night, because the workers were coming out of a lit hangar into darkness, a rope was strung between the door and the shelter to help them to feel their way. One night during the rush to the shelter, everyone fell in a heap, as they had run into a surprised horse, which had stopped with its head over the rope.

Alan Copas was sent to Salisbury Hall as a boy trainee under Ted Lovatt to be part of the team to build the first secret Mosquito, which was still a de Havilland-funded private venture. Copas worked all round the site, with particular responsibility for the installation of the hydraulics systems. The basis for the Mosquito hydraulics was using components from the Airspeed Oxford. When there was a shortage of parts, Copas would ride over to Hatfield on his motor cycle and, if necessary, remove components from the aircraft on the production line.

Copas remembers the prototype being completed at Salisbury Hall, and then dismantled for moving by road to Hatfield, where, after reassembly and preparation for flight, it was taken up for the first time by Geoffrey de Havilland Jnr, the elder son of the founder, on 25 November 1940. To save the one month taken for this move by road to Hatfield, it was decided to fly the third aircraft, the night-fighter prototype, W4052, from the fields adjacent to Salisbury Hall. Copas did the daily check of the appropriate systems, while other members of the team completed their checks. It had been intended that a tractor would be borrowed from the local farmer, but at the last minute he decided he would use it to plough the field from which the aircraft was going to fly. The Mosquito was therefore manhandled to the top of the field and across a ditch filled with timbers, ready for Geoffrey de Havilland Jnr to make a lightly loaded take-off on 15 May 1941, just two days after Richter had landed nearby by parachute. He had the works manager, Fred Plum, as a passenger, as Plum had bet him that he would not fly the aircraft from Salisbury Hall. Two later Mosquitos were flown out from the local fields, but a route to the west was taken to avoid having to pull the aircraft across the ditch. Alan Copas started at de Havilland at Hatfield in January 1935, working in the print room where the DH.88 Comet Racer drawings were being issued for the later aircraft after 'Grosvenor House' had won the race from Mildenhall to Melbourne. He left Salisbury Hall in 1942, returning to Hatfield and finishing his training, working on the hydraulic systems for all of the Hatfield-produced aircraft to the 146, before retiring in 1985. Copas still spends time at Salisbury Hall, acting as a guide at the de Havilland Heritage, formerly the Mosquito Aircraft Museum, where he keeps an eye on his old charge, the Mosquito prototype W4050.

For the construction of the first prototype Mosquito, only a single barn-like hangar was erected. However, when it was decided to build more Mosquitos at Salisbury Hall, a second, similar barn was built alongside, for the construction of the major assemblies before erection in the original building. Not everything was built at Salisbury Hall for the prototype but, because secrecy was required for everything built at Hatfield, the ultimate aircraft type was not identified. Stan Clayton was given the task of building the exhaust stubs for the Merlin engines, but it was a long time before he knew what they were for. The site of the original hangar can still be seen, as the metal door track is still located in the ground. The sheet metal workshop was in a wooden hut close to the front of the hangar, and 'Nell Gwynn's' moat-side cottage was a raw material store.

Two of the members of the day shift at Salisbury Hall were Tommy Adamson and Frank Eldridge, who were part of the team of up to 150 people working on the Mosquito mock-up and prototypes. An advantage of flying the Mosquitos from Salisbury Hall rather than moving them by road was that the wing was too wide for the gate. When moving the prototype to Hatfield, the wing had to be carefully lifted over the gate-posts as the lorry went through. Both Adamson and Eldridge worked in the Experimental Department, later Technical Services, until their retirement, their woodworking skills being used on the construction of the aircraft mock-ups.

Conditions during the winter were sometimes harsh, with little heating, and if the public transport failed, some of the workers were faced with up to 10 miles to walk from Welwyn Garden City, and the return journey home in the evening. This made the long working days even longer. The Mosquito construction team returned to Hatfield in February 1942, leaving the Horsa team building a special bomber version of the glider. This secret project was intended to carry a Barnes Wallis 12,000 lb (5,443 kg) Tallboy bomb to be used against the battleship *Tirpitz*, but fortunately the Lancaster was incapable of towing the glider that far and the project was abandoned after its first flight.

2. The Bomber

Externally the shape of the Mosquito changed little throughout the entire development, apart from the adaptations for various specialist roles. Conceived as an unarmed bomber, the Mosquito featured the clear nose for bomb-aiming, together with a V windscreen, and the crew door below the cockpit floor, entry being by a somewhat rickety set of telescopic steps.

During the early design progress of the Mosquito, Lord Beaverbrook, the Minister of Aircraft Production, told Sir Wilfred Freeman at least three times that work should stop on the Mosquito and effort be directed to something believed to contribute more directly to the war effort, but he never gave a definite instruction for work to cease. Lord Beaverbrook was only interested in aircraft that would be available by early 1941, so, to keep the project alive, 50 Mosquitos were promised for service by July of that year.

With the fall of Paris and the subsequent evacuation from Dunkirk, full priority was given to existing types of combat aircraft. Particular attention was paid to fighters, including Hurricane and Spitfire, for defence against enemy raiders, and for some form of retaliation, the Wellington and Blenheim bombers, which proved somewhat ineffective and vulnerable. Work continued at Hatfield on Oxford and Dominie trainers, with emergency bomb racks being installed under the fuselage of Tiger Moths, to be used as a last ditch attempt to repel any invaders. More effective defensive work was being done in the factory on the repair of Hurricanes for return to the squadrons engaged in the Battle of Britain.

Although design work continued on the Mosquito at Salisbury Hall, construction of the prototype came practically to a halt owing to the non-availability of materials. A strong plea was made to Lord Beaverbrook to sanction the reinstatement of the work on B.1/40, the case being made for the minimum use of strategic materials. The use of metal would be minimal with high-strength castings weighing a total of only 250 lb (113.4 kg), as an alternative to the more expensive forgings, which would weigh only 30 lb (13.6 kg). Precision machining was reduced to a minimum, one example being the main undercarriage legs consisting of pressings riveted together, with rubber in compression blocks used for shock absorption. This gave a simple, rugged undercarriage, which was cheap to build and easy to maintain. With de Havilland making a firm promise to deliver 50 Mosquitos in 1941, despite the delays, work was allowed to continue, providing it did not interfere with other activities.

In addition to the bombs falling on the Hatfield factory in October 1940 by a chance German raider, who had been unable to find his Reading target as a result of poor weather, delays were also caused by regular air-raid warnings, bombs falling within a mile of the factory one day in every five.

On 3 November 1940 the yellow-painted Mosquito prototype was moved in two main sections to Hatfield by road. One section was the fuselage and fin, while the other was the one-piece wing, with the Merlin engines and tailplane loaded separately. The aircraft was still a private venture, and therefore carried the Class B markings E0234 for its early flight trials before adoption as W4050. The new aircraft was reassembled in a remote hangar at the west

The prototype Mosquito structurally complete during the early autumn of 1940, with the Merlin engines and undercarriage fitted. The propellers, nose cone and cowlings are yet to be fitted, and components for the second Mosquito are in the foreground. (de Havilland photo)

The prototype Mosquito pulled out for the first time after reassembly at Hatfield was partially covered by tarpaulins to camouflage the new yellow combat aircraft from enemy photo-reconnaissance. Even with covers over most of the aircraft, the sleek lines are apparent. (de Havilland photo)

end of the factory, and when it was pulled out its bright-yellow shape was disguised on the ground by tarpaulins draped over the wings and fuselage. The aircraft was painted yellow as a protection to try to avoid misidentification by allied fighters and anti-aircraft guns, because it was undesirable to lose such a vital aircraft to 'friendly fire'. Following engine runs, Geoffrey de Havilland Jnr commenced taxiing trials on the grass at Hatfield on 24 November. The next day, following a short hop to check the controls, he made the maiden flight for a trouble-free 30 minutes. During the flight the undercarriage was retracted and a speed of 220 mph (353 km) was reached, and Geoffrey was very happy with the handling of the aircraft.

The prototype W4050 became the principal experimental Mosquito, used for testing the aerodynamics and performance. As a result of buffet of the tailplane, it was found necessary to extend the engine nacelles rearward beyond the wing trailing edge, the one-piece flaps being split into two interconnected portions on either side of the nacelles. This cured the buffet but, as already mentioned, the elevators had to have metal skins to replace the fabric to avoid flutter. Problems with the engine cowlings caused a Merlin to be shut down on the thirtieth test flight, but all of these snags were comparatively minor and easy to rectify.

On 29 December, just over a month after the first flight, the Mosquito prototype as well as other significant new British combat aircraft, was shown to Lord Beaverbrook, together with other senior Government Ministers and RAF officers at Langley. As a result of the good impression made, the next day de Havilland was instructed to increase production capacity in anticipation of a further batch of 150 Mosquitos, to add to the original 50 aircraft.

On 11 January 1941, de Havilland was instructed to produce a reconnaissance prototype, followed by 19 production aircraft, and the balance of 28 aircraft would be fighter versions, with bombers likely to be included in

the next batch of 150 planes. Development and testing therefore included all three roles, the fighter prototype having been called up in the first batch of 50 aircraft. As the early flight testing continued, the predicted speed of 386 mph (621 km/h) was achieved, and on 17 January an altitude of 22,000 ft was reached. The aircraft was then prepared for despatch to Boscombe Down for initial service trials, the upper surfaces being camouflaged, and a prototype 'P' was marked in a circle on either side of the fuselage. The aircraft was flown to the A&AEE at Boscombe Down on 19 February, but service testing was slow to commence, owing to continued scepticism about the aircraft. However, when testing did start, the performance was so exceptional that the figures were double-checked, and the results confirmed the top speed of 20 mph faster than the current Spitfires. As a result of the favourable reports, considerable enthusiasm was generated for the Mosquito, with many visitors from London to see the aircraft.

Fortunately the Mosquito had begun to prove itself, and was creating a great deal of interest, when an incident occurred which, had it happened earlier, could have spelt disaster for the project. At that time Boscombe Down was without paved runways. While the prototype was being taxied for its fifty-seventh flight, the pilot felt some odd oscillations. On inspection it was found that, while travelling over the soggy surface of the airfield, the rear fuselage had fractured around the starboard side access hatch, because the tailwheel had castoring troubles and caught in a rut. This hatch was later strengthened by adding a wooden strip above the door, which also helped to keep moisture out of the fuselage. The damage was serious enough for the decision to be made to change the fuselage, the replacement being made using the fuselage of the nearly completed PR prototype W4051, which was later finished at Hatfield. The new fuselage was transported to

The Mosquito prototype, carrying the class B markings E0234 used before it was officially adopted, is prepared for initial engine runs at Hatfield. (de Havilland photo)

Mosquito prototype E0234 having the Merlin engines run on 19 November 1940 in preparation for its maiden flight. The ground crew holding the tail down probably had the coldest job of all. (de Havilland photo)

Using orthochromatic film, the prototype looks almost matt black and the red of the fin flash has merged into the yellow. In this side view, the undercarriage doors have yet to be fitted. (MOS press photo)

The prototype Mosquito almost ready for its first flight. Final preparations are being made and the undercarriage doors have been fitted. (de Havilland photo)

On 25 November 1940 in poor light, the Mosquito prototype E0234 made its maiden flight in the hands of Geoffrey de Havilland Jnr, lifting off the grass surface in a northerly direction with the houses of Manor Road in the background. (de Havilland photo)

Following its successful early test flights, the Mosquito was adopted by the British Government and was allocated the identity W4050. It is seen here taking off from the grass surface at Hatfield on 10 January 1941 during the early stages of the flight development programme. (de Havilland photo)

The cleanness of the design and attention to detail which made the Mosquito 20mph faster than the Spitfire is apparent. During early test flying the Mosquito had short engine nacelles and undivided flaps. However, during testing buffet was caused with the tailplane, and the nacelles were extended rearwards with the flaps divided. This was the only major aerodynamic change needed. (de Havilland photo)

Boscombe Down and the repairs were made by a de Havilland working party.

Despite the failure of the fuselage, the A&AEE report was most satisfactory. The Initial Handling Report dated 3 March stated that the aircraft was pleasant to fly, with light and effective aileron control. The plane was found to stall in the clean configuration at 105 mph (168.7 km/h), and with flaps down the stall was at 90 mph (144.7 km/h), Take-off and landing were straightforward, with an easily controlled tendency to swing on take-off at full power. The top speed using full supercharger was found to be 388 mph (624 km/h) at 22,000 ft (6,706 m) and although the maximum altitude reached during the test programme was 29,700 ft (9,052.5 m), the estimated service ceiling was 33,900 ft (10,332.7 m).

Thus the overall impression of the Mosquito was favourable, allowing official adoption without any problems. No longer was the aircraft 'Freeman's Folly'. The rate of climb and acceleration were good, and the plane handled well at all speeds. If Geoffrey de Havilland Jnr had not drawn attention to some mild buffeting, it would probably not have been noticed. The side-by-side seating for the two crew was rather snug, with the width of the fuselage not allowing any improvement, but the heating was adequate; in fact the close proximity of the radiators sometimes made the cockpit a little too warm. The aircraft handled well on the ground, with a pleasant ride and effective brakes. One criticism, which was soon corrected, was the lack of an internal handle for the crew entry door, although in an emergency a quick exit could be made by jettisoning the canopy top hatch.

After the repairs, the aircraft was flying again by 14 March, when it returned to Hatfield for further adjustments, before recommencing the handling trials four days later. This time it was fitted with the extended engine nacelles, and it remained at Boscombe Down until 23 March. On 4 May the prototype made its hundredth flight, returning to Boscombe Down, and achieved a maximum level speed of 392 mph at 22,000 ft with an all-up weight of 16,000 lb. During further handling tests at Boscombe Down, the fuselage was again damaged as a result of a heavy landing, but this time the fracture on the port side, just behind the wing trailing edge, was repaired. An irregular patch was glued to the inner and outer fuselage skin, demonstrating the ease of repair in the field, which can still be seen on the prototype preserved at Salisbury Hall in the de Havilland Heritage. Service tests were completed on the prototype on 23 May, to be continued on more representative service aircraft.

Returning to Hatfield, W4050 was used by de Havilland for stall testing in a number of configurations, and was then flown at high speeds with the bomb doors open to observe the flutter of the doors. On 23 July 1941 a mock-up of the unpopular defensive gun turret was fitted to W4050 and, although the aircraft handling was satisfactory, as expected it lost all of the speed advantage, because of the extra drag.

The flight testing duties were shared by Geoffrey de Havilland Jnr and his younger brother John, George Gibbins and Pat Fillingham. While involved with production testing of Mosquitos HX849 and 850 on 23 August 1943, the aircraft collided close to the airfield, killing John and Gibbins, as well as their observers, G.J. Carter and J.H.F. Scrope. The wreckage fell near Hill End, on the boundary of St Albans. Fillingham continued on test-flying duties into the jet age, finally retiring from the Trident development programme.

In late October, W4050 was grounded for the fitting of the more powerful 1,705 hp supercharged Merlin 61 engines. It returned to the flight-test programme on 20 June 1942, attaining an altitude of 40,000 ft on the second flight with the new engines. Merlin 77s developing 1,710 hp were then fitted, the Mosquito flew again on 8 October. A top speed of 439 mph was reached in

John de Havilland in the cockpit of a Mosquito fighter-bomber. He was killed, together with George Gibbins and the two flight test observers on 23 August 1943 when Mosquito FB.MkVIs HX849 and HX850 collided near Hatfield. (de Havilland photo)

November, the highest achieved by any Mosquito in level flight.

The first fully equipped Mosquito bomber prototype, W4057, was completed in the Experimental Department at Hatfield, having been originally started as the similar reconnaissance version. The initial flight was during the first week of September 1941, and the plane was delivered to Boscombe Down on 27 September, to be followed by the first production version, W4064, on 18 October. Both were returned to Hatfield for trials to increase the war load to four 500 lb (227 kg) bombs, the limitation being not the weight but the space. Initially, telescopic fins were tried, but it was found much simpler to crop the existing fins, which did not impair the ballistics, and this was adopted as standard.

The main initial production of the bomber Mosquito was the B.MkIV, powered by two Merlin 21 or 23 engines, developing 1,460 hp. By fitting the two-stage Merlin 61 engines, the aircraft was redesignated the B.MkIX, replacing the earlier versions on the production lines in early March 1943, mainly centred at Hatfield, where bomber and PR airframes were built, in addition to fighters and fighter-bombers.

A number of conversions were made of the

In September 1942 the prototype was fitted with two-stage Merlin 61 engines for the development of the later high altitude pressure cabin aircraft. (de Havilland photo)

Night-fighter Mosquito prototype W4052 flying over the bomber prototype W4057 at Hatfield during the early trials programme. (de Havilland photo)

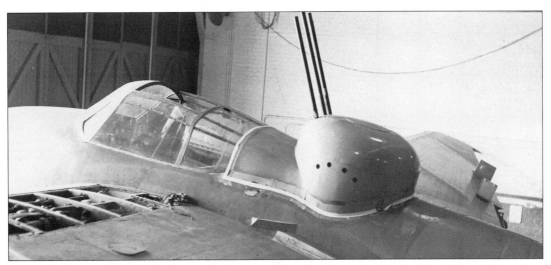

An upward offensive gun installation was tried out in mock-up form but not adopted, although it would have been very useful in the night-fighters when they had to identify the enemy visually from underneath, and then fall back and climb to get the hostile aircraft in the gun sights, by which time they could have escaped. (de Havilland photo)

The Mosquito Bomber cockpit had the spectacle-type control wheel, with the main flying instruments in the centre and the engine indicators on the left. On the right is the access to the nose for the bomb aimer. (de Havilland photo)

Early Mosquito B.MkIV W4072, part of the first batch of 50 aircraft, parked on the grass at Hatfield in March 1942. (AM press photo)

Mosquito B.MkIV DK328 at Hatfield prior to delivery. This aircraft was issued to No. 105 Squadron, coded GB-V, but was shot down on the 13th sortie on 7 November 1942 during an attack on shipping in the Gironde Estuary. Both the crew survived to be taken prisoner. (de Havilland photo)

A Mosquito during the Second World War shows B.MkIV Series ii DK339 which first flew from Hatfield in September 1942. It was delivered to No. 105 Squadron coded GB-O completing 23 sorties from 12 September 1942 to 1 May 1943. (de Havilland photo)

Mosquito LR495 was the first B.MkIX trials aircraft and had provision for the carriage of additional bombs under the universal wing then being fitted. This particular aircraft was delivered to Boscombe Down on 17 April 1943, but was destroyed during take-off overload trials on 29 January 1944. (MOD press photo)

Mosquito B.MkXVI ML991 with the enlarged bomb-bay doors to accommodate the 4,000 lb 'Cookie' bomb during a test flight on 25 April 1944. (de Havilland photo)

Mosquito B.MkXVI ML926/G was delivered to Defford for radar bomb sight, 'Oboe' and H2S trials. (de Havilland photo)

Mosquito B.MkIV Series ii DZ313 with mobile trolley-ack battery plugged in ready for the engine start. (de Havilland photo)

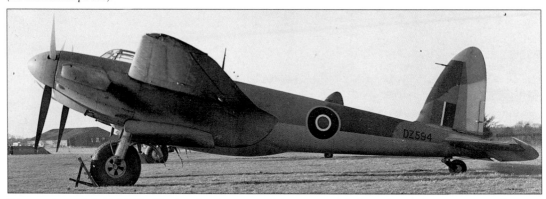

The carriage of the 4,000 lb 'Cookie' bomb was tried first on modified B.MkIV DK594 in November 1943. This was the prototype conversion with the enlarged bomb-bay doors to house the larger bomb, the conversion taking about seven weeks. It was tested at the A&AEE at Boscombe Down to an all-up weight of 25,200 lb and was issued to No. 627 Squadron on 15 February 1945 coded AZ-X until struck off charge on 28 June 1945. (de Havilland photo)

Mosquito B.MkIX photographed at Hatfield on 6 September 1943 with the broader chord paddle blade propellers fitted and underwing fuel drop tanks. (de Havilland photo)

The ultimate Mosquito bomber, the B.Mk35 TJ150 on completion at Hatfield on 15 October 1945. This version was too late to enter combat during the war. (de Havilland photo)

Having been retired from flying and used for training apprentices, the Mosquito prototype was brought out into public view again for the first post-war SBAC display, held at Radlett in September 1946. It is surrounded with a selection of the weapon loads including underwing fuel tanks, a torpedo, a Molins cannon and various cameras. The trainer version is shown by dual rudder pedals, and there is a fighter-bomber canopy and a night-fighter radar antenna. (de Havilland photo)

B.MkIV for the carriage of a pair of 'Highball' mines in tandem, recessed in the bomb bay. The prototype conversion was DZ471, followed by 26 others, all for service with No. 618 Squadron. With the decision at the end of the war in Europe to move the Highball Mosquitos to Asian operations, 29 airframes were further modified, many of them the original batch, with Merlin 24 engines, motors and drives for spinning the stores, arrester hooks, armour plating and new windscreens.

The first B.MkIX off the Hatfield line, LR495, made its maiden flight on 24 March, and, following initial company trials, it was delivered to Farnborough, where it was flown at a take-off weight of 23,000 lb (10,433 kg), the highest to that date. These trials were in preparation for the carriage of not only four 500 lb (227 kg) bombs internally, but also a further 500 lb bomb under each wing, plus 540 gallons (2,455 l) of fuel and 200 lb (90.7 kg) of desert equipment. By the end of April, the first MkIX had been delivered to No. 109 Squadron, to be followed by the re-equipping of nos 105 and 139 squadrons.

The final major bomber development was the B.MkXVI, which had a pressure cabin added to the MkIX as well as the capability of dropping the 4,000 lb (18,144 kg) 'Cookie'. To accommodate this large blast fragmentation bomb, the bomb bay was enlarged by fitting bulged doors to increase the depth. This brought the Mosquito up to the same load-carrying capability as the B-17 Flying Fortress. Design work commencing in April 1943, and DZ540, a converted MkIV, made its first flight in late July as the pressure cabin prototype, reaching an altitude of 40,000 ft (12,192 m) which was good for a wooden airframe.

The first of 12 initial production B.MkXVIs (ML926), all without modified bomb doors, was rolled out at Hatfield in October 1943. Deliveries to No. 109 Squadron started in December. The first of the B.MkXVIs (ML937), with the capability of carrying the 4,000 lb Cookie, was first flown by Geoffrey de Havilland Jnr on 1 January 1944. Following company flight-testing it was delivered to Boscombe Down on 5 February. A small number of Mosquito MkIXs were also fitted with the enlarged bomb-bay doors to allow the Cookie to be carried, the empty weight of this conversion being 14,644 lb (6,642 kg), compared with the empty weight of the MkXVI of 14,901 lb (6,758 kg).

The final bomber version, the B.Mk35, made its first flight from Hatfield on 12 March 1945, not entering service until after the end of the war, although fifty-seven had been delivered by the end of May. The major difference from the earlier B.MkXVI was that the power came from a pair of Merlin 113/114 engines, developing 1,690 hp. These engines gave this version a top speed of 422 mph (679 km/hr) at 30,000 ft (9,144 m). The B.Mk35s served with nos 109 and 139 squadrons at Coningsby and Hemswell in the pathfinding role until they were replaced by Canberras from 1952.

During the early 1950s a number of surplus Mk35s were converted for target towing by Brooklands Aviation at Sywell, some being fitted with an external target winch. No doubt the most inelegant conversion of the Mosquito was by General Aircraft, the TT.Mk39 for the Royal Navy, with a lengthened glass-house nose and small dorsal turret – few of these saw service.

The prototype continued its contribution to the development programme, including exhaust stack development with Rolls-Royce from 1 March until 10 June 1943. In 1944, W4050 was finally grounded and subsequently used by the apprentices for practical ground instruction. It was displayed publicly at the post-war SBAC displays held at Radlett in 1946 and 1947, surrounded by representative war loads. It was finally struck off charge on 21 June 1947. It was stored at various locations, until its return to Salisbury Hall for permanent public display on 15 May 1959.

3. PHOTO-RECONNAISSANCE DEVELOPMENTS

The photo-reconnaissance versions of the Mosquito were based on the bomber airframe. Instead of being armed with bombs, however, they carried cameras and extra fuel tanks to undertake high-speed unarmed reconnaissance at low and high altitudes for both tactical and strategic purposes. Out of the initial batch of 50 Mosquitos ordered under contract 69990 to Spec B.1/40, a PR prototype and 19 production aircraft were specified. The prototype was the second airframe, W4051, which was started at Salisbury Hall, but delayed when its fuselage was donated to the damaged W4050 and completed with a new fuselage at Hatfield. Many of the PR versions were produced in parallel with the bombers, often taking the same or adjacent Mark number designations. Most versions were painted in overall PR blue as camouflage for higher altitudes.

The assembly of W4051 was completed at Hatfield on 24 May 1941, the same day that the first production PR aircraft, W4054, went into the paint shop. In addition to the fuselage replacement, delays had been caused by the scrapping of the fabric-covered elevators and then replacement with metal-skinned versions. W4051 made its maiden flight on 10 June, and two days later it was flown by Wg Cdr G. Tuttle, commanding officer of the Photo-Reconnaissance Unit (PRU) at Benson, which was eager to put the new aircraft into service. Following company flight-testing from Hatfield, W4051 was delivered to Boscombe Down on 25 June for the service trials to commence.

During the summer of 1941, W4051 and the first production PR Mosquito were used to assess the camera installations, and the measurement of performance parameters. The PRU at Benson had 5 Mosquito PR.MkIs in operation by September, with a sixth aircraft on test. The initial aircraft suffered from insufficient endurance for the longer-range sorties. However, with the adequate space in the empty bomb bay and more than enough weight-carrying capability, additional tanks were installed to give a further 700 gal (3,182 l) of fuel. The first of these longer-range PR.MkIs, W4060, was flying by September 1941 and had been delivered to Boscombe Down by the end of the month for service testing.

On 17 September 1941, Mosquito PR operations started from Benson with W4055. Despite being a great success, it was difficult to obtain enough aircraft for the tasks required, owing to the demand for Mosquitos for other roles. To meet this need, de Havilland had to face the continuous and rapidly changing requirements of the RAF. The first batch of 10 Mosquitos were in operation on PR duties, but the next 10 were allocated as bombers. The balance of the first 50 aircraft were to be completed as fighters, which featured a different fuselage configuration. For the PRU to achieve its goals, 2 F.MkIIs were issued from a maintenance unit, where airborne inter-

The second Mosquito W4051 was completed as the PR prototype and was assembled at Hatfield after donating its original fuselage to the prototype W4050. (de Havilland photo)

The Mosquito PR prototype W4051 was delivered to the PRU at Benson following its flight test programme. It featured the short engine nacelles. (Aeroplane photo)

Mosquito PR.MkIV DZ383 was issued to No. 540 Squadron in May 1943. (AM press photo)

The Hatfield-built Mosquito B.MkIV DK324 converted to PR.MkVIII prototype. (IWM photo)

Mosquito PR.MkXVI NS705 showing the enlarged bomb-bay doors, which gave more room for additional fuel tanks in the bomb bay. (Charles E. Brown photo)

Mosquito PR.MkXVI MM308/G which was not fitted with the enlarged bomb-bay doors, but was equipped with American H2X radar in the nose, and was delivered to 8th USAAF in Britain; 100 gallon drop tanks are fitted under the wings. (de Havilland photo)

Mosquito PR.Mk32 NS589 was a high altitude pressure cabin version powered by Merlin 72/73s. (MAP press photo)

The ultimate PR development of the Mosquito was the PR.Mk34, an example being RG176 at Hatfield in January 1945, which was later modified to a PR.Mk34A and used for trials at the A&AEE at Boscombe Down. (MAP press photo)

ception (AI) radar was being installed, and 2 B.MkIVs were allocated direct from the production line, all 4 aircraft being equipped with cameras.

For even greater ranges, and also to outrun the newly introduced Fw.190 fighters, the PR.MkIV was modified by installing a pair of two-stage Merlins, as tested on the prototype W4050, resulting in the PR.MkVIII. Five of this mark were ordered new, with additional fuel being carried in a pair of 50 gal (227 l) underwing drop tanks. Twenty-six PR.MkIVs were converted from bombers with provision for drop tanks, and powered by Merlin XXIs. The two-stage Merlins gave an improved high-altitude performance, and further crew comfort was promised with the addition of a pressure cabin later. As an interim measure, 90 of the PR.MkIX were produced at Hatfield with deliveries from May to November 1943, the first one flying in April. These aircraft were powered by 1,680 hp Merlin 72/73 engines with 18 lb maximum boost, and the range was increased to 1,500 miles (2,414 km).

The pressure cabin PR version of the MkIX took priority over the bomber, with authorisation being received on 3 April 1943. The pressure cabin was based on the one developed for the high-altitude MkXV fighter, the prototype PR.MkXVI making its maiden flight in July 1943. During testing, this prototype, DZ540, reached 40,000 ft

(12,192 m). However, although deliveries began in November, problems with condensation misting the laminated windscreen delayed the start of full operations until February 1944.

The PR.Mk32 was lightened and fitted with extended wingtips for regular operations at around 40,000 ft, to attempt to avoid the enemy jet fighters. Only 5 of this version were built, and these served in the latter stages of the war in Europe.

The ultimate PR Mosquito development was the PR.Mk34. This was similar to the B.Mk35 but, instead of carrying bombs, additional fuel tanks were located in the enlarged bomb bay, giving a very long range, particularly for operations in Asia. Wing drop tanks could contain either 100 or 200 gal (454 or 909 l), making the total fuel capacity up to 1,262 gal (5,737 l). This fuel load gave a range of up to 3,600 miles (5,794 km) with an airspeed of 300 mph (482 km/h) at 25,000 ft (7,620 m). The all-up weight had increased from the PR.MkI at 19,413 lb (8,805 kg) to 25,500 lb (11,567 kg), making the Mosquito less pleasant to fly. However, despite these major improvements in performance, the airframe configuration changed very little, the bulged bomb bay being the most prominent new feature. The PR.Mk34 entered operational service after the end of the Second World War.

4. THE FIGHTER

Although the Mosquito was originally conceived as an unarmed bomber and never carried defensive armament in service, it was clear that, with its outstanding performance, it could be adapted to fighter and ground attack operations by fitting offensive armament. This armament generally consisted of four fixed .303 inch machine-guns in the nose and four fixed 20 mm cannons under the forward fuselage, and did not involve the installation of drag-producing gun turrets. The machine-guns were located in the nose position, replacing the perspex dome of the bomber version. Because the cannons were under the floor, the crew entry door was relocated to the starboard side of the cabin, from the under-floor position in the bomber. The crew had the protection of a flat, bullet-proof windscreen and an armour-plated bulkhead in front of the instrument panel, to help to shield them against not only hostile fire from other fighters, but also the ground in the ground attack role.

The original contract, No. 69990, had called for a bomber prototype, followed by forty-nine production bombers. However, on 18 July 1940 de Havilland received the instruction to complete one aircraft as a fighter prototype. The third airframe, W4052, was allocated at Salisbury Hall to be completed as the night-fighter prototype, under contract 135522, issued on 16 November 1940, to cover the work on this variant, which was built to Spec. F18/40. The threat was from long-range Focke-Wulf Condors against Allied shipping, where a long-endurance effective fighter was required, as well as a high-performance night-fighter, to replace the Beaufighters, which were too slow for the higher-performance German aircraft entering service.

The defensive gun turret was still being considered at this time, with the machine-guns moved from the nose to a turret located on top of the fuselage, operated by a third crew member. Although weight was not increased significantly, the drag of the installation reduced both speed and range unacceptably. Two prototypes, W4053 and W4073, were allocated to the turret development and assembled at Salisbury Hall, making a total of 5 Mosquitos built at this location.

In January 1941 de Havilland received a further change of instructions: to convert 28 bombers to production fighters with fixed guns, in addition to the already ordered prototype. As previously mentioned, Geoffrey de Havilland Jnr flew W4052 from fields adjacent to Salisbury Hall to avoid a one month delay in dismantling and reassembly. This flight was made on 15 May 1941, the day that Richter was taken to Hatfield Police Station. Taking the place of W4052 in final assembly at Salisbury Hall was the first turret fighter prototype, W4053, which was flown out of Salisbury Hall on 14 September, using a different departure route to avoid having to move the aircraft across a ditch. By the time the aircraft landed at Hatfield, pieces of the turret had become detached. The second turret fighter was flown out of Salisbury Hall by George Gibbins on 5 December 1941, this time fitted with a mock-up turret, which was removed soon after.

Meanwhile the Fighter prototype W4052, painted matt black, had been delivered to

The four .303 in machine guns fitted in the nose of the Mosquito NF.MkII with the feed channels from the ammunition boxes on top, to the breach of each individual gun. (de Havilland photo)

Modifications were made to the Youngman airbrake installation to avoid turbulence over the fin and tailplane. However, it was found that these airbrakes were an unnecessary complication and they were deleted. (de Havilland photo)

Early production Mosquito NF.MkIIs including W4090, W4092 and W4088 ready for delivery at Hatfield on 12 February 1942. (de Havilland photo)

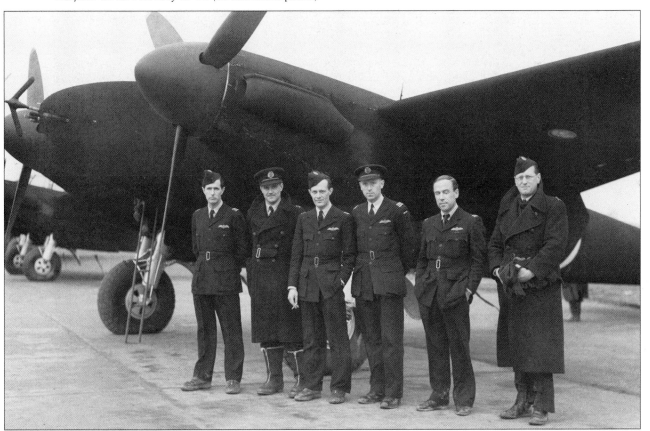

Many of the Mosquitos were delivered to the RAF by civilian aircrew of the Air Transport Auxiliary, both male and female. In this case the six aircrew, including Jim Mollinson second from the right, are ready to deliver NF.MkIIs W4090, W4092 and W4088. (de Havilland photo)

The original Salisbury Hall-built Mosquito fighter prototype W4052 was later painted in the modified day fighter camouflage adopted for all night-fighters. (de Havilland photo)

Test flying has its hazards, and when Geoffrey de Havilland Jnr had the port engine fail over Bedford in the night-fighter prototype, his approach to Hatfield was balked by an aircraft taking off, and he struggled across Welwyn Garden City to make a wheels-up landing at Panshanger on 19 April 1942. (de Havilland photo)

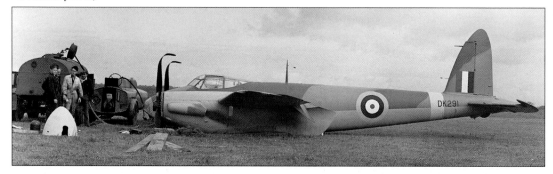

A modest mishap with Mosquito B.MkIV Series ii DK291 after a wheels-up landing at Hatfield on 29 May 1942 by Geoffrey de Havilland Jnr, when the undercarriage refused to lower. The aircraft is being defuelled prior to lifting and return to the hangar for repair. (de Havilland photo)

Mosquito NF.MkII DD737 painted overall matt black as used on the early night-fighters. However, this was not found to be an effective camouflage, as well as increasing drag, and a modified day fighter scheme was adopted. DD737 was delivered to No. 85 Squadron in May 1942. (de Havilland photo)

The wing leading-edge radiators were found prone to damage from debris from the destruction of hostile aircraft. Mosquito NF.MkII DD723 was fitted experimentally in February 1944 with underslung radiator intakes for the Merlin engines, but this configuration was not adopted. (de Havilland photo)

Hatfield-built Mosquito FB.MkVI prototype converted from B.MkIV. (IWM photo)

The Mosquito FB.MkVI was probably the most versatile of all the variants with four machine guns in the nose, four 20 mm cannons under the cockpit and bombs in the bomb bay and under the wings. LR356 ready for a test flight in March 1944. (de Havilland photo)

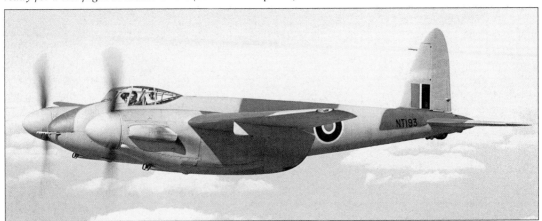

The overall configuration of the Mosquito FB.MkVI stayed the same throughout its service, and more of this version were produced than any others. (de Havilland photo)

As an alternative to underwing bombs, rocket rails could be fitted for use against shipping. Mosquito FB.VI PZ202 has four rocket rails fitted under each wing. (de Havilland photo)

The 37 mm Molins gun fitted neatly under the floor of the Mosquito with the breach block extending back into the bomb bay. The armourer gives scale to the shell fired from the gun. (Photo Chaz Bowyer collection)

When underwing fuel drop tanks were introduced to increase endurance on shipping strikes, the rocket fire power was maintained by mounting the RP in pairs one above the other. (de Havilland photo)

The ship-busting Mosquito FB.MkVI with its .303 in nose mounted machine guns, underfloor 20 mm cannons, eight wing mounted rocket projectiles packed quite a destructive punch, believed to be the equivalent to a broadside from a cruiser. A camera was mounted just above the machine guns to record the effect of the attack. (de Havilland photo)

This close-up of the Mosquito night-fighter shows the double arrow head antenna fitted between the pairs of machine-guns in the nose. (de Havilland photo)

Mosquito DZ659/G, a modified F.MkII and fitted with AI MkX (US SCR.720/729) nose-mounted radar in March 1943. (de Havilland photo)

Mosquito NF.MkXII HK117 powered by Merlin 21 engines later served with No. 29 Squadron. (AM press photo)

Leavesden-built Mosquito NF.MkXIII MM478 equipped with AI MkVIII under the universal radome, the first flight of this variant being in August 1943. (MAP press photo)

Leavesden-built Mosquito NF.Mk30, May 1944.

Mosquito NF.MkXVII DZ659 modified from a Hatfield-built F.MkII and fitted with SCR.720/729 or AI MkX radar under a universal radome. (MAP press photo)

Leavesden-built Mosquito NF.Mk36 RK957, the last of the night-fighter variants to enter service with the RAF. (MAP press photo)

The prototype Mosquito NF.Mk38 RL248 was converted from a Leavesden-built NF.Mk36. (MOS press photo)

The crews reported a definite retardation of the Mosquito MkXVIII when the Molins gun was fired. (de Havilland photo)

Leavesden-built Mosquito F.MkII HK129 converted to NF.MkXII by Marshall of Cambridge.

Mosquito NF.Mk38 VT653 in March 1948 was one of the last Mosquitos to be built at Hatfield and was the ultimate night-fighter version. (de Havilland photo)

The last Mosquito to be built was NF.Mk38 VT670 at the Hawarden factory near Chester. It made its maiden flight on 30 September 1948. This version did not enter service with the RAF, but some were sold overseas. The AI radar antenna can be seen in the transparent nose. A total of 65 Mosquitos were built at Chester. (de Havilland photo)

Boscombe Down for service trials on 23 June. It was fitted with an early standard AI radar, the first airborne tests being against a target Blenheim on 5 September. The design of the Mosquito was so smooth and drag-free that the crews had difficulty slowing down for interceptions, and a Youngman frill type airbrake was fitted round the fuselage just aft of the wing trailing edge. Flight-testing continued from 1 January to 1 August 1942. However, in practice it was found to be just as effective to use the flaps to slow down, without all of the additional complication and weight of the airbrake installation.

The matt black finish was found to reduce the top speed by up to 10 per cent, or the equivalent of 26 mph (42 km/h), owing to the extra drag, so this was replaced by normal day-fighter camouflage. The flight development programme generally went well, but problems were found with the flutter of the fabric-covered elevators, particularly with the original short engine nacelles. The engine exhaust system caused other headaches. It was not unknown for the individual stubs to become detached from the base, and there were difficulties with the saxophone flame-damping exhaust fitted to the night-fighters to help to avoid detection by the target aircraft. W4052 was fitted with new, stronger engine cowlings to cope with the extra weight of the night-fighter exhausts.

Like any powerful twin-engined aircraft, the Mosquito could fly on one engine in the event of a power failure, but the ease of control was reduced. On Sunday 19 April 1942, Geoffrey de Havilland Jnr was flying at 20,000 ft (6,096 m) over Bedford when the port engine began vibrating. As a precaution, he shut down the faulty engine, and with plenty of height he headed back to Hatfield. Once committed to land, a departing Proctor, the pilot not realising the emergency, took off in the way of the Mosquito, and Geoffrey had to struggle over Welwyn Garden City with the Mosquito on one engine at low speed, trying to retract the flaps and undercarriage to reduce drag, but without losing the lift at such a low speed. He saw Panshanger in front, formerly a decoy airfield site, but by then the home of the de Havilland-operated flying school equipped with Tiger Moths. He made a wheels-up emergency landing on the grass, demonstrating the resilience and ease of repair of the wooden structure. The aircraft was jacked up the next day and, after repair, was flown out of Panshanger on 5 May. Geoffrey had to make a further wheels-up landing at Hatfield on 29 May, when the undercarriage failed to lower on B.MkIV DK291.

In early 1941 the development of the fighter-bomber Mosquito commenced, using the basic fighter airframe but with the AI radar left out, and the smaller bomb bay, owing to the 20 mm cannon installation, fitted out to carry two 250 lb (113.5 kg) bombs internally, with two more under the wings. These aircraft were initially known as intruders, optimised for ground attack, and the capability was further increased when the bomb vanes were clipped, allowing space for two 500 lb (227 kg) bombs internally. Not only did the Mosquito make an effective ground attack aircraft, but it could also share the precision attacks with the bombers, with the forward-firing guns helping to combat the defences of the more active targets. DZ434 was the first FB.MkVI, and made its maiden flight on 1 June 1942. However, by the time it had been delivered to Boscombe Down for service trials, it had become HJ662. The FB.MkVI continued in production for the remainder of the war with little change, the Leavesden factory near Watford specialising in the fighter airframes.

The only significant development of the FB.MkVI was the MkXVIII, which was adapted for maritime duties against German U-boats in the Bay of Biscay. This was known as the Tsetse, and, in place of the four 20 mm cannons under the cockpit floor, a single 57 mm 6 lb Molins cannon was fitted. There was concern that the firing of this cannon would be too much for the wooden structure of the Mosquito, but in fact the plane was found to absorb the loads better than a metal structure. The initial installation was made in a scrap fuselage, and the first gun was installed at Hatfield in HJ732 during April 1943. Firing trials started in early June at the Hatfield gun-butts, where high-speed photography was used to identify any reasons for stoppages. After two days of ground firing the aircraft was flown on 8 June and delivered to Boscombe Down four days later for service trials, which covered the firing of some 800 rounds over a two-month period. Only a small number of these conversions were made. As on normal ship-busting operations, a salvo of unguided rockets fired from under the Mosquito wings was equivalent to a broadside from a cruiser. However, the conning tower of a submarine was a more precise target, where the machine-guns in the nose could help with aiming, and the shell from the Molins cannon could punch a hole in the U-boat hull. The rate of fire of the Molins gun was twenty-five shells in 20 sec, and, when fired, the Mosquito momentarily slowed as a result of the recoil. The MkXVIII Mosquito could also carry eight 60 lb rockets, two 500 lb bombs or two 100 gal (454 l) drop tanks under the wings. No. 618 Squadron was the main user of this version of the Mosquito and started operations from Predannack in Cornwall on 24 October 1943.

With all the available space where the load could be carried in the Mosquito bombers, the fighter versions could take advantage by the installation of additional fuel tanks under the wing centre section. Where the fighter-bomber had space behind the cannons for bombs and a 50 gal (227 l) fuel tank, the fighter versions had capacity for an additional 151 gal (686 l), the first trial installation being made on W4096. To simplify production the Mosquito wing was strengthened for the carriage of bombs and fuel tanks and standardised across all versions.

The early night-fighter Mosquitos were fitted with a basic AI radar system, recognised by an arrowhead antenna pointing out of the nose between the machine-guns, with additional antennae fitted near the wing-tips. As the radar technology improved, a scanner was fitted on the nose with the protection of a radome, displacing the machine-guns. The radome was made from early composite materials, which were electronically transparent, allowing efficient operation of the airborne radar.

The first thimble radome installation, housing AI MkVII, was on Mosquito DD715 in July 1942. After successful trials at the Royal Radar Establishment (RRE) at Defford, authority was given for ninety-seven MkIIs to be taken from the Leavesden production line and delivered to Marshall at Cambridge for the fitting of the radomes. The first two aircraft were HJ945 and HJ946, with work commencing on 2 January 1943. When the airframe conversion was completed, the aircraft were flown to Defford for the fitting of the secret radar. These aircraft became the Mosquito NF.MkXII, and initial deliveries were to No. 85 Squadron on 28 February, ready for operational service. The NF.MkXIII was developed from the FB.MkVI airframe, powered by Merlin 21 or 23 engines, fitted with the universal wing and with the endurance increased further by the increase of fuel capacity from 547 to 716 gal (2,486 to 3,255 l).

Because of the parallel development of airborne radar by both Britain and the USA, it was important to make provision for both in the Mosquito, and a new universal nose radome was produced for this purpose. Powered by Merlin 25s, this became the NF.MkXIX, the initial conversion being DZ659, which was fitted with the first of 2,000 American AI/SCR720 radars in January 1943. Marshall was again involved in the conversion programme, with a further ninety-eight NF.IIs taken from the Leavesden

The cockpit of the Mosquito FB.MkVI featured the fighter-type stick, and on the right is the rear side of the protective armour-plated bulkhead. The main flying instruments are in the top centre, and engine indications are on the left side of the panel. (de Havilland photo)

production line to be configured for the American radar as the NF.MkXVII. Meanwhile the first NF.MkXIX was delivered to Ford for trials on 1 April, only eight weeks after the conversion was started.

In April 1944 the NF.Mk30 was developed from the MkXIX, with power coming from a pair of two-stage Merlin 72s, MM686 being the first example. Fortunately the earlier marks were still effective in combat, as the Mk30 suffered from exhaust shroud problems, delaying its service entry until late in 1944. Once in service, the Mk30 served with great success in Fighter

Command, 100 Group, the 8th USAAF and, post-war, in the Belgian Air Force.

The Mosquito NF.Mk36 was the final version to see RAF service. As well as having improvements to the radar, it was also fitted with the more powerful Merlin 113 engines. The ultimate Mosquito night-fighter was the NF.Mk38, which had an even better radar, but this was not adopted by the RAF. Much of the production was diverted to the emerging Yugoslav Air Force, an NF.Mk38 being the last Mosquito built when it was completed at Hawarden near Chester.

5. Special Variants

The Mosquito excelled not only as a bomber, fighter and photo-reconnaissance aircraft, but also in a number of additional tasks. These developments included further specialist bomber and fighter variants, as well as adaptations for carrying passengers and the more mundane task of target towing. The Mosquito was truly a multi-role combat aircraft, performing all of its duties with success and demonstrating its adaptability.

In all of the developments, the basic airframe was retained, but the shape was changed by the addition of equipment and role-demanded requirements. During the summer of 1942 a new threat came from high flying Junkers Ju.86P bombers, which were too high for the ground-based anti-aircraft guns and beyond the reach of most of the defensive aircraft within the timescale for interception, before the aircraft could escape. These aircraft carried a small bomb load of 250 kg (551 lb), owing to being at the extremity of their performance, and were infrequent visitors on what were mainly nuisance raids. They are known to have dropped bombs in the Bristol, Cheltenham and South Wales areas initially, and the Spitfire was considered for the defence against these high raiders, but the combination of a pressure cabin and the two-stage Merlin 61 was not available. Even if the Spitfire could have got close to the raider, which usually came over Britain in clear weather, the Ju.86P could drop its load and dive away rapidly to escape.

On 24 August 1942 a Ju.86P dropped a 50 kg (110 lb) bomb on Camberley from an estimated altitude of 38,000 ft (11,582 m). The next day a second Ju.86P dropped a 250 kg bomb over Hertfordshire. On 29 August another high flyer dropped its bomb on Histon, Cambridgeshire, the defending Spitfires from Debden failing to intercept. A week later a further bomb was dropped from high altitude on Luton, and the raider flew directly over the Hatfield factory on the route home and was seen clearly by members of the Mosquito design team. A Spitfire sent up from Manston in Kent managed to shoot at the raider, but stalled at the extreme altitude and missed.

It was at this stage that Phil Smith and other members of the team commenced work on the high-altitude Mosquito MkXV, selecting the pressure cabin bomber prototype, MP469, for conversion with two Merlin 61 engines driving four-blade propellers and an increased wingspan to 59 ft (18 m). The surplus four-gun nose, which had been removed from DD715 when the radome was fitted, was grafted on MP469 to replace the original bomber nose. To aim for an altitude of around 43,000 ft (13,106 m), the weight was reduced by removing the armour plating and reducing fuel tankage, as well as many other detail changes.

Once again demonstrating the versatility of the Mosquito and the dedication of the de Havilland team, the modified aircraft was rolled out for engine runs only a week after being given the go-ahead, weighing 2,300 lb (1043 kg) lighter than a standard MkII Mosquito. John de Havilland made the first flight on 14 September, and the next day he flew it to an altitude of 43,500 ft (13,259 m), well above that being achieved by the Ju.86P

To combat the high flying German Ju.86P aircraft the Mosquito MkXV was rapidly developed from the pressure cabin bomber prototype MP469 with the surplus four-gun nose grafted on from DD715. This was the only version of the Mosquito fighter to have a Vee windscreen and lower crew access door. (de Havilland photo)

With the high flying day threat over, it was believed that the Germans may have planned high flying night attacks. Mosquito MkXV MP469 was further modified to have the nose with machine guns replaced with one housing AI MkVIII radar. With no cannon armament in this aircraft that was built as a bomber, a ventral gun pack housing four .303 in machine guns was attached below the bomb bay. (MOS press photo)

Pressure cabin Mosquito NF.MkXV DZ366 was one of four conversions from the B.MkIV fitted with AI MkVIII in the nose. This aircraft was delivered to No. 85 Squadron in March 1943, by which time the four-blade propellers had been replaced with three-blade units. DZ366 remained with the squadron until the high altitude threat had passed in August 1943, and was later used for ground instruction at Cranwell. (de Havilland photo)

Mosquito NF.MkXV DZ385 was another conversion from the MkIV, the .303 in ventral gun pack being lighter and easier to install than a pack with four 20 mm cannons. (MOS press photo)

The first trial installation of 'Highball' was made in Mosquito DK290/G which was flown to Heston for the modifications to commence on 24 March 1943.

Another role for the Mosquito was conversion training, and the T.MkIII was produced in Britain, based on the fighter airframe but with the guns deleted. The T.MkIII had dual controls and TV959 and RR299 both served with the Home Command Communications Squadron based at White Waltham. TV959 is now stored at Duxford pending restoration, and RR299 was lost in a fatal crash at Barton on 21 July 1996 while being operated as a historic aircraft by British Aerospace.

Mosquito T.MkIII served with 204 AFS at Driffield for aircrew conversion to the Mosquito.

Redundant Mosquito T.MkIIIs LR539, LR554 and TW112 with useful parts being salvaged at 27 MU Shawbury in July 1956 before being scrapped. (Shanks photo)

aircraft. On 16 September the first aircraft was collected by a member of No. 151 Squadron and flown to RAF Northolt to await the German raiders, who in fact never came. Only five Ju.86s had been converted to pressure cabin versions, and, with the deteriorating winter weather, flights ceased after twelve operations unknown to the RAF.

During practice patrols, to keep weight to a minimum, the aircraft was operated by a pilot only. It took about 35 min to reach 42,000 ft (12,800 m) with sufficient fuel remaining for 2 hrs endurance. By reducing fuel further, and therefore the endurance, the Mosquito was able to reach 45,000 ft (13,715 m). Pressurisation was only 2 lb/sq in (0.14 kg/sq cm), but it reduced the cabin altitude by about 12,000 ft (3,658 m), although the pilot still had to breathe oxygen.

With the approaching winter and the high-altitude day threat apparently gone, there was concern that the Germans could fly similar operations at night. Once again, MP469 entered the workshops and had a further change of nose, this time having a radome fitted over AI MkVIII, with associated power systems. Because this aircraft had started life as a bomber, there were no 20 mm cannons under the fuselage, and it still had the lower fuselage bomber-type entry door. To provide offensive armament, four 303 in machine-guns, as they were lighter than the cannons, were fitted in a special ventral fairing under the fuselage centre section. Because of the radar installation, the second crew member was restored and two 24 gal (109 l) internal wing fuel tanks were put back, increasing the overall weight to 17,400 lb (7,829 kg). However the performance was still sufficient that, at 42,000 ft (12,800 m), the rate of climb was still a surprising 500 ft/m (2.54 m/sec). As a result, it was decided to convert a further four B.MkIVs – DZ366, DZ385, DZ409, and DZ417 – to the same configuration with the designation NF.MkXV.

By the middle of March 1943 the new fighters were delivered to the Fighter Interception Unit (FIU) at Ford for service trials. They were then taken to No. 85 Squadron at Hunsdon in Hertfordshire, which was commanded by Gp Capt. John Cunningham. These specialist Mosquitos were formed into a C Flight for operational trials from the end of April until the middle of August. The greatest height reached was 44,600 ft (13,593 m), in MP469, but no contact was made with the enemy. The aircraft were withdrawn from operational service, two of them being delivered to Farnborough for pressure cabin trials. One of these was written off in an accident, and the survivors were later allocated to ground instruction duties.

Dr Barnes Wallis and No. 617 Squadron are well known for the dam-busting raid on the Mohne, Eder and Sorpe dams, in an effort to disrupt the industrial might of the Ruhr Valley. What is less well known is that the dam-busting 'Upkeep' bouncing mines used by No. 617 Squadron were scaled down, to be known as 'Highball' mines, and two of these could be carried by the Mosquito. The principle of 'Highball' was very similar to 'Upkeep', but it was intended as an anti-shipping weapon. Two were dropped simultaneously by a Mosquito, and bounced across the water until they hit the side of a ship. They then sank beside the hull, until the explosion was set off by a hydrostatic fuse, blowing the underside out of the ship. The obvious target was the *Tirpitz* sheltering in Alten Fiord in Northern Norway, but any such operation was beyond the return endurance of the Mosquito. Thus after a long flight over the North Sea, and the hazards of the attack against a well-defended and difficult target, the crews would have to find somewhere to force-land in enemy territory.

The two mines were carried in tandem by the Mosquito, with the bomb doors removed to give clearance. The mines were rotated backwards at 1,000 rpm before dropping, and had to be released in daylight from a height of 25 ft (7.6 m) about a mile (1,600 m) from the target. The need for the bouncing bombs was to clear the defensive torpedo netting and other countermeasures, and the mines would sink down the side of the ship's hull, exploding the 600 lb (272 kg) charge at a pre-set depth.

The first Mosquito for the trial installation of the conversion, DK290, was flown into Heston on 24 March 1943 for the modifications to commence. The planned date for the attack on the *Tirpitz* was 15 May, so No. 618 Squadron, led by Sqn Ldr C.F. Rose, borrowed some Mosquitos from Marham to begin intensive training with the hand-picked crews.

The flight trials with the Mosquito showed up similar problems to those experienced with the original 'Upkeep' weapon for the dams raid. The effects of the compromise between weight and strength were difficult to predict, and in early tests a number of the mine cases broke on impact with the water. In addition, the release gear caused problems, resulting in an inevitable delay of the attack date.

The first two of the converted Mosquitos were delivered to No. 618 Squadron at Skitten in the north of Scotland on 14 May, with the balance of 13 arriving by the end of the month, even though 'Highball' was still not operating successfully under test. By the end of the first week in July, the 32 in (81 cm) mine, with a ⅛ in (7 mm) steel case was withstanding the impact of the drop, but an accurate form of sighting still needed to be developed. The use of 'Highball' dropped by Mosquitos was only one of a number of schemes being considered for the attack on the *Tirpitz*. Because the raid would have to be in daylight, not only would it be hazardous, but also there was concern that Germany might discover the secrets of the bouncing bomb and use it against the Allies. What was not realised at the

time was that one of the 'Upkeep' bombs had been dropped on the earth Sorpe Dam on the dams raid and was found lying unexploded on the top of the wall. It had therefore been dismantled and its secrets revealed.

In mid-August 'Highball' was considered as an anti-submarine weapon by being used as a depth charge. The overall anti-shipping trials went well enough to encourage the ordering of another 250 mines from Vickers, and further training was started from the new No. 618 Squadron base at Wick. Another scheme tried with 'Highball' was to drop it on land aimed at the mouth of a tunnel, where, after entering, it would blow up, thus bringing the tunnel down. However, as with all of the operations, a practical form of sighting was still causing a problem. Another headache was manning a special squadron with highly skilled and motivated crews, but not providing them with any operations. To maintain morale, therefore, a number of crews were detached to No. 248 Squadron at Predannack to fly Mosquito MkXVIIIs on anti-U-boat operations over the Bay of Biscay.

With the Allies progressing across the continent after D-Day, it was decided on 9 July 1944 that No. 618 Squadron, with the 'Highball' mines, should be deployed to the Asian War and be used in anti-shipping operations against the Japanese Navy. For this the Mosquitos required some modifications, including more powerful Merlin 25 engines with a 36 lb boost driving four-blade propellers, arrester hooks for carrier operations, additional armour plating and air turbines for spinning the stores. The urgent conversion work was contracted to Marshall in Cambridge and Airspeed in Portsmouth. The first two B.MkIVs, DZ554/G and DZ555/G, were flown to RAF Thorney Island on 6 July 1944, as the RAF pilots were hesitant to try to land the aircraft at the rather small airfield at Portsmouth. Airspeed test pilots Ron Clear and Bob Milne collected the aircraft from Thorney Island and managed

Mosquito Mk35 RS719 was the first conversion to the target-towing configuration by Airspeed at Christchurch fitted with the winch under the bomb bay. (MOS press photo)

the challenging task of landing them at Portsmouth, despite the fact that they had never flown the type previously. Milne's landing was incredibly short, and a distance that Clear was unable to match, but he later found the reason was that the emergency hatch had blown off on take-off from Thorney Island, giving Milne a very accurate stalling speed indication for the approach to Portsmouth, a feature that Clear did not have for his landing on the 1,000 yd (914 m) grass strip.

Following the conversion of the Mosquitos, they were delivered to No. 618 Squadron at Beccles, where the runway had been marked to represent the deck of a carrier for deck operational training. All 24 Mosquito MkIVs modified for 'Highball' operations had been returned to No. 618 Squadron by September 1944, with the addition of three PR.MkXVIs. Capt. Eric 'Winkle' Brown had already proved the Mosquito to be capable of deck operations when he made the first landing of a twin-engined plane on an aircraft carrier on 25 March 1944. Although successful landings and take-offs were made with the PR.MkXVIs on

10 October, it was decided to minimise the risks. Thus all of the Mosquitos were loaded on to the carriers HMS *Fencer* and HMS *Striker* in Glasgow docks ready for the ships to sail on 31 October, reaching Melbourne on 23 December.

On their arrival, the crews started further training, but no operations were sanctioned, despite many tempting targets, owing largely to the American domination of the war against Japan. The dropping of the atom bombs brought an abrupt end to hostilities, and No. 618 Squadron was disbanded in Australia on 29 July. Thus a highly trained and motivated squadron had not made a single offensive sortie in its intended role. The aircraft were left where they were, eventually being broken up, although enough metal parts of one of them survived and are forming part of a challenging restoration more than 50 years after the aircraft were abandoned. The stock of 125 'Highball' mines was statically detonated to avoid the concept getting into hostile hands, although they were somewhat specialised.

Mosquitos were also used as trainers, high-

Mosquito FB.MkVI LR359 on the final approach to HMS Indefatigable *on 25 March 1944, to make the first landing by a twin engined aircraft on a carrier at sea. (FAAM photo)*

value cargo and courier carriers, and target tugs, as already mentioned. The Mosquito T.MkIII was based on the fighter-bomber airframe, and it had all offensive armament removed and the bomb doors locked closed. The T.III, and the equivalents from Australia and Canada, provided a useful conversion trainer for new Mosquito aircrews, as well as checking currency and flying instrument rating tests. T.MkIII RR299, operated by British Aerospace, was the last Mosquito flying, and it was lost with its crew in a tragic crash at Barton near Manchester on 21 July 1996.

Mention has already been made of the target-towing capability, a number of the later B.Mk35s being converted by Brooklands Aviation into TT.Mk35s. The major modification was to fit a target-towing winch below the bomb bay, and wire guards around the tail to avoid the controls being fouled by the target cable. The aircraft were painted silver overall, with yellow and black diagonal stripes on the undersides to improve visibility.

These Mosquitos could be used for air-to-air target practice, and for ground-to-air practice for shipping and coastal guns. A number were based with 3 CAACU at Exeter and were the last Mosquitos to serve with the RAF, although they were operated by civilian crews under contract. Some of them were used in the films *633 Squadron* and *Mosquito Squadron*, both made at Bovingdon, and a few of those that have survived are now preserved.

Any further developments of the Mosquito, involving greater power, higher altitude and greater load-carrying ability, were overtaken by other projects as aerospace began to enter the jet age.

Many surplus Mosquitos were sold overseas after the Second World War, both to Allied air forces and, in some cases, to civilian operators for photo-survey work in the more remote regions of the world. These operations will be covered in more detail in later chapters, as well as the 'Ball-bearing' flights to Sweden operated by BOAC crews from Leuchars.

6. PRODUCTION IN BRITAIN

The Mosquito was designed for ease of production and repair, but, as it turned out, it was also ideally suited for everything from major assemblies, such as the one-piece wing and the fuselage shell, to the smallest electrical components being built in widely dispersed factories and workshops. De Havilland set up a number of its own dispersed workshops around the assembly-line locations, as well as subcontracting other parts to a range of specialist companies around the country. Complete wings were made at the now closed ESA factory in Stevenage, and the former bus overhaul works at Aldenham made fuselages for the Leavesden production line. These facilities were not the only producers of wings and fuselages: to avoid any major disruption by enemy attack, a number of other factories in the woodworking industry were employed on this vital work. The broad commonality of parts, for both the fighter and bomber variants, helped to sustain volume production.

The fuselages were formed in two half shells over concrete moulds, like half lobster shells, to allow ease of access for the installation of the systems and equipment. The monocoque structure consisted of the fuselage formers, bulkheads and structural members located in pre-formed slots in the moulds. Glue was applied, and thin layers of birch ply laid over and held in place by metal straps while the glue set. The stabilising balsa, threaded ferrules for the location of components and any spruce structural members were in turn glued into place and strapped down for curing. It was then time for the final outer layer of birch ply to be glued

and hardened, before the removal of the shell, and then mounted in vertical jigs for the installation of the equipment in locations that would otherwise have been difficult to gain access to. For the more maintenance-intensive systems, the location was in more accessible parts of the fuselage shell to ease rectification in service. The stressed fuselage shell was then joined with a strap around the entire centre line to form a lightweight smooth structure.

The one-piece wing was initially built in a vertical jig with the leading edge down, resting on the straight front spar. The front and rear spars were built from spruce laminated planks about ½ in thick, and in between were the ribs made up with spruce members and birch ply webs. The thicker birch ply wing-skins were double layer on the top surface overall but the outer wingtip area, separated by Douglas fir formed stringers, which were glued and attached to the skins as well as using many brass screws. The underside skins on the outboard wing section were a single birch ply layer. However, where the fuel tanks were located in the wing on either side of the Merlin engine mountings, stressed engine bay doors were bolted on, made from birch ply skins with balsa infill, complying with the airfoil shape of the undersurface. The one-piece wing was then laid horizontally for the fitting of the leading edges, the flap and aileron shrouds, and the wingtips, before doping and covering with light medapolan fabric, ready for painting in whatever colours were required. The wings were then ready for delivery to the production line to which they were allocated.

The tailplane was structurally a scaled-down version of the wing, and the fin was made similarly. The flaps were a simple wood, plain structure involving a spruce spar with spruce and ply ribs, covered by birch ply.

Engine cowlings, ailerons and elevators were of aluminium construction, and the rudder was of aluminium structure with fabric covering.

A total of 7,619 Mosquitos were produced in Britain, Canada and Australia, 6,710 during the Second World War. Of these totals, the Hatfield factory produced 3,054 during the war, in addition to repairing 1,252 more in the factory or in the field, keeping the aircraft in operation. Often the more complex metal combat aircraft took longer to repair or were more easily written off. The wooden structure of the Mosquito was no more susceptible to fire damage than the metal aircraft. It did, however, suffer more from the elements, particularly before the casein glue was replaced by the Ciba-Geigy developed formaldehyde adhesive, which was later developed into the Redux bonding of metal to metal to replace riveting.

In addition to the Hatfield production lines, which tended to specialise, though not exclusively, in the building of the bomber/PR variants, the de Havilland shadow factory was set up at Leavesden to produce Mosquito fighter/fighter-bomber airframes, as well as another part of the factory building Handley Page Halifax under licence. Standard Motors at Coventry also built the fighter/fighter-bomber versions, using its expertise in volume production. Percival Aircraft at Luton and the Airspeed factory at Portsmouth assembled bombers, while the de Havilland factories in Australia and Canada developed their own versions based on the parent company's aircraft, but, where appropriate, using locally produced equipment and engines.

After the war, the Hatfield factory became busy with a number of other projects, particularly the Comet jet airliner, so additional production capacity was acquired at Hawarden near Chester in the old wartime Vickers factory used for the assembly of Wellingtons and, later, Lincolns. In 1948 de Havilland took over this factory, where most of the remaining Mosquitos were built. Small batches were also made at the Airspeed factory at Christchurch, where some were converted to target tugs. Marshall in Cambridge also played a major part in the modification, repair and support of the Mosquito during the hostilities.

In all of the production facilities, female labour played a vital part in building the Mosquitos, alongside the men who had not been called up for military service. In addition to de Havilland Aircraft being responsible for the massive task of controlling Mosquito production, the de Havilland engine factories overhauled more than 9,000 Rolls-Royce Merlin engines – not just for Mosquitos, but also for Spitfires, Hurricanes and Lancasters. Having acquired licences from Hamilton Standard in 1934, de Havilland also manufactured more than 12,000 propellers for Mosquitos and a further 90,000 propellers for many other types of Allied aircraft. In addition, nearly 41,000 propellers were repaired or overhauled, the technique being perfected for straightening blades that had been damaged during forced landings.

To keep the project alive, de Havilland had to promise 50 Mosquitos to be delivered by the end of 1941. This was considered by some to be almost impossible to achieve, and further delays were caused by the constant changes of versions. If the original requirement had remained for bombers only, that deadline would have been achievable. However, with the changes to 20 PR Mosquitos, and 30 of the fighters with the modified fuselage, only 20 aircraft were completed by the deadline. The fiftieth Mosquito was delivered by the middle of

On the flight line in October 1943 is a mixed batch of Mosquitos including an FB.Mk VI and an unidentified PR version. (de Havilland photo)

The fighter/fighter-bomber production line at the Leavesden factory near Watford, where a total of 1,566 Mosquitos were built. (de Havilland photo)

Mosquito fighter-bomber production at Hatfield. The aircraft were built sideways on a rolling track developed from Standard Motors expertise. The bomber line is beyond.

Lined up at Hatfield in November 1942 during the production flight test programme are Mosquito B.MkIVs DZ372, DZ371 and DZ362 together with F.MkIIs DZ253 and DZ255. (de Havilland photo)

March 1942. However, by this time, the Mosquito was well established, and not only was there total acceptance, but the demand and enthusiasm was growing continually.

The first Mosquito to enter operational service was PR.MkI W4055, which was delivered to the PRU at Benson on 7 August 1941. The first active bomber was W4057, which was delivered on 23 September. The Leavesden production turned out their first Mosquito, a dual-control fighter, at the end of January 1942, and it was flown to Hatfield for flight testing. As the Hatfield production on the Mosquito grew, the earlier established assembly lines were moved out, the Tiger Moth going to Morris Motors at Cowley, Oxford, the Dominie to Brush at Loughborough and the Airspeed Oxfords back to Airspeed.

There was a great deal of confusion in the early days while the RAF decided exactly which versions of the Mosquito were to take priority. Because of this it was difficult to settle on a contract, which would then authorise de Havilland to order the materials for the aircraft, as well as the jigs and tools, and to commence training the labour to build them. With production started on the bomber variants, and then the change to fighters, the noses had to be cut off and replaced by fighter types. This at least demonstrated the ease of repair and modification, which could almost certainly not have been achieved with a metal construction.

In preparation for the anticipated high rates of aircraft production, de Havilland had been setting up the Leavesden factory. The factory was initially intended for building Armstrong Whitworth Albemarles, but because this aircraft was not very successful, the production order was changed to Vickers Wellington bombers at a rate of up to thirty aircraft per month. De Havilland was quite naturally less than enthusiastic about building the products of other design teams, and was thus relieved when the factory was allocated to Mosquito production. The new factory complex had to

be designed and built before setting up the self-contained Mosquito production line, which was supported by the Aldenham bus depot making fuselages, and the First World War Acton factory of Alliance which supplied the wings. The Hatfield factory dispersed 60 per cent of Mosquito production to the surrounding area, leaving about 3,500 people employed in the main factory, which was about the number later employed in peacetime.

The subcontract organisation started in 1940 with two High Wycombe furniture makers, E. Gomme Ltd and Dancer & Hearne Ltd, making wing spars and other wooden assemblies, plus some jigs and tools. The specialist motor engineers Van den Plas and H.J. Mulliners produced some metal fittings. The subcontracting organisation continued to grow in 1941, the smallest supplier being a domestic group of housewives and retired men who assembled electrical components in an enlarged garden shed at Welwyn.

The factory buildings that had been destroyed by the German bomber in October 1941, previously known as the 94 Shop, where the pre-war Moth Minor had been constructed, were rebuilt as the Mosquito Repair Organisation (MRO), and a supplementary production was set up for the workers to gain experience with the aircraft before the department became busy with salvage and repair once the Mosquito had entered service.

To gain experience in large-scale production from the motor manufacturers, Ernest Grinham was seconded from Standard Motors at Coventry to organise the production line at Hatfield. His experience was later used to operate additional production at Coventry, so it was perhaps not surprising that a number of the de Havilland directors selected the Standard Vanguard car after the end of the war.

Some of the early fighter Mosquitos were provided with dual controls, not to be used as trainers but to allow the navigator to share the flying duties on longer endurance operations. In the event of the pilot being incapacitated, this feature also gave the navigator a sporting chance of flying back to friendly territory and attempting a forced landing.

By the end of July 1941, plans were well advanced for Mosquito production in the de Havilland Canada factory at Downsview, close to Toronto, and production in the USA was considered, but not proceeded with. The Ministry of Aircraft production was considering ordering up to 500 Mosquitos, with the production rate of 150 aircraft per month being planned from Hatfield, Leavesden and Downsview. In mid-July, bombers were produced by the fairly simple conversion of 10 PR aircraft in Contract 69990, and the last 50 in Contract 555 were completed as bombers.

It was important for de Havilland to keep the Ministry of Aircraft Production supplying the early contract cover at a sufficient rate for the ordering of long-lead materials and equipment in advance, to obtain the levels of priority required to match the desired delivery rate to the ever eager RAF squadrons. With only relatively small initial orders, the growing production rate satisfied the requirements quickly, with the potential of having gaps in the production process. The monthly production rate grew from 150 to 160, and then up to a possible 200 Mosquitos, with bombers coming off the lines from January 1942.

Canadian production, starting with the supply of British equipment and parts to reduce delays, started in September 1942, supplying both the RAF and the RCAF squadrons operating from Britain, with the rate building up to fifty aircraft a month by May 1943. It was not just a case of building Mosquitos for delivery into operational service; spares also had to be produced to keep the existing aircraft operational, accounting for about 20 per cent additional effort.

By January 1942, orders placed had reached 1,778 Mosquitos of all types, Hatfield being responsible for 928, Leavesden 450 and Canada 400. To achieve the required rate of delivery, many of the employees were working at least a 50-hour week, while management were working 12-hour days, with one half-day off a week if the time could be spared. Also, in early 1942 it was decided to set up a further Mosquito production line in Australia at the de Havilland factory at Bankstown near Sydney. The exercise of setting up production in Canada had to be repeated, but much further away, increasing the risk of losses to enemy action of drawings, tools, parts and the technical experts used to reduce the delays in starting production to a minimum. The Australian production supplied the Pacific theatre, as the distances were too far to bring Australian-produced aircraft to Europe, when there was a need anyway for the planes in the war against Japan.

In the early stages of ordering Mosquitos, priority had been given to fighter variants, but in April 1942 it was realised that not enough bombers were being built to meet the urgent demand. The next month a further 261 Mosquito bombers were ordered from Hatfield, followed at the end of the month by 350 FB.MkVIs, with another 360 FB.MkVIs from Leavesden. The Canadian factories were advised to prepare for the production of up to another 1,100 aircraft. In one month, total orders had reached 3,849 Mosquitos. In parallel with the increased production at the main assembly lines, the sub-contract organisation had to grow to ensure that there were no critical shortages. The most effective way to manage the flow of parts was for de Havilland to order the materials, gaining better prices for bulk orders, besides which it was the parent company that had the overall contract authority to order materials and equipment. Some 400 subcontractors would then manufacture the parts to high levels of accuracy to ensure interchangeability, and deliver them to the allocated final assembly

Reprinted from "The Aeroplane," May 7, 1943

THE DE HAVILLAND MOSQUITO

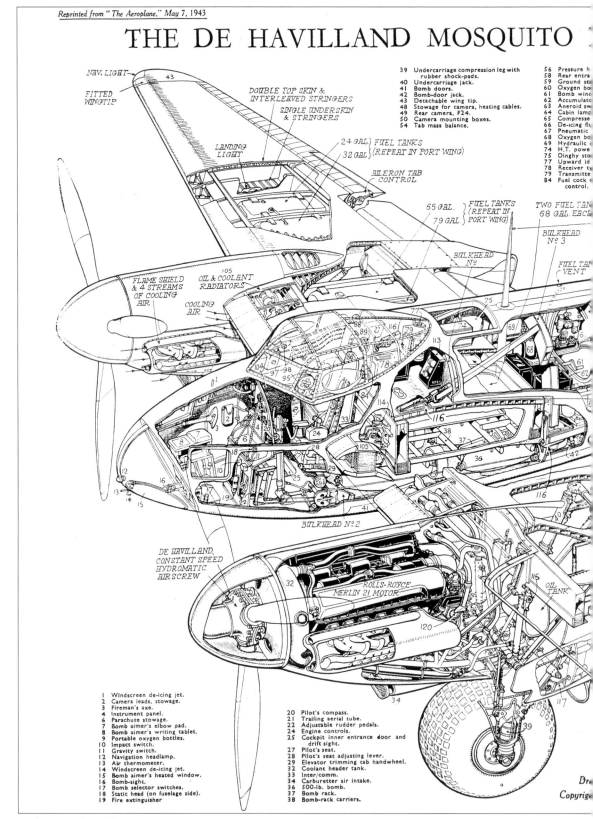

NAV. LIGHT

FITTED WINGTIP

DOUBLE TOP SKIN & INTERLEAVED STRINGERS

SINGLE UNDERSKIN & STRINGERS

LANDING LIGHT

24 GAL. FUEL TANKS
32 GAL. (REPEAT IN PORT WING)

AILERON TAB CONTROL

65 GAL. FUEL TANKS
79 GAL. (REPEAT IN PORT WING)

TWO FUEL TANKS
68 GAL. EACH

BULKHEAD Nº 3

FUEL TANK VENT

FLAME SHIELD & 4 STREAMS OF COOLING AIR

OIL & COOLANT RADIATORS

COOLING AIR

BULKHEAD Nº 2

DE HAVILLAND CONSTANT SPEED HYDROMATIC AIRSCREW

ROLLS-ROYCE MERLIN 21 MOTOR

OIL TANK

BULKHEAD Nº 2

39	Undercarriage compression leg with rubber shock-pads.
40	Undercarriage jack.
41	Bomb doors.
42	Bomb-door jack.
43	Detachable wing tip.
48	Stowage for camera, heating cables.
49	Rear camera, F24.
50	Camera mounting boxes.
54	Tab mass balance.

56	Pressure h
58	Rear entra
59	Ground sta
60	Oxygen b
61	Bomb win
62	Accumulat
63	Aneroid sw
64	Cabin lamp
65	Compresse
66	De-icing fl
67	Pneumatic
68	Oxygen bo
69	Hydraulic
74	H.T. powe
75	Dinghy sto
77	Upward id
78	Receiver ty
79	Transmitte
84	Fuel cock control.

1	Windscreen de-icing jet.
2	Camera leads, stowage.
3	Fireman's axe.
4	Instrument panel.
6	Parachute stowage.
7	Bomb aimer's elbow pad.
8	Bomb aimer's writing tablet.
9	Portable oxygen bottles.
10	Impact switch.
11	Gravity switch.
12	Navigation headlamp.
13	Air thermometer.
14	Windscreen de-icing jet.
15	Bomb aimer's heated window.
16	Bomb-sight.
17	Bomb selector switches.
18	Static head (on fuselage side).
19	Fire extinguisher

20	Pilot's compass.
21	Trailing aerial tube.
22	Adjustable rudder pedals.
24	Engine controls.
25	Cockpit inner entrance door and drift sight.
27	Pilot's seat.
28	Pilot's seat adjusting lever.
29	Elevator trimming tab handwheel.
32	Coolant header tank.
33	Inter/comm.
34	Carburetter air intake.
36	500-lb. bomb.
37	Bomb rack.
38	Bomb-rack carriers.

Dr

Copyrig

('The Aeroplane' drawing)

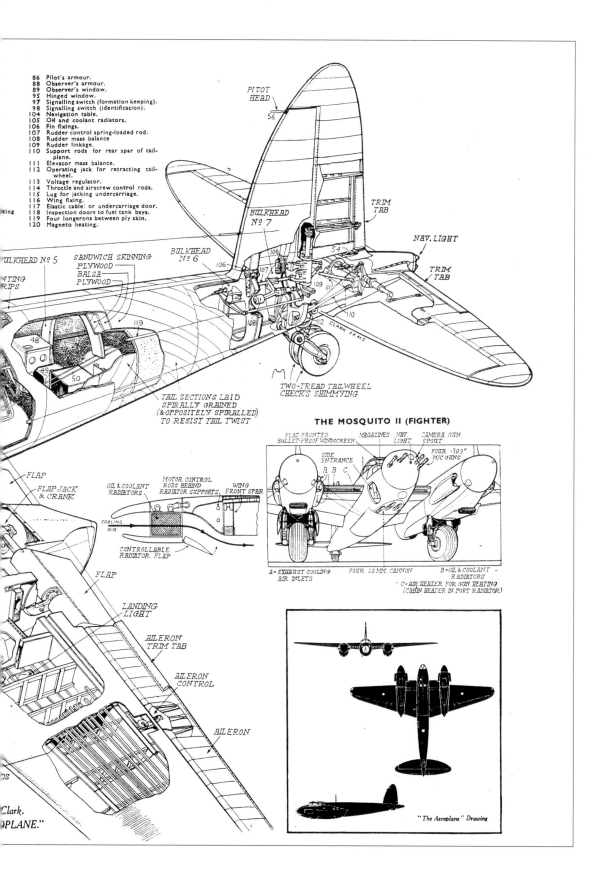

86 Pilot's armour.
88 Observer's armour.
89 Observer's window.
95 Hinged window.
97 Signalling switch (formation keeping).
98 Signalling switch (identification).
104 Navigation table.
105 OH and coolant radiators.
106 Fin fixings.
107 Rudder control spring-loaded rod.
108 Rudder mass balance.
109 Rudder linkage.
110 Support rods for rear spar of tail-plane.
111 Elevator mass balance.
112 Operating jack for retracting tail-wheel.
113 Voltage regulator.
114 Throttle and airscrew control rods.
115 Lug for jacking undercarriage.
116 Wing fixing.
117 Elastic cable for undercarriage door.
118 Inspection doors to fuel tank bays.
119 Four longerons between ply skin.
120 Magneto heating.

PITOT HEAD
56

BULKHEAD Nº 7

TRIM TAB

NAV. LIGHT

TRIM TAB

54

BULKHEAD Nº 6

BULKHEAD Nº 5

SANDWICH SKINNING
PLYWOOD
BALSA
PLYWOOD

106

107

109 111

110

CLARK ARMS

119

108

112

48

49

50

TAIL SECTIONS LAID
SPIRALLY GRAINED
(& OPPOSITELY SPIRALLED)
TO RESIST TAIL TWIST

TWO-TREAD TAILWHEEL
CHECKS SHIMMYING

THE MOSQUITO II (FIGHTER)

FLAT-FRONTED
BULLET-PROOF WINDSCREEN

MAGAZINES

NAV. LIGHT

CAMERA GUN
SPOUT

SIDE
ENTRANCE

FOUR ·303"
M/C GUNS

A B C

OIL & COOLANT
RADIATORS

MOTOR CONTROL
RODS BEHIND
RADIATOR SUPPORTS

WING
FRONT SPAR

COOLING
AIR

CONTROLLABLE
RADIATOR FLAP

A = EXHAUST COOLING
AIR INLETS

FOUR 20 M.M. CANNON

B = OIL & COOLANT
RADIATORS

C = AIR HEATER FOR GUN HEATING
(CABIN HEATER IN PORT RADIATOR)

FLAP

FLAP JACK
& CRANK

FLAP

LANDING
LIGHT

AILERON
TRIM TAB

AILERON
CONTROL

AILERON

"The Aeroplane" Drawing

Clark.

OPLANE."

The Hatfield flight line was often busy with many different Mosquitos waiting for testing to be completed. This was a typical scene in February 1944. (de Havilland photo)

The last Hatfield-built Mosquito B.Mk35 TK656 is rolled out on 10 April 1946 and was delivered on 12 May. A total of 3,349 Mosquitos were built at Hatfield and Salisbury Hall, out of a grand total of 7,781 aircraft. (de Havilland photo)

In addition to building new Mosquitos, Hatfield was the base for the Mosquito Repair Organisation (MRO). At this facility parts were salvaged from written-off Mosquitos before the remainder was scrapped. Much repair work was done in the field by the MRO as well. (de Havilland photo)

One of the major subcontractors was Wrighton Aircraft of Walthamstow in East London who, despite the bombing of London, produced their 1,000th fuselage in July 1944. (de Havilland photo)

line. Manpower at the Hatfield factory increased to about 4,700, with another 2,000 dispersed in the local area, while the Leavesden factory supported around 3,000 workers. Leavesden was basically a production unit, while Hatfield provided support for the entire programme, as well as working on the development of future projects, including the Vampire jet fighter.

A further boost to the production capability was achieved in December 1942 with the award of a contract to Standard Motors for 500 FB.MkVIs, to be built at the Ansty factory and airfield near Coventry and supplied with parts from the suburban factory at Canley. The first Mosquito from this line, HP848, was rolled out in mid-June, replacing Airspeed Oxfords in the factory, and the production rate rose to 35 Mosquitos a month by December. A second order was placed with Standard Motors for another 300 aircraft, the eventual total built at Ansty reaching 1,066, when the last FB.MkVI TE932 was completed on 21 December 1945.

Percival Aircraft at Luton was the next production factory to start building Mosquitos when it was awarded a contract for 250 B.MkIXs on 4 May 1943. Mr Grinham left Hatfield in mid-May and returned to Coventry, having boosted the capability of the production line by setting up a track assembly system, as well as making many other improvements. This allowed 71 Mosquitos to be produced that month, with a further 36 being built at Leavesden. By the end of June 1943 the combined production lines at Hatfield and Leavesden had delivered 1,000 Mosquitos, the production rate having reached around 20 aircraft a week. By the end of the year, total orders for Mosquitos were approaching 5,000 aircraft to be built in Britain alone, 2,548 coming from Hatfield, 1,544 fighter variants from Leavesden, 500 FB.MkVIs from Coventry plus the 250 bombers already ordered from Percival. Production plans were being made for

further Mosquitos to be built at the Airspeed factory at Christchurch. This was not established until after the end of the war, 12 FB.MkVIs being produced by the end of 1945, followed later by two batches of B.Mk35s, starting with VP178 in March 1946.

Mosquito production did not start at the Hawarden factory until de Havilland took it over from the production of prefabricated houses in 1948. The first de Havilland aircraft to be produced in this vast factory was a Mosquito NF.Mk38, rolled out that September, and the last Mosquito to be built, also a NF.Mk38, was completed in the same factory in November 1950.

Having experienced the close encounter with an enemy spy near Salisbury Hall in 1941, Hatfield was the subject of the attentions of a British-born double agent in early 1943. His name was Eddie Chapman. He had been convicted in Jersey for safe-breaking and was in prison when the Germans took over the Channel Islands. In return for his freedom, the Germans wanted to use his skills against the Allies. However, to ensure his loyalty, they set him a number of tests. In the first he was to be given a radio and dropped by parachute over Britain, reporting back when he had arrived successfully. His immediate reaction was to abandon the radio and give himself up to the authorities, but, by chance, he found that he had been dropped in France, and therefore quickly radioed back. By the time of his second test, he was already known to MI5 as a double agent with the codename Zigzag, and he was dropped by a German aircraft near Ely with his task to make his way to Hatfield, to sabotage the factory and delay Mosquito production. He was lucky to survive this test, as the German aircraft was shot down shortly after he made his jump by parachute.

Once at Hatfield, Chapman put on overalls and mixed with the workers during lunchtime, identifying his target as the powerhouse just inside the main gate. Although the entire plan was known to the British security service, no one in the factory was aware of it, and Chapman had to make his entry as if he was a real German spy in order to maintain the effectiveness of the planned sabotage. On the night of 2 January 1943 he was driven to the small group of houses at Smallford on the road from Hatfield to St Albans, and there he started out across the fields to the wartime boundary of the airfield. He climbed through the fence, proving that it was possible to penetrate the factory without being detected. As the Germans had not supplied him with explosives, to maintain his cover he had to steal some from a quarry at Sevenoaks in Kent. The theft was reported in local newspapers.

The so-called sabotage was planned for the night of 29 January, and with the change of shift the powerhouse was cordoned off ready for a camouflage expert and illusionist called Maskelyn to prepare the scene. A small controlled explosion was used to remove part of the roof. Some of the buildings were covered in pieces of camouflage netting to suggest damage, and pieces of electrical transformer were scattered around the site. The following day a German reconnaissance aircraft was 'allowed' through the defences to photograph the damage and thus give Chapman credibility, allowing him to return to Germany and use his safe-breaking skills to obtain top-secret German documents for the Allies.

The workers at Hatfield were told that there had been an explosion but that production would not be affected, and a report appeared in the national press announcing the sabotage of an aircraft factory without giving the location, in the normal bland way of reporting wartime activities.

7. PRODUCTION OVERSEAS

As already mentioned, in addition to production lines in Britain, further capacity was provided in the de Havilland factories in Canada and Australia, where there was not the threat of enemy action that could disrupt the efforts of building the aircraft. The Canadian production was particularly important: not only was it to provide additional Mosquitos, but, in the event of Britain being invaded by the Germans, the Canadian organisation would take over full responsibility for the aircraft. It was in July 1941 that the decision was taken to set up another Mosquito production line in Canada, to be supplied by licence-built Merlin engines produced by Packard, the first two US-built engines running on the test-bed in August 1941.

The first two Mosquitos were to be completed in Canada by September 1942 with a target production rate of fifty aircraft every month by early 1943. The Ministry of Aircraft Production was to place an order for 400 Mosquitos on Hatfield under Contract 555, which would then be subcontracted to de Havilland Canada. To assist in the start-up of the Canadian production lines, a number of key people were seconded, or sent out on extended stays, to support their colleagues. One of these people was W.D. Hunter, who took charge of design, incorporating locally produced materials and equipment, while maintaining interchangeability for ease of maintenance and repair. The chief production engineer at Hatfield, Harry Povey, went to Downsview to help to organise the new production line.

The logistical problems of sending drawings, information, jigs and tools to Canada, with the hazards of enemy action against the convoys, caused many delays and, by the time the fuselage jigs reached Downsview, the Canadians had built their own. The British-built jigs were then diverted to help to start the Australian production, but the ship carrying them was lost to the Japanese before reaching Australia.

With priority given to fighter production in Britain, to the detriment of the bombers, initial Canadian production concentrated on the bomber versions. However, the RCAF also wanted Mosquitos. To satisfy this need, the Canadian Government placed its own orders direct with de Havilland Canada. To help to differentiate the Canadian Mosquitos, they were allocated mark numbers from 20 onwards, starting with the B.MkXX. In addition, twenty-five B.MkVIIs were built for the USAAF.

It was de Havilland Canada that started making the fuselage forming jigs from concrete, a much cheaper and quicker form of construction than the wooden moulds originally produced in Britain. They were also harder wearing, and this form of construction was adopted for production in Britain's factories.

In June 1942 the production orders for the Canadian factory had increased to 1,100 Mosquitos. To assist in defining the aircraft, B.MkIV DK287 was shipped from Liverpool to Canada on 13 September as a pattern. It was, however, rather late to be of any use, as by the time it arrived the first Canadian Mosquito was nearly ready for its maiden flight. This pattern aircraft was also damaged during unloading at Halifax. On 24 September, B.MkVII KB300 was flown by

Ralph Spradbrow, the chief test pilot. Geoffrey de Havilland Jnr arrived three days later to compare the flying characteristics with British production standards. Finding the first Canadian Mosquito acceptable, only a year and three days since Hunter and Povey had arrived in Canada, he then gave one of his usual spirited demonstrations for the benefit of the Canadians and visiting Americans.

Geoffrey de Havilland remained to assist the Canadian flight-test team until his return to Britain in January 1943. Unfortunately, Spradbrow was taken ill and Pat Fillingham was sent to Canada on 4 February with an ex-PRU pilot named Wooll, who had been interned after a forced landing in Switzerland and was not permitted to fly on operations again. During his six-month stay in Canada, Fillingham participated in the production flight-testing, instructing the Canadian flight-test team on how to take over responsibility for the flight-test schedule, as well as identifying and curing faults.

John de Havilland was intended to go to Australia to set up the flight-test procedures, but with his loss in the crash near Hatfield, Fillingham was sent from Canada to Australia to start testing there. After eight months in Australia, he returned via Canada, leaving there by ferrying Mosquito KB221 to Prestwick via Goose Bay, Greenland and Iceland. This route was always fraught with hazards, mainly owing to the unpredictable weather, and while on the approach to the land-locked airfield in Greenland, with high cliffs on either side, cloud obscured the airfield and a return had to be made to Goose Bay, to await improved conditions. Fillingham finally arrived home on 16 June 1944 after being away for seventeen months. He then continued flight-testing at Hatfield. While he had been away, George Errington had been seconded from Airspeed, where he was chief test pilot, to help out with the flight-testing at Hatfield.

With bomber production established at Downsview, fighter-bomber production started in January 1943. A T.MkIII was sent over on 20 January, initially as a pattern for the local production of trainers, but later to be used to convert RCAF pilots and ferry crews for the delivery of Mosquitos across the Atlantic to Europe. With the Downsview factory busy turning out bombers, the first fifty of which were retained in Canada to equip an operational conversion unit, and the FB.MkXXI production becoming established, a further ten T.MkIIIs were released from British stocks to cope with the growing conversion programme.

Although the Mosquito was kept as simple as possible, there were still a number of specialised parts that were causing delays in the Canadian production programme, as well as in Britain. By the middle of April, only seventeen Mosquitos had been completed at Downsview. The changes of role, as well as the adaptation to locally produced materials, did not help. However, by hard work and effort the Downsview factory was able to produce 67 aircraft in the first year, by which time output had reached 14 Mosquitos per month. By the middle of 1943, 92 Mosquitos had been completed, with priority given to bombers, and a year later 268 had been delivered, the production rate having reached 40 per month.

Up to this time the Mosquitos from Downsview had been powered by Rolls-Royce-produced Merlin engines. However, on 7 July 1944, the two hundred and seventy-first Mosquito completed in Canada, KB370, was accepted as the first to be fitted with Packard-built Merlin 225s with 18 lb boost. This version was designated as the B.MkXXV, to be followed in late 1944 by the main Canadian fighter-bomber, the FB.MkXXVI, also powered by Packard Merlin 225s. A shortage of cannons and radios was turned to an advantage in mid-1943 by completing some MkXXVs as T.MkXXIIs with dual controls to fulfil an urgent training need. With the war in Europe

A total of 1,034 Mosquitos were built in Canada by the local de Havilland company based at Downsview near Toronto. The main production version for use in Europe was the B.MkXX, followed by the B.MkXXV. One of the first two Canadian built bombers was B.MkXX KB328 donated by Acton, Ontario, which made the transatlantic flight to Hatfield, arriving on 12 August 1943. (de Havilland photo)

Mosquito B.MkVII KB303 was the fourth of 25 of this version, all of which remained in North America, six being delivered to the USAAF. (de Havilland Canada photo)

In addition to the bomber variants of the Mosquito, de Havilland Canada also produced large numbers of fighter-bombers. KA100 was the first of three Canadian-built Mosquito FB.MkXXIs. (de Havilland Canada photo)

The Canadian-produced Mosquito B.MkXXV was a more powerful development of the B.MkXX with 1,620 hp single-stage Packard Merlin 225s. (MAP press photo)

Following Mosquito FB.MkXXI KA102, the fighter-bomber production concentrated on the FB.MkXXVI. (de Havilland Canada photo)

Most of the surplus Mosquito FB.MkXXVIs were sold to China for the Nationalists to defend against the communists. The aircraft were prepared at Downsview and then shipped to China where they were reassembled and test flown ready for the training programme and combat. (de Havilland Canada photo)

The Canadian-built Mosquito T.MkXXII was developed from the FB.MkXXI and was also similar to the British T.MkIII. (de Havilland Canada photo)

The other initial delivery from Canada was Mosquito B.MkXX KB162 donated by New Glasgow, Nova Scotia, and delivered to Hatfield on 12 August 1943 before entering service with the RAF. (de Havilland photo)

Canadian Mosquito B.Mk25 KB669. (Flypast Collection)

The Canadian Mosquito FB.Mk26 was developed from the earlier MkXXI and was similar to the British FB.MkVI, but its power came from Merlin 225 engines. (de Havilland Canada photo)

Canadian-built Mosquito T.Mk29 KA117 and powered by a pair of Packard-built Merlins later served with No. 85 Squadron. (MAP press photo)

In Australia, where 212 Mosquitos were built, the main version was the FB.Mk40, all the remaining versions being conversions from these. Mosquito FB.Mk40 A52-41 was the 41st production aircraft from the Bankstown factory. (de Havilland Australia photo)

Mosquito PR.Mk41 A52-327 was the last to leave the Bankstown factory near Sydney. It was a conversion of one of the earlier FB.Mk40s and was delivered on 22 July 1948 to be used on a large-scale photographic survey of Australia. (DHA photo)

Nine Mosquito FB.Mk40s lined up at the de Havilland Australia airfield at Bankstown near Sydney. (de Havilland Australia photo)

coming to an obvious end, Canadian production had reached 887 Mosquitos, with the monthly average rate of production exceeding 80 aircraft. Of this total, 430 bombers and 59 fighter-bombers had been delivered for service in Europe.

The first Canadian deliveries to Britain were B.MkXXs KB162 New Glasgow and KB328 Acton, both of which arrived at Hatfield on 12 August 1943. By November, five B.MkXXs had been delivered to 13 Maintenance Unit (MU) at Henlow and KB161 was issued to No. 139 Squadron on 11 November. The first operational sortie by a Canadian-built Mosquito was on 2 December, when bombs were dropped on Berlin. Some MkXXVs were prepared at Henlow for service with No. 614 Squadron in the Middle East, and a batch of MkXXVs were modified for special duties with the Royal Navy, in the same theatre. Nos 162 and 163 squadrons were equipped with Canadian-built aircraft, as were nos 139, 608 and 627 squadrons, with 1655 Mosquito Training Unit supplying crews.

Ninety B.MkXXs were allocated to the USA with the new designation of F-8, and the 8th USAAF in Britain was issued with 30 FB.MkVIs from British production. Eleven F-8s were issued to No. 375 Servicing Squadron at Watton in Norfolk, some of the aircraft being used to photograph the Allied advances across Normandy from D-Day.

With the end of the war in Europe, deliveries from Canada ceased, many of the completed aircraft being stored at Downsview and the despatch airfield at London, Ontario. By the time of VJ-Day on 15 August 1945, 1,032 Mosquitos had rolled off the Canadian production line, with the final total completed being 1,076 when all Downsview production came to an end. Not all of the surplus Mosquitos were wasted, as 200 fighter-bombers were sold to China in 1947.

The only other Canadian developments were the T.Mk27, modified from the T.MkXXII with more powerful engines, and the T.Mk29, which was converted from FB.MkXXVIs. The de Havilland Aircraft Company of Canada and the associated industries had overcome major problems to deliver Mosquito bombers to Britain when they were in short supply from the home factories owing to the difficult priority with ordering. The Canadian production was around one-seventh of the overall total and therefore made a significant contribution to the Allied successes.

The challenge of setting up Mosquito production in Australia faced problems similar to the Canadian programme, but it was compounded by the longer supply routes and the lack of suitable existing factories with the right skills, materials and tooling. Because of the shortage of production facilities and local raw materials, many of the parts were supplied from Britain, together with some personnel seconded to Australia when the RAAF placed the first order. In addition, a pattern aircraft, F.MkII DD664, was shipped to Australia to help with familiarisation. As de Havilland Australia was only building for RAAF use, the overall totals were smaller, but the same problems had to be overcome.

In July 1942, much of the initial vital design information reached Sydney, allowing detailed engineering and planning to start. Although the target was for the first Australian-built Mosquito to fly by August 1943, this was not achieved by A52-1001, the renumbered DD664, until 17 December. Hatfield was able to provide some 95 per cent of the parts and materials without a problem, but it was harder to get the 5 per cent holding up production in Britain, which also delayed the Australian programme. A new factory was built at Bankstown near Sydney, and by May 1943 most of the machine tools were available, and the sub-contractor organisation was set up and beginning to work.

Australian production was also allocated dedicated mark numbers, in this case starting with 40, the Roman numerals having become rather ponderous. The first Australian Mosquito to be completed was FB.Mk40 A51-1, which was first flown on 23 July 1943 by Wg Cdr Gibson Lee, the locally based de Havilland test pilot. Pat Fillingham arrived to set up the production flight-test team on 19 October, having had to experience the discomfort of the long Pacific crossing from Canada in a Liberator bomber transport conversion.

Once established, the shipping of components to Australia went well, with far fewer losses to enemy action then expected. To allow local effort to concentrate on offensive Mosquitos, and rather than having diversions for small batches, 14 T.MkIIIs were shipped to Australia without engines, arriving towards the end of 1943. This allowed conversion training to start once the locally available Packard-built Merlin 31s had been fitted. The change from casein glue to formaldehyde, which was more suited to the hotter climate, caused some delays and the shortage of skilled labour continued to be a problem.

The first delivery to the RAAF was made on 4 March 1944, but subsequent deliveries were delayed by gluing problems, where the joint between the top skin and the top of the main spar delaminated. To overcome this, all of the wings had to be rectified, and the fiftieth was already in the jigs, with some 20 aircraft completed. The crash of Mosquito FB.Mk40 A52-12 on the pre-acceptance test-flight, killing the crew, was believed to have been caused by the failure of the glue joints, but on investigation was found to have been the result of wing flutter at high speed and high g, possibly caused by the approach of compressibility when the airspeed over the airfoil was close to the speed of sound. However, the problem appeared to be unique to Australian production and may have been caused by local conditions.

A further crash at Bankstown on 8 November 1944, of FB.Mk40 A52-18 while under severe manoeuvring loads led to further delays in production while the investigation was proceeding. Despite a thorough investigation of the glue joints, torsional stiffness, flutter and aileron balance, no obvious cause could be determined, although a variety of indeterminate theories were suggested from experts in Britain and Australia. By this time the results of the war in Europe were a foregone conclusion, but the Japanese were still a very real threat in Asia.

From the period March 1944–May 1945, the total Mosquito deliveries from Bankstown were 75, with a production rate of about 12 aircraft per month. By the time of the Japanese surrender on 15 August 1945, 108 Mosquitos had been produced by the Australian industry, with the eventual total reaching 212 aircraft, by which time the basic aircraft and many of the special parts were being produced locally.

Following the FB.Mk40 was the PR.Mk41, powered by two-stage Packard-built Merlin 69s, a total of 28 being delivered to the RAAF between May 1947 and July 1948. These aircraft were used for the important large-scale photographic survey of Australia until 1953, and some of the surplus aircraft were acquired by New Zealand. Only one Packard Merlin 69 Mosquito, FB.Mk42 A52-300, was built, and the final batch consisted of 21 T.Mk43s powered by Packard Merlin 33s, but otherwise similar to the RAF T.MkIIIs. These were converted from FB.Mk40s and delivered between June 1944 and May 1947.

In addition to the T.MkIIIs originally supplied from Britain, 23 PR.MkXVIs and 38 FB.MkVIs were also supplied from RAF stocks for use in Asia, the PR.MkXVIs serving with No. 87 Squadron RAAF and the FB.MkVIs with No. 1 Squadron RAAF.

8. BUILDING THE WOODEN WONDER

Although some mention has already been made of the construction of the Mosquito, it is appropriate to provide a more detailed account of how this remarkable high-performance, versatile aircraft was precision-engineered from timber. The Mosquito was unique in being the only all-wooden frontline combat aircraft to see service during the Second World War, using the exceptional de Havilland experience of using this form of construction. The company had used metal construction in the fuselage frame of the Tiger Moth trainer, and produced the all-metal Flamingo airliner, the production of which was stopped owing to the start of the war.

Wooden construction could be built more quickly than metal, and any damage would be both easier to repair and more localised. Materials would be more readily available as a result of their not being required for other combat aircraft, and the non-strategic labour would be able to make a significant contribution to the Allied war effort. Although de Havilland had not previously built a high-performance combat aircraft, its experience with the DH.88 Comet Racer, and later the Albatross all-wood airliner, helped to establish a strong basis. This allowed the Mosquito to enter service less than two years after the start of design, as well as making it the fastest combat aircraft in the world at that time.

As mentioned previously, the fuselage shells were produced in two halves with the join along the vertical centre line. The moulds were mounted in sections on frames with the inside of the shell downwards. They were initially made from mahogany, until the cheaper method using smooth concrete sections was adopted. The fuselage bulkheads were mounted in the gaps between the sections of the mould, with the 1½ or 2 mm thick inner plywood skin spread over the mould, and glued to the recessed bulkhead frames and other internal structural members, including the main wing attachment brackets. Neither heat nor pressure chambers were used, the various layers being held down by metal straps. Once the first layer of glue had hardened the pre-prepared spruce internal structural members were put in place, and the remainder of the interior of the sandwich was stabilised with sections of ⅜ in thick balsa wood, all of which was glued to the inner surface of the inside skin. Once the glue had cured, the outer birch ply skin was applied. The cut-outs, such as the bomb doors, lower side panels beneath the wing, and the entry and access doors were made integrally and later removed for individual assembly.

Once the fuselage shells were complete, the two halves were removed from the moulds and mounted vertically at a convenient height for the installation of the equipment and systems. These were attached to the fuselage by using ferrules consisting of plywood discs mounted on wooden plugs, with a threaded brass bush set in the centre to pick up with the attachment bolts. The ferrules were located by drilling the inner fuselage skin, using special location templates, to a sufficient depth to accept the plugs, without breaking the outer skin surface.

While the fuselage shells were in two halves, the opportunity was taken to instal as much as possible of the internal fittings, including the cockpit floors, the control linkages and the initial stages of the electrical wiring. About 60 per cent of the equipment installation was completed before the fuselage shells were joined and the system types were separated to assist in the pre-assembly, most of the flying control cables being located on the port side of the fuselage and the hydraulic piping on the starboard side. The interior of the shells was sprayed with protective paint before joining the two portions.

The joining of the fuselage shells was done by a V-butt joint of multi-ply spruce, reinforced by plywood strips set in rebates internally and externally to give a smooth, flush finish. Great care was taken to locate the two halves together accurately to avoid distortion and twisting. While the glue was setting, laminated wooden 'O' ring clamps held the rear fuselage shells together, as well as trunnion mountings in the centre section located on the wing attachment fittings. With the wing centre section and lower fuselage side panels removed for later assembly, the lower part of the cut-out was supported by a pair of jury-struts to avoid the weakened top of the fuselage breaking, and all lifting of the fuselage was done with great care to provide the correct support.

Following the assembly of the fuselage, fitting-out continued with the addition of the instrument panels and the completion and connection of the plumbing and wiring. Bulkheads six and seven were fitted at the rear end to carry the fin and tailplane attachments, followed by the tailwheel pick-up and retraction jack. The complete exterior of the fuselage, including the various cut-outs, were then doped and covered with light medapolam fabric to protect the wood and give a smooth finish. Following the attachment of the cockpit canopy, the fitting of the remaining equipment and services was completed. The stability of the supported and moulded monocoque structure gave a similar tensile strength to a light alloy construction, but in compression and sheer it was far superior in strength.

As already mentioned, the wing was a one-piece assembly from tip to tip. There was a slight sweep-back taper to the front spar, with a marked taper to the rear spar, giving the wing its distinctive planform. The wing spars were of laminated spruce construction, with sections spindled out for lightness and then covered with plywood webs on both sides. As well as the slight backward sweep of the front spar and the considerable forward sweep of the laminated rear spar, account had also to be taken of the modest dihedral, giving some stability when the plane was being flown. Each wing spar, when completed, was around 50 ft (15 m) long, the spar booms being built out from the centre section, with the outer sections and wingtip extensions scarf-jointed with 1:15 tapers and glued together. The spars were made from spruce laminations cut to an accuracy of 0.01 in, and the slightly rough finish helped the glue to bond strongly. The top spar boom was originally made from 1.45 in thick laminations, but, because thicker laminations called for a higher standard of timber, they were reduced to 0.4 in, to make the best use of the material available. The spar booms were rough-finished using overhead planers, and the accurate final finishing was done by hand, using hand planers with straight edges laid across datum blocks on each side.

The birch ply spar webs were made from fairly short lengths, routered to shape, and drilled in batches of two or three at a time, using hand drills guided by bushes mounted in wooden templates. The complete spar web was assembled by scarfing the sections together and bonding them with clamps while the glue set.

The Mosquito fuselage was built in two half shells over wooden moulds. Later these were made from concrete. Once the first layer of birch ply had been formed over the mould and glued to the bulkhead

sections, the reinforcing pieces were laid on, and the gaps between filled with stabilising balsa wood. The outer skin was then glued into place and held with steel straps until cured. (Aircraft Production photo)

The port side shell of a Mosquito bomber fuselage has part of the cockpit floor installed and the mounting for the pilot's instrument, as well as some other equipment. (de Havilland photo)

Each pair of fuselage shells was mounted side by side for easy access to equipment and wiring. (BICC photo)

When the initial fitting of equipment was completed, the fuselage shells were joined around the centre line and held with straps until the glue had cured. (de Havilland photo)

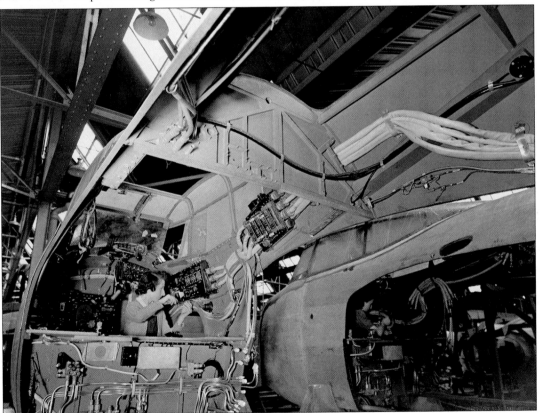

Once the fuselage was assembled more detailed fitting of wiring, hydraulic piping and systems continued before assembly to the wing. (BICC photo)

While the completion of equipping was continuing, the cockpit canopies were also fitted, and the fin attached. (de Havilland photo)

Much detailed work was done by subcontractors all over Britain, and women played a vital part in building the Mosquitos, particularly in the more intricate work such as the electrical equipment. (BICC photo)

ESA of Stevenage was one of the major subcontractors for Mosquito wings. (ESA photo)

When removed from the assembly jig, the wings were located upside-down to allow the fitting of the pre-formed and load-bearing fuel tank bay doors. Between each pair of fuel tank bays was the space for the main undercarriage retraction, with the engine mount pick-ups on the front spar. (de Havilland photo)

Wing spar assembly was achieved using large fixtures, the rear spar requiring sloping access platforms to cope with the rearward taper of the wing. Once located in the fixture, the spar booms were trimmed in length to an accuracy of 0.020 in on each side, and the webs were bonded and screwed down to complete the assembly, the screws providing the extra joint strength as well as acting as clamps while the glue hardened. As no other work could be done on the spars while the glue was setting at normal temperatures, a complex system of thermostatically controlled heating pads was devised to provide an increased temperature accurate to within ± 1.5°F. The rib posts were also bonded into place at this stage. Once the bonding of the spars was completed, they were placed in a drilling jig for all of the holes (such as for the undercarriage pick-up points, engine bearer brackets and aileron hinge brackets) to be located for the metal fittings, using bush plates as guides.

It would have been impossible to obtain sufficiently high-quality ply to make the wing skins in one piece, so they were produced in sections similar to the spar webs, but to a larger scale. They were joined by gluing the tapered scarf joints. In preparation for assembly, the Douglas fir stringers were located in metal slots in horizontal tables. The skins were pre-drilled and countersunk before being bonded to the stringers, and the screws again assisted with bonding. The large numbers of brass screws were fixed using pump-action screwdrivers. Once assembled, the access panels were cut out and the outer surface of the skin was sprayed with red primer dope. The inner surfaces were painted with a white, damp-resistant cellulose paint. Once the paint had dried, the skins were ready to be joined to the spars and ribs in the final assembly jig.

The final assembly of the wing was done in large, paired vertical fixtures with the lower side inside. The spar assemblies were located against double-wedge hardwood blocks, which could be knocked out to release the wing on completion. The spars were located with the front spar at the base, located by the engine bearer fittings on the front face. The rear spar was located by the undercarriage radius-rod attachments. With the spars in position, assembly of the thirty-two ribs commenced, the inner higher load-bearing ones being double-skinned box section with spruce formers, and the outer ribs just single skinned. The heavier load-bearing ribs at the centre section and around the undercarriage retraction bays were bolted to the spars, while the others in the inboard areas were glued and screwed into position. The lighter outboard single-skinned ribs were glued and tacked to the rib posts.

The lower outboard skin from rib six was attached first by bonding and brass screws, the inboard sections being where the tank-bay doors were later assembled, and the undercarriage retraction stowage. The inner top skin was assembled next, with the stringers already mounted on its upper surface, the attachment to the spars and ribs being drilled using templates in the inner shell. The spar and rib booms were counterbored to depth for attachment screws, the shell skin being used as the locating jig. The pre-formed stringers over the centre section were joined to the outer stringers by tapering and scarfing them together, the joints being held by a number of small, wooden wedge clamps while the glue set. The entire assembly had been pre-dry-fitted to check locations before final gluing and screwing.

Water-resistant cellulose was applied to the inner shell, and the pre-drilled three top-wing skin panels were offered up for attachment to the inner shell. The inner face was coated with adhesive, for both bonding and damp-proofing, and the top outer skin was offered up to the wing structure by a gang of men and then fixed by screws, additional pressure being achieved by clamping battens. On the undersides, from rib one to rib six, anchor bolts were inserted through the skin and inner shell into the rib former, and walnut mounting pads were attached over the two number one ribs for the forward fuselage location.

To provide a smooth finish, the recessed countersunk screw heads were filled and sanded before the main wing box was removed from the jig. This was done sideways on wheeled stands, which allowed the wing to be lifted and turned by crane and lowered onto stands resting on the lower skin. At this stage the leading edge, flap and aileron shrouds were fitted, the leading edges being of pre-formed plywood skin with supporting nose ribs. These and the shrouds were glued and screwed into position, and held in place by canvas bands over the wing. Clearances were checked by installing slave flaps and ailerons. The pre-formed, stressed fuel tank covers were bolted through to the anchor nuts around the openings covering the fuel tanks, along with the remainder of the undercarriage fittings and wing-to-fuselage brackets.

Equipping began with the fitting of the leading edge radiators between the engines and the fuselage, and the control cables were located ready for connection. The wing was transported to the paint shop for a protective coating of red dope, a madapolam covering and a final paint, ready for the installation of the electrical wiring and hydraulic systems. It was then ready for final attachment to the fuselage on the main production line, when the pre-formed detachable wingtips were added.

The fin and tailplane were of a similar construction to the wing, the fin being fitted just forward of the one-piece tailplane. The structure of each was based on two spars, the rear one being a straight member, with the front spar swept back to accommodate the curved leading edges. Ribs and nose ribs completed the structure, the tailplane being built leading edge first. The overall span of the tailplane had to be maintained to tight tolerances to allow clearance for the elevator mass balances at the tip. The trim tab brackets and the elevator hinge brackets were fitted to the rear spar before it was attached to the structure. The skin was a single layer of birch ply with scarf joints and inspection holes cut out prior to assembly by bonding and screwing, as with the wing. Following the assembly of the first skin, the inner surfaces were waterproofed and the metal fittings assembled. After fitting the second skin, the entire assembly was doped, madapolam covered and painted.

The all-wooden ply-covered flaps were in two sections, located either side of the rear end of the engine nacelle and joined by a torque tube to ensure that they operated as a single unit. The torque tube was joined in the centre by a cranked fitting to locate with the flap-operating hydraulic control jack. The flaps were of conventional single-skin ply construction formed round the spruce structure with the interior damp-proofed. On completion, the exterior was doped, covered and painted, similar to the other assemblies.

The ailerons and elevators were of conventional metal structure with metal skins riveted in place, the ailerons having mass balance weights in the leading edge, and the elevators being fitted with forward facing horn balances. The rudder was a conventional metal structure with a fabric covering.

The main undercarriage was of rugged and simple design, the only hydraulics being the retraction jack. To absorb the shock of landing, twelve rubber moulded blocks were used inside an outer leg, which consisted of two semi-elliptical pressed shells made from 16 swg 124 steel, riveted together around the rubber blocks, which had duralumin spacers. This method was not uncommon for lighter aircraft, but the Mosquito was the heaviest application, and it proved to be very robust and maintenance-free. The advantages were the elimination of precision machining and more relaxed tolerances, together with cheap and easy assembly. The main shock-absorption

The wings were fabric covered, doped and painted before delivery to the production line. (de Havilland photo)

Before the wings were delivered for final assembly, the wiring, hydraulic piping, coolant piping, control runs and main undercarriage mounting were installed. (BICC photo)

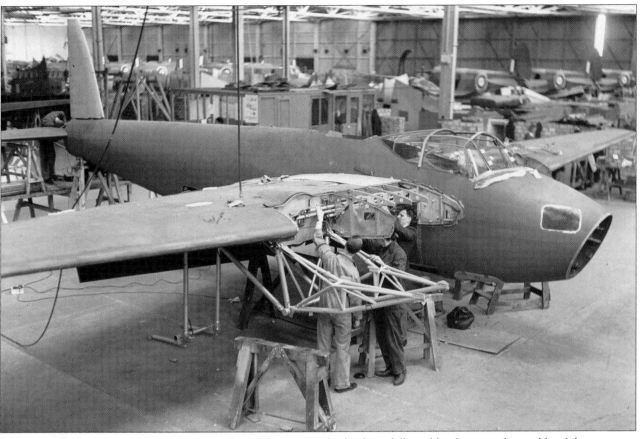

Final assembly started with the joining of the wing to the fuselage, followed by the start of assembly of the tail surfaces and the Merlin engine mounts. (de Havilland photo)

The fighter/fighter-bomber production line at Hatfield with assembly just commenced on another Mosquito before it moves sideways on tracks around the line. (de Havilland photo)

The main undercarriage leg was a very simple assembly of a pressed steel split outer shell, with the shocks taken by rubber blocks in compression. (Aircraft Production photo)

leg was a piston tube connected directly to the axle at the base. At the top was an elliptical piston of laminated, fabric reinforced Bakelite, an early composite material. The rubber blocks and the inside of the casing were lubricated with graphite powder.

Final assembly of the Mosquitos was carried out on a U-shaped track, the major components being delivered at one end and the aircraft being moved progressively down as parts and equipment were added, across the end of the assembly hall, and then back down the other side. The progression ended at the paint shop for completion of the surface finish. The plane was then rolled out ready for flight-test. Two of these lines were set up at Hatfield, one for bombers and the other for fighter airframes. For ease of access, the aircraft were mounted as close as possible to the floor, on frames that were pushed sideways along the track until the time came to fit the undercarriage.

Assembly commenced with the mainplane mounted on cradles supporting the wings just outboard of the engine nacelles. The fuselage was then carefully lowered into position, supported neutrally to avoid damage to the fuselage shell above the wing centre section and picking up with the five wing-to-fuselage locations, which were bolted together. The fuselage side panels were then fitted below the wing to ensure structural integrity, followed by the fin, tailplane and tailwheel. The third stage was the fitting of the undercarriage, followed by the tubular steel engine mounts and the radiators. The inboard fuel and oil tanks, including fuel tanks in the top of the bomb bay, were fitted and the remainder of the radio equipment and other systems were completed in the fuselage. The bombers and fighter-bombers had the bomb racks installed under the wing centre section, and the fighters and fighter-bombers had the machine-guns fitted in the nose and the cannons under the floor.

The Merlin engines came as fully assembled power units with all of the accessories, and they were offered up, followed by the connection of the controls from the cockpit and the radiator plumbing. With the engines in place, the aluminium engine nacelle fairings, cowlings and main undercarriage doors could be fitted. The various control surfaces were fitted and connected with the control column, rudder pedals and trim wheels in the cockpit. This brought the aircraft to the turning point of the track, where it was essentially complete and ready for testing the functions. The wheels and axles were fitted, and the undercarriage lowered into pits in the floor, still keeping the aircraft at an accessible level, and the de Havilland Hydromatic propellers were attached to the prop shafts by using an overhead crane. The Aeronautical Inspection Directorate (AID) representative made the inspection on behalf of the customer, and the aircraft was finally jacked up on to its own undercarriage to check the coolant system operation. This was followed by a final inspection, and the wheeling of the plane into the paint shop for the application of the markings.

Among the differences in the cockpit was that the bomber and PR versions had a horn-type control wheel, which was more suitable for precision bombing runs and gave access down on the right for the navigator to do his bomb aiming. The fighter cockpits had a stick control column, and on the right side of the night-fighters was the radar scope. In addition, there was armour plating right across the front of the cockpit to protect the crew from defensive fire from hostile aircraft or from the ground.

The initial production test-flight lasted for about an hour and was used to check general handling and overall systems operation. Normally each Mosquito required an average of three test-flights, unless it was classed as a 'Lulu', in which case it was off-test after one flight. Occasionally a 'rogue' aircraft would be produced, with all of the tolerances compounding, which would take more time to adjust and correct. Often it would only just be cleared and would then have a bad reputation for the rest of its operational service. About thirty Mosquitos were cleared for delivery each week but, in the winter months, when fog delayed flight-testing, a backlog of up to 100 aircraft could accumulate. With the well-drained grass surface of the airfield at Hatfield, the Mosquitos could take off directly into the wind, making the take-off swing easier to control. The busy team of test pilots and flight-test observers not only undertook the production and development testing at Hatfield, but also helped out at Leavesden, Luton and Coventry from time to time to ensure that the correct standards were being upheld. In addition, repaired Mosquitos both

The Mosquito tailwheel was retractable, and mounted on the rearmost fuselage bulkhead. (MOI press photo)

at Hatfield and at service airfields had to be flight-tested before they were returned to operation.

Although the Mosquitos were fitted with radio, there was no ground radio at Hatfield, all control being handled through signal lamps from the watch office. When flying above cloud, the pilot had to estimate where he was before descending. If he became lost, he would land at any airfield he could find through the gaps in the cloud to wait for conditions to improve, and to ask the way back to Hatfield.

Pat Fillingham started with the de Havilland Aeronautical School and learned to fly with the RAF Volunteer Reserve. He began his test-flying career by flying Tiger Moths and Oxfords, before joining the Mosquito

A Mosquito fighter-bomber receives the final touches before completion. (BICC photo)

team at about the same time as John de Havilland, when the tenth Mosquito was under test. The majority of testing up to that time had been done by Geoffrey de Havilland Jnr and George Gibbins. In the early stages there were no dual-control Mosquitos to be taught on, so the first flight followed a pre-flight briefing. As well as testing the aircraft, the pilot was also learning how to fly it. Flight-test observers were not always carried, leaving the pilot the total responsibility of checking the aircraft, including its performance parameters. Fillingham eventually flew about 2,000 Mosquitos, the major problem being to ensure that the ailerons were not too heavy at high speeds.

The swing on take-off could sometimes be difficult to control, particularly on the new aircraft, as the constant speed unit oil could be sticky, resulting in full power engaging rather suddenly, and not at the same time for both engines. The best way to avoid this hazard was to exercise the propellers thoroughly during the initial run-up.

Once a Mosquito was off-test it was ready for collection, often by one of the pilots from the Air Transport Auxiliary (ATA), many of whom were women. A group of these pilots were based at Hatfield, and they would fly the Mosquitos, usually single-handed, to an RAF Maintenance Unit (MU) for preparation for delivery to an operational squadron.

9. EYES UNSEEN: PHOTO-RECONNAISSANCE

Although the Mosquito was initially designed as an offensive bomber, it first entered service in the photo-reconnaissance role. Knowing intelligence about an enemy is vital to winning a battle, and it was also important to know to what extent the Allied bomber fleets were hitting their targets, so that the damage could be assessed. Since the American Civil War, tethered balloons were used to see behind enemy lines, but at the start of the Second World War, neither side had made any plans of how they were going to monitor progress over, or behind, the front lines, nor how to supply the war machine.

Although the RAF had been using aerial photography since the First World War, there had been no special development of the cameras or techniques used to take the pictures. It took a civilian, Australian Sidney Cotton, to convince the RAF that better results could be obtained. With the the Second World War inevitable, Cotton undertook a programme of photo-reconnaissance flights over Germany using Lockheed 12a based at Heston. Among the improvements to the equipment was the blowing of warm air over the lenses to stop them from frosting up at high altitudes. He finally convinced the RAF by taking some photos from a civil aircraft over the Dutch coast two weeks after the war had started, in a search for elements of the German Navy. The results were so clear compared with the standards currently available that Cotton was given the task of assisting the Allies with major improvements and was made a squadron leader in command of the specially formed Heston Flight.

The RAF PR operations in the Second World War started with unarmed Spitfires fitted with special cameras for the shorter-range tactical requirements. However, the unarmed Mosquito could undertake the deeper-penetration missions into hostile territory, at low level for tactical requirements and at maximum altitude, when weather allowed, for more strategic needs. The Mosquito not only had greater endurance, but was faster, had the security of two engines, could carry more cameras and had a navigator who could pinpoint the target with greater accuracy using more sophisticated aids. The availability of the Mosquito gave the RAF the advantage of good photographic coverage of the enemy in all theatres of the war.

No.1 Photo-Reconnaissance Unit (1 PRU) had been set up at RAF Benson in Oxfordshire as the specialists in these vital requirements. Only eight months after the maiden flight of the prototype, the first PR Mosquito, W4051, was delivered to 1 PRU on 13 July 1941 from Boscombe Down. To ensure an early entry into service in this vital role, the prototype had undertaken some PR development flying, with camera ports located in the front end of the bomb-bay doors, and another oblique position in the rear fuselage access door. The next aircraft to arrive at Benson was W4054, on 22 July,

Mosquito PR.MkI W5051 LY-J:PRU based at Benson. This aircraft later went on to operate with nos 521 and 540 squadrons, and 8 OTU, until struck off charge on 22 June 1945.

Cameras being loaded into the rear equipment bay of the Mosquito ready for the next reconnaissance sortie. (AM press photo)

followed by W4055, in August, giving an opportunity for the air and ground crews to train on the new aircraft before commencing operations. A short delay was caused by the need to change the camera mounts from metal to wood, to damp out some unwanted vibration, and there were some oil tank swelling problems to overcome. Once ready, the first operational sortie was flown by Sqn Ldr Clarke in W4055 on 17 September, the target areas being Brest and down as far as the Franco-Spanish border. The pictures were taken from an altitude of 24,000 ft (7,315 m) and the results were not entirely successful, as the generator became unserviceable and cut off the power to the cameras.

The RAF groundcrews were somewhat sceptical about working on wooden aeroplanes, feeling that this was a retrograde step, but once the Mosquito was established in regular operations, it proved to be rugged and easy to maintain, with plenty of metalwork for the fitters, and at the same time employing the skilled woodworking trades, which found the damage easy to repair.

In October, three of the PR Mosquitos were sent on detachment to Wick in Scotland to obtain strategic information from occupied Norway. On completion of sixteen successful sorties, Sqn Ldr Clarke demonstrated the high speed of the Mosquito by flying from Wick to Benson in the record time of 1 hr 32 min on 15 October. In December, a return was made to Wick by four Mosquitos, to cover reconnaissance needs in Norway and surrounding areas. Unfortunately, the first loss of a Mosquito and crew occurred on this detachment, when Sqn Ldr Taylor and his navigator, Sgt Horsfall, flying W4055 on its fifteenth sortie, failed to return from a flight to the Trondheim–Bergen area on 4 December.

The winter months in the far north restricted the length of daylight. Also because photo-reconnaissance required clear weather, sorties were often abandoned owing to cloud cover

Instead of dropping bombs and allowing for drift, the PR navigator waits until the target is in his viewfinder and then presses the button to take the photos. (AM press photo)

over the target. Weather forecasting was even less precise than it is nowadays with the help of satellites, and after a long flight it was not uncommon to find the target area obscured and impossible to photograph. During December, January and February, the aircraft were moved south to Leuchars, north of Edinburgh.

With the start of delivery of the longer-range PR.MkIs, commencing with W4060 in early 1942, deeper-penetration sorties could be achieved as far afield as Poland. On 22 February, Flt Lt Victor Rickets and Sgt Lukhmanoff in W4051 took excellent photos of the German battlecruiser *Gneisenau* in dry dock in Kiel, and later a Spitfire located the sister ship, *Scharnhorst*, under repair at Wilhelmshaven. Both of these ships were then

Flash bombs for night photographs.

Photo-reconnaissance sorties were flown at both high and low level, depending on the target to be covered. This photograph of a V-weapon site was taken at very low level by a PR Mosquito to assess damage in July 1944. (AM press photo)

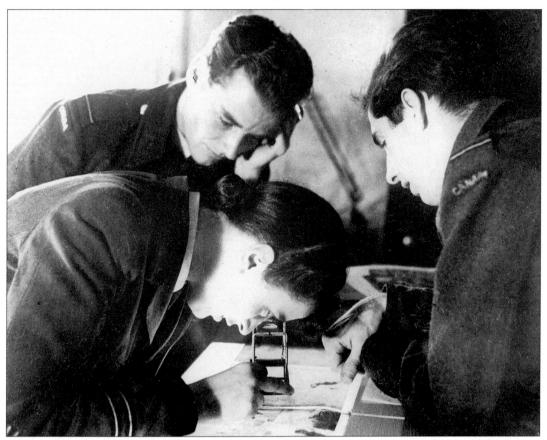

On return from a sortie, once the photos were processed, the intelligence interpreters make a thorough analysis of the damage caused, or if it is a new target, where the primary aiming point will be, and what type of bombs will be used. (AM press photo)

kept under regular observation by PRU Mosquitos. In preparation for the commando attack on St Nazaire, Mosquitos W4051 and W4060 photographed the French coastline in the area. A PRU Mosquito operating from Leuchars flew the round trip to Murmansk and back in a day, locating and photographing the *Tirpitz* in the shelter of a Norwegian fiord.

Many of the photo-reconnaissance sorties were flown at altitudes of around 22,000 ft (6,700 m) depending on the weather, cloud cover and visibility. When the crews arrived at a target area and found it covered by cloud, they often came down to as low as 400 ft

(120 m) so that they could return to base with at least some results. Good intelligence and photographic coverage was always required of a potential target to allow detailed and correct planning. However, it was important not to alert the enemy to future targets. Therefore, like the bomber raids, flights were not made direct to the potential target and back, but diversions were made to make it difficult for the enemy to identify a potential target. It was also important to be able to assess the damage to a target as soon as possible after the raid – often as soon as the dust had settled and the area was no longer obscured by smoke. The

first time that a Mosquito was used to assess bomb damage was on 4 March following a Bomber Command raid on the Renault factory in Paris, where it was important to ensure accurate bombing, thereby avoiding damage and deaths to the French Allies. The Mosquito took off from Benson in appalling weather and the crew lost sight of the ground until they descended to 900 ft (275 m) over the River Seine in heavy rain. With the cloud base becoming lower and lower, the crew were eventually able to locate and photograph the damaged target at 400 ft (120 m), spending about 35 minutes over Paris. Despite having radio, there were none of the modern aids available for navigating, but Benson was found through a lucky gap in the clouds.

With the delivery of four F.IIs and two B.IVs from the Hatfield production lines to satisfy the urgent need for additional Mosquitos, the camera equipment was installed at Benson. The converted PR.MkIIs were limited in range owing to a lack of the long-range tanks, but the PR.MkIVs were capable of much greater endurance and deeper penetrations into hostile territory. By the middle of 1942 the new F.Mk52 36-in airborne camera was becoming available, to replace the F.Mk24, which was normally operated at 1/300th second at f5.6, giving a 1:8000 scale from 24,000 ft (7,315 m), with excellent definition and detail.

The Mosquito and its Merlin engines had a good reputation for reliability, but, on occasion, faults still occurred. In August 1942, Flt Lt Wooll was flying DK310 on a photo sortie to Venice when his starboard engine developed a coolant leak, causing it to be shut down. Normally the Mosquito could fly easily on one engine, but when, owing to the extra work, the temperature of the port engine started to rise, it was obvious that the crew were not going to be able to return to Benson. They therefore made a precautionary landing at Belp, near Berne, in neutral Switzerland.

The efforts to destroy the Mosquito after landing were unsuccessful, and the crew and aircraft were interned. The crew were later exchanged for two German pilots, returning to Britain, but a condition of the release was that they would not return to combat. As mentioned earlier, Flt Lt Wooll assisted with production test-flying at de Havilland Canada. The Mosquito, meanwhile, was retained by the Swiss, who planned to use it for night-time mail flights, but these never took place. The aircraft logged 76 hr development test-flying of equipment from September 1943 until it was retired in March 1953.

The early success of the Mosquitos and Spitfires, with the PRU bringing a continually expanding task, resulted in a total of four dedicated photo-reconnaissance squadrons being formed. Their training was undertaken by 8 PR OTU at the somewhat bleak and exposed Fraserburgh airfield in Aberdeenshire, where the first Mosquito was delivered in December 1942.

The first of the new units was No. 540 Squadron, which was formed at Leuchars on 19 October 1942 from H and L flights of the PRU and equipped with twelve Mosquitos. Flights continued from Leuchars over the Scandinavian region, especially keeping a regular check on the *Tirpitz*, but a number of detachments were made to as far away as Malta in preparation for the North African landings. On 19 January, DZ364 was intercepted while attempting to reach Berlin, and it flew to the alternative destination of Peenemunde. This was not considered a major potential target until, during the evaluation of the photographs, a V-1 flying bomb was identified for the first time by Flg Off Constance Babington-Smith. On rechecking earlier photos, further V-1s were identified, which resulted in a major Bomber Command raid, known as Operation Crossbow, during the night of 17–18 August 1943. This delayed the entry into service of

Mosquito PR.MkIX ML897:D of Bomber Command's 1409 Met Flight based at Wyton flew a total of 161 sorties in advance of Bomber Command and US 8th AF raids. During its service ML897 operated as a bomber, marker, high and low altitude reconnaissance and weather recce.

these pilotless flying bombs, although some of the launch sites were identified in northern France by the end of October and No. 140 Squadron was used in the tactical photographic low-level role to help to identify what became known as 'ski sites'.

As a stop-gap measure before the PR.MkIXs became available, two of the five MkVIIIs were delivered to No. 540 Squadron in January 1943. These were similar to the MkIVs but were powered by the two-stage supercharged Merlin 61s for operations at higher altitudes, and they were fitted with two 50 gal (227 l) wing drop tanks to increase their range. The first operational sortie with

the MkVIII was with DZ342 on 19 February, but no results were achieved owing to the failure of the rear camera mudflap to lower. The PR.MkIXs began equipping No. 540 Squadron, when LR405 and LR406 were delivered on 29 May 1943, and operations commenced with this version on 20 June. The PR.MkIX was powered by two-stage Merlin 72s, although the aircraft was not pressurised, and a distinguishing feature was a perspex observation blister in the canopy roof.

With the winter of 1942/3 bringing shorter days, there was a need for night photography and successful trials were made with the American-produced M.46 600,000 candlepower photoflashes. Operational trials were then carried out by No. 544 Squadron, starting with DZ538 from 26 March initially using MkIVs, until sufficient MkIXs were available. No. 544 Squadron began operations with MkIXs, using Benson pool aircraft on 13 September flown by Flt Lt Dickie Blythe, who later joined the Hatfield post-war sales team. The first MkIX LR478 was delivered on 22 October, providing a much greater endurance. Typically, trips were to Frier, Regensburg, Linz, Vienna, Budapest, back to Vienna and then to Sarbono, Bucharest, Foggia, finally landing at Catania. In the 6½ hr sortie a total of 1,900 miles (3,060 km) had been flown at an average speed of 292 mph (470 km/hr) and with a fuel consumption of 2.5 miles/gal (0.884 km/l). While taxiing at Catania after landing, the engines stopped as a result of fuel exhaustion.

A special Norwegian No. 333 Squadron was formed at Leuchars in May 1943 for the crews to photograph their homeland, with which they would be more familiar than RAF aircrew. While A Flight was equipped with Catalinas, B Flight had camera-equipped Mosquito F.MkIIs, the guns being useful against enemy targets and for retaliation against hostile fighters. Following training with 8 OTU, operations commenced on 27 May and the first combat victory occurred when a Dornier Do.24 was shot down on 13 June. The MkIIs were replaced by camera-equipped FB.MkVIs from September 1943, and they continued in operation with Coastal Command until the end of the war.

No. 541 Squadron commenced operations from Gibraltar when it was formed from B Flight of No. 544 Squadron in October 1943 to cover photo-reconnaissance duties in the eastern Mediterranean and North Africa.

Once sufficient numbers of the PR.MkIXs were established in service, the earlier marks were withdrawn from operations, the last PR.MkIV sortie being flown using DZ473 on

10 September 1943, followed soon after by the MkVIIIs. Not only were the Mosquitos achieving excellent photographic results, but they were largely immune from the enemy defences. In the winter months, the high altitude of operation was given away by contrails during clear weather, but the defending fighters were equally visible as they climbed to attempt to intercept. To avoid anti-aircraft fire from the ground, commonly known as flak, the Mosquitos needed to operate at even higher altitudes. To achieve this, eight of the MkIXs were fitted with Merlin 76/77 engines driving paddle-blade airscrews, which not only improved the ceiling but also gave an increase in speed. However, as cockpit heating was not available, visibility was reduced by the icing of the cockpit canopy, even in the pressurised MkXVI, which was delivered to 140 and 400 squadrons in December 1943. Following some introductory problems during the early part of 1944, No. 140 Squadron made its first operational sortie with a MkXVI on 4 February. Forward-facing cameras were being fitted by then, especially for low-level targets, where clarity was improved by the reduced relative movement. Berlin was high on the priority list for photo-reconnaissance during the winter of 1943/4, but the weather did not clear sufficiently for good results until 19 February, when No. 540 Squadron was able to obtain clear pictures.

To help with the build-up and preparations for the Allied invasion of Europe, nos 4, 140 and 400 squadrons were assigned to the 2nd Tactical Air Force (TAF) in early 1944, the target area being northern France. Conversion training for No. 4 Squadron was completed at Aston Down, ready for the Squadron to move to a very muddy Sawbridgeworth in Hertfordshire on 3 March, equipped with a mixture of Mosquito PR.MkXVIs, Spitfires and Mustangs. Mosquito operations began on 20 March, but by April the squadron had moved to

Mosquito PR.MkXVI NS581 used by Air Marshal Sir Arthur Coningham visited Hatfield in August 1944. (de Havilland photo)

No. 140 Squadron commenced operations with Mosquito PR.MkXVIs on 4 February 1944 and was based at Melsbroek in March 1945 as part of 34 PR Wing.

Mosquito PR.MkXVI NS777 of No. 140 Squadron during the winter of 1944/5 parked on a forward airfield with the hangar disguised as a derelict farmhouse.

No. 4 Squadron operated
PR.MkXVI aircraft briefly at
Sawbridgeworth and then
Gatwick. Mosquito PR.MkXVI
MM273 was operated from
Gatwick in 1944, and was
later issued to the Fleet Air
Arm. (Freddy Andrews photo)

The pre-raid target picture taken by a PR
Mosquito of the Fw.190 factory, which
attracted the attention of the US 8th AF
B-17 Flying Fortresses in a daylight attack.

The Fw.190 factory after being bombed in a daylight attack
by B-17s of the US 8th AF photographed by a PR Mosquito.

Mosquito PR.MkXVI NS502 served as M of No. 544 Squadron.

Gatwick, which was a relatively small grass field, but was closer to the V-1 launch sites along the French coast. A navigator with this unit was the late Flt Lt Freddy Andrews, whose options, after training with Coastal Command, were to fly with coastal Beaufighters or PR Mosquitos. He was happy to be allocated to the Mosquito, and joined No. 4 Squadron at Aston Down for the conversion training. Many of the pilots had converted from the single-engine, single-crew Spitfires and were not used to sharing the tasks with a navigator. After only a short period it was decided to withdraw the Mosquitos from No. 4 Squadron, and the last Mosquito sortie with the squadron was flown on 20 May, leaving the Spitfires to cope with operations

from the advanced frontline airfields, although the Mosquito was a more rugged design and capable of rough-field operations.

Similarly, No. 400 Squadron only operated Mosquitos for a relatively short period, the first MkXVIs being delivered on 22 December 1943, although the first operational sortie was not until the following March. After only forty-three sorties, the Mosquitos were withdrawn on 12 May and had left the squadron by 29 May.

No. 140 Squadron specialised in tactical operations, the Mosquitos replacing Spitfires by 10 April, the main duties being to obtain material for the planning of the D-Day landings. To provide the full range of cover required in the timescale, night photography

Canadian-built B.MkXX USAAF Mosquito F8 334826, 'The Spook'. (FlyPast Collection)

was used for the first time on 4 May. From 1 March, with D-Day only three months away, No. 540 Squadron concentrated its major operations at Benson, flying operations over France and southern Europe. The squadron received the first PR.MkXVI on 31 May, but, owing to bad weather immediately prior to the invasion of Europe, no information could be gathered. No. 544 Squadron shared the photo-reconnaissance duties with nos 140 and 540 squadrons; their task was to concentrate on the situation with the vital rail communications in central and southern France, often operating at very low altitudes and fitted with forward-facing cameras. The ability of the Mosquito to cope with damage and return the crew safely to base was demonstrated when one of the No. 544 Squadron aircraft was damaged by flak. The rudder cables were cut, the electrics had failed, there were no engine instruments and the radiators had jammed shut, in addition to

other damage, but the plane was still flown home by the crew. When the PR.MkXVIs were issued to No. 544 Squadron, the aircraft were able to fly to virtually all parts of Germany.

By the middle of 1944 the equipment fit was improved with the addition of K.19 cameras in the No. 140 Squadron Mosquitos, and the strategic operations of nos 540 and 544 squadrons had improved accuracy by installing Rebecca, H and Gee. The close teamwork between the pilot and navigator enabled more accurate coverage to be obtained, even when operating under low cloud cover. With the invasion of France under way, the two strategic squadrons were allocated to the tactical tasks of photographing troop movements and supply routes.

In February 1944 the 8th USAAF commenced taking deliveries of Mosquito PR.MkXVIs, which were to be used initially for weather reconnaissance over Europe. Six of the aircraft based with the 482nd Bomb

Mosquito PR.MkXVI NS591:S of 25th (Reconnaissance) Group, US 8th AF on the approach to land at RAF Watton on 22 February 1945. This aircraft was sold to the French Air Force on 17 July 1946.

Hatfield-built Mosquito PR.MkXVI NS538:F of 25th (Reconnaissance) Group at RAF Watten, one of six of this version fitted with H2X in the nose and used initially by the 482nd Bomb Group at Alconbury. (Photo Chaz Bowyer collection)

Group at Alconbury were fitted with special radomes under the fuselage to test H2X radar, the American equivalent of the British H2S, which gave clear radar pictures of target areas through cloud cover. Mosquito PR.MkXVIs were based with the 25th Bomb Group at Watton from August 1944, although USAAF photo-reconnaissance operations with Mosquitos had commenced in time for the D-Day landings. When used on night operations, the aircraft carried a dozen 700,000 candlepower M.46 photoflashes. Other USAAF uses for the Mosquito included some operated by 492nd Group on carpetbagger operations from Harrington, where they assisted Allied agents in occupied Europe.

Mosquito PR.MkXVIs were used to confirm the location of the German battleship *Tirpitz* in Tromso Fiord in Norway, which required a flight of 2,100 miles (3,380 km) achieved by carrying a pair of 100 gal (454 l) underwing fuel drop tanks. On 25 July 1944, No. 544 Squadron Mosquito MM273 was one of the first to come up against the German Me.262 jet fighter when it was flying in the Munich–Stuttgart area, but it made its escape by flying into cloud cover.

The need for even higher altitudes was recognised during 1942, but it was not until early 1944 that Merlin 15 SM engines were available, the first installation being in Mosquito MkXVI MM328. Among the improvements were higher supercharger gear ratios, an increase in wingspan and a decrease in the empty weight. Service trials began at Benson on 20 May, when it was found that the ceiling increased by between 4,000 and 5,000 ft (1,220 to 1,525 m). Five more similarly modified Mosquitos, designated PR.Mk32, were delivered from August 1944, shared between nos 540 and 544 squadrons. These were to meet up with German jet- and rocket-powered fighters. Service trials continued with PR.Mk32 NS587, operated by No. 544 Squadron in November, but

problems with icing, overheating engines and a lack of sufficient cockpit heating had to be corrected before No. 540 Squadron flew NS580 on the first operation on 5 December 1944. The original conversion was destroyed in an accident at Benson on 1 April 1945.

To help with achieving the desired results from low-level missions, forward-facing cameras were fitted into the nose of each of the underwing fuel tanks, although there was no intention to jettison these except in a dire emergency. The first MkIX to be modified for this configuration, MM235, was lost on 11 August 1944 and replaced by another MkIX LR432. It was, however, found that, with the more hazardous low-level photographic operations, a similarly modified FB.MkVI was more effective as it could shoot back at the defenders, and keep them sheltering from the Mosquito cannons and machine-gun fire. As more of Europe came under Allied control, advanced airfields could be used by Mosquitos, and No. 140 Squadron operating with the 2nd TAF was able to make deeper penetrations into enemy territory, rarely encountering hostile fighters.

Using the endurance of the Mosquitos, No. 544 Squadron was diverted on to flying long-range diplomatic mail flights between London and Moscow, operating from Northolt under the codename Operation 'Frugal', starting on 9 October 1944. Flying at an average speed of 300 mph the duration of the flights was around 6½ hrs. Similar diplomatic mail flights were flown to Cairo and Naples, and later to support the Potsdam Conference.

The defeat of Germany became inevitable during the early months of 1945, keeping the PR Mosquito units increasingly busy, flying round the clock to keep track of the enemy supply lines. The longer-range Mosquito PR.Mk34s joined No. 544 Squadron in April 1945, carrying 200 gal (910 l) fuel drop tanks under the wings, in addition to the internal fuel load. However, the arrival of these aircraft was too late for hostilities in Europe, as the final

Mosquito PR.Mk34A PF662 was built by Percival at Luton and delivered to No. 540 Squadron at Benson and coded DH-T. In addition to the normal camera installation in the fuselage, one of which can be seen ahead of the roundel, cameras were also fitted in the leading edge of the underwing fuel tanks.

sorties by MkIXs of nos 540 and 544 squadrons were flown in early March, and, following a move to advanced airfields in France by No. 540 Squadron on 29 March, MkXVI RF970 made the unit's last operational sortie on 26 April from Benson. Despite the great success of the Mosquito PR operations from Benson and other airfields during the Second World War, the German Air Force never attempted similar operations themselves, no doubt owing to their lack of mastery of the air.

With the end of the war, the need for photo-reconnaissance operations with Mosquitos continued. At Benson, No. 58 Squadron operated Mosquito PR.Mk34s with A Flight, and the Ansons with B Flight were replaced by Mosquito PR.Mk35s in 1951.

Only eight of these conversions are recorded from B.Mk35s, made at Leavesden, and No. 58 Squadron used four of these aircraft, as the only operators of this version. The advantages of using the converted bomber variant was the provision for carrying photographic flares for night photography internally, instead of under the wings, and the bomb bay provided room for additional camera equipment. The PR.Mk34's bomb bay was filled with extra fuel tanks, and the doors were fixed shut, except for access on the ground. The PR.Mk35s were used to develop improved night photography, later to benefit the PR sorties with Canberra jet bombers. The operations were later moved to Wyton.

The high, all-up weight with full fuel load

Mosquito PR.Mk34 RG300 being manhandled out of the hangar at Benson. It was sold in the USA as N9871F and the remains of the aircraft are now in storage with the Confederate Air Force. (de Havilland photo)

Because of their long endurance, Mosquito PR.Mk34s, including PF623, were used for navigation assistance to No. 54 Squadron Vampires across the Atlantic in August 1948, when they were returning from the tour of the USA. (de Havilland photo)

made the PR.Mk34 Mosquitos probably the least pleasant version of the aircraft to fly. Unlike the other versions, the PR.Mk34 had a tendency not to want to fly, and an increased elevator balance weight helped to lift the tail off the ground during take-off. Even with the bomb bay fuel tanks empty, and similarly loaded to the B.Mk35, the PR.Mk34 was less pleasant to fly, although in most respects the aircraft were identical. However, the 7 hrs endurance of the PR.Mk34 was essential for the longer-range sorties, although the cockpit could be somewhat cramped. An example of a typical operation was Benson to Gibraltar, then to Castel Benito in North Africa, and the return to Benson after a few days away on detachment for further training. The PR.34s were so heavy with full fuel on take-off that, if a problem occurred, it was necessary to fly around for an hour to burn off enough fuel, and bring the aircraft down to a safe landing weight, as there was no provision for fuel jettison in an emergency. It was not normal to jettison the underwing fuel tanks when they were full, in case only one released, and caused major control problems with the out-of-balance forces.

Crews were converted to the Mosquito after the war by flying T.MkIIIs and FB.MkVIs with 204 AFS at Brize Norton, and then progressed on to operational training with PR.Mk34s at 237 OCU at Leuchars. One B.Mk35 with all of its operational equipment removed was used for pilot familiarisation with No. 58 Squadron. It was popular with the aircrew because it was a delight to fly.

Mosquito PR.Mk34s of No. 58 Squadron were used on Operation Dimple, which entailed the crews flying to Germany to refuel, then flying east over Eastern Europe and the Soviet Bloc at very high altitudes, a task that was later adopted by the Canberra U-2 spy-plane and is now done by satellites.

Although Europe was the main theatre for wartime Mosquito PR operations, they also occurred to a lesser extent in the Mediterranean, the Middle East and Asia, where information about enemy dispositions was just as vital. The Mediterranean operations complemented the UK-based reconnaissance over northern Europe by covering the southern flank, but the UK-based units were given priority for the latest versions of the PR Mosquitos, making them in short supply overseas.

For operations in hotter climates, the change from casein glue to formaldehyde provided a more reliable bonding. The initial Mediterranean operations were carried out from Malta using a pair of tropicalised long-range PR.MkIs, which took photographs over Italy on the way to Malta. Both of the aircraft were written off in Malta, due either to enemy action or landing on soft ground.

Many of the British dominions and colonies helped to fight in the Second World War, and No. 60 Squadron SAAF was one of the examples. The squadron was allocated to photo-reconnaissance to cover the North African battles, but was only equipped with the relatively short-range and vulnerable Baltimores and Marylands. Any coverage into southern Europe would require the range of Mosquitos. A pair of Mosquito MkIIs, DD743 and DD744, had been allocated to hot weather trials to determine how the wooden structure and adhesives would stand up to the high temperatures. The trial involved their being left to stand out in the sun, until General Montgomery persuaded Winston Churchill to have them released for operations. They would still experience the temperatures, but would at least make a more positive contribution and achieve more realistic trials, although the hazards of combat were not conducive to long service.

The two aircraft were delivered to Castel Benito for the use of No. 60 Squadron SAAF on 4 February 1943, where a camera was fitted under the cockpit floor. The aircraft operated with success, despite the

Mosquito PR.MkXVI MM366 served with No. 60 Squadron SAAF in the Mediterranean theatre. (O.G. Davies photo)

unfamiliarity of both the air and ground crews with the Mosquito. Up to four sorties a day were soon being achieved, starting with DD744 on 12 February. These two aircraft continued in service until DD743 was lost on 5 July and DD744 was damaged and withdrawn from use on 6 August 1943. However, more Mosquitos had begun to be issued to the squadron following the successes with the first two aircraft. In June, PR.MkIV DZ553 arrived, but was shot down on 27 July on the seventh sortie. During August, PR.MkIXs LR411 and LR437 were issued to the squadron, followed by four more in September to permit more effective high-level operations ranging over Italy, Austria and other parts of southern Europe. An important tactical operation was the

photography of Sicily in preparation for the Allied landings, and by January 1944 the squadron had reached its maximum number of 13 Mosquitos, with the first PR.MkXVI MM287 commencing the update of the aircraft in February.

When No. 4 Squadron ceased Mosquito operations, the trained aircrew were dispersed to other units, and Freddy Andrews was sent to Dyce near Aberdeen to join up with a South African pilot, Lt P. Stofberg. Once they had completed their refresher training, they collected Mosquito PR.MkXVI NS644 from Benson and ferried the aircraft to No. 60 Squadron SAAF, then based at San Severo in Italy which was shared with No. 680 Squadron. Because the SAAF was short of trained navigators, a number were

No. 60 Squadron (SAAF) used red and white diagonal stripes on the fin to help with recognition from allied fighters, an example being PR.MkXVI NS644. (Freddy Andrews photo)

seconded from the RAF, which is why Andrews joined the squadron. Two USAAF Lightning units were also based at San Severo, one of their tasks being to provide defensive cover for the Mosquitos against attacks by German jet fighters, but the Lightnings had difficulty keeping up with the Mosquitos.

The normal operating height was around 27,000 ft (8,230 m). Sorties were flown over the Balkans, eastern Germany and as far as Poland, the targets including railway tunnels in the Balkans suspected of being used as underground factories. It was hoped that the pictures would be able to determine which tunnels were being used as factories and what

they were producing. Although flak was a threat, particularly if the Mosquitos were at a height where contrails were formed, the main hazard was from German jet fighters. Escorting Mustangs or Lightnings would accompany the Mosquitos on all but the longest-range flights, and it was on one of these unescorted flights that NS649 was damaged. Andrews was in the nose taking photographs over the Salzburg–Innsbruck area on 26 November 1944 when there was a loud bang. On returning quickly to his seat, he saw that an Me262 jet fighter had followed their trails and fired at the Mosquito. The first shells hit along the top of the port engine cowling and were deflected down by the

No. 60 Squadron (SAAF) operated photo-reconnaissance flights from the Mediterranean throughout southern Europe, and up north as far as Poland. (Freddy Andrews photo)

propeller blade into the reduction gear, causing a runaway. Fortunately there was just enough power to feather the propeller, and the Mosquito dived rapidly towards a lower altitude cloud layer. The Me262 overshot the Mosquito twice in the dive, despite an estimated speed of around 500 mph (800 km/h), but once in cloud the Mosquito was able to shake off the German jet.

The next challenge was to fly back to base, when the Mosquito had descended to 9,000 ft (2,740 m) and had to climb back up to at least 14,000 ft (4,270 m) to clear the Alps. Lt Stofberg selected full boost on the starboard engine for 30 minutes, well beyond the

recommended time, but achieved enough height to go over the tops of the mountains. Despite bad weather over Italy, the crew were able to locate the airfield through a gap in the cloud, using Gee as an aid. They landed at about 180 kt (333 km/h) and overshot into mud at the end of the runway. The damaged port engine was changed before the aircraft went back on operations, but it was not long before the overstrained starboard engine also needed changing.

On 15 August 1944, No. 60 Squadron's Mosquito NS520, which was being flown by Capt Pienaar in the Cunzberg–Leiphein area, was attacked by an Me262. The interception

Damage to Mosquito PR.MkXVI NS649 of No. 60 Squadron (SAAF) after being shot at by a Me.262 jet fighter over the Salzburg–Innsbruck area on 26 November 1944. The South African pilot Lt P. Stofberg is on the left, and navigator Freddy Andrews is on the right. (Freddy Andrews photo)

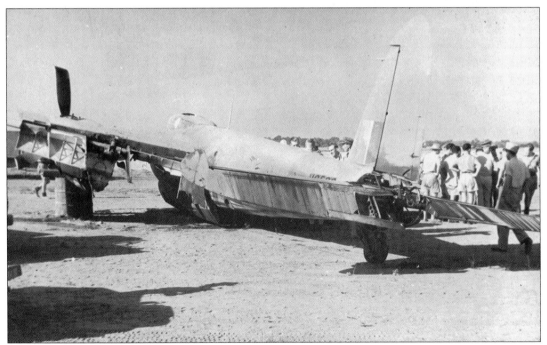

The substantially damaged No. 60 Squadron (SAAF) Mosquito PR.MkXVI NS520 after the wheels-up crash-landing by Captain Pienaar following repeated attacks by an enemy Me.262 jet fighter. Damage includes the almost complete destruction of the port flaps and elevator controls. (de Havilland photo)

started at 30,000 ft (9,145 m). In the running battle the Mosquito was damaged in the port flaps, port aileron, port tailplane, rear of the engine nacelle, and tailcone. During the 40 min skirmish, the Mosquito lost 11,000 ft of altitude and had its speed reduced owing to the damage. The aircraft survived twelve attacks and made a wheels-up crash-landing in Italy, the crew being awarded an immediate DFC.

Freddy Andrews' duties as a PR navigator were to guide his pilot to and from the target and, once over it, instead of releasing the bombs before the aiming point so that they would land in the right place, he pressed the camera button. As well as navigating, Freddy was also responsible for sharing the duties of lookout for any hostile aircraft. Care had even to be taken when a 'friendly' aircraft was spotted, as they could be hostile if the pilot had not properly identified the Mosquito. As well as black and white invasion stripes painted under the wings and fuselage, the No. 60 Squadron Mosquitos were painted with red and white diagonal stripes on the fin and rudder as a means of identification. With hostilities obviously coming to an end, the squadron was allocated to aerial mapping survey duties over Austria, the Franco-Italian borders and the associated Italian Alps region. When the war in Europe ceased, No. 60 Squadron was allocated to further large-scale mapping survey duties of Greece, the Aegean Islands, southern Italy and the islands of Sardinia, Corsica and Sicily. The official stand-down came on 15 July 1945, and, in August, ten of the Mosquitos were flown from San Severo to the home base of No. 60 Squadron at Zwarkop in South Africa. The aircraft were put into storage and were seldom flown, eventually being retired from service.

Not being a South African, Freddy Andrews did not go with No. 60 Squadron to South Africa but instead joined No. 680 Squadron, which at that time was based in Iraq, the task being to conduct a

photographic survey of the featureless desert. By February 1944, No. 680 Squadron had begun to replace its Spitfires with Mosquitos, and by the end of April it had one PR.MkIX and nine PR.MkXVIs. The aircrafts' area of operations was to provide photographic coverage of Greece and the Balkans, complementing the work of No. 60 Squadron SAAF. For the longer-range flights over Austria and Bavaria, No. 680 Squadron often had escort cover from Mustangs and Lightnings of the 31st Fighter Group USAAF. For the peacetime operations over Iraq, it operated PR.MkXVIs and later the less popular but very long-range PR.Mk34s.

Another unit to operate PR Mosquitos in the Mediterranean area was No. 683 Squadron, which started operations with a PR.MkII from Malta in February 1943 flying over southern Italy. However, only twenty sorties were flown before the aircraft were withdrawn by June. In the summer of 1943, a detachment of three PR.MkIXs were flown by No. 540 Squadron to the Mediterranean, and a PR.MkXVI was flown to Gibraltar in January 1944 to check the operation of the two-stage Merlins in a warmer climate.

Asia was the other major area for Mosquito PR operations. To check the suitability of the aircraft in the extreme climatic conditions, six Mosquitos of varying age were sent to India to be picketed out in different places to determine how the structure would stand up to the hot and humid climate. Despite the fact that the worst way to treat an aircraft, particularly one made from wood, is to leave it outside unattended, the Mosquitos stood up well to temperatures reaching 130°F, 88 per cent humidity and a rainfall during the period of nearly 64 inches.

PR operations started with Mosquitos in Asia when No. 681 Squadron at Dum Dum had the first aircraft delivered on 2 August 1943. The first active sortie was on 23 August with DZ697 flying over the Mandalay,

Hatfield-built Mosquito PR.MkXVI NS688 being prepared for departure from an Indian-based maintenance unit.

Shewbo-ye U-Monywa and Wunthe areas. Its sister aircraft, DZ696, had to force land close to enemy territory, having suffered bullet holes in both oil tanks. Despite appalling conditions, including torrential rain, illness among the working party and a shortage of spares and tools, the aircraft had new engines and an undercarriage fitted in three weeks and was flown out of a specially prepared jungle strip.

Meanwhile a PR.MkVI, HJ730, was delivered, to be followed by PR.MkIX LR440 in September. LR440 made its first operational sortie on 21 October over Japanese positions at Rangoon and Magwe. Despite successful results, the Mosquitos were withdrawn from the squadron by the end of the month. No. 684 Squadron was

formed at Dum Dum to replace No. 681 Squadron, equipped with a selection of Mitchells and Mosquito Mks II, VI and IX, commencing operations on 1 November. Many of the operations were of long duration, but the Mosquitos were very reliable, which was helpful, as they were in short supply initially. On 9 December, No. 681 Squadron moved to Camilla, allowing long-duration flights over northern Burma, Thailand and the Andamans, mostly flying at between 28,000 and 33,000 ft (8,500 to 10,000 m). Towards the end of January 1944 the squadron was operating Mosquito PR.MkVIs and IXs, but that February these were supplemented by the arrival of the first PR.MkXVIs, which gradually replaced the

No. 684 Squadron commenced operations from Dum Dum on 1 November 1943 and later received Mosquito PR.MkXVIs, including NS787:M.

earlier aircraft. The newer Mosquitos allowed deep-penetration flight over the inhospitable terrain of Burma and Siam (now Thailand), where the two Merlin engines provided the crews with much needed security. As an example of the type of operations involved, one of the longer flights took 7 hr 20 min, covering 2,256 miles (3,630 km) at an average speed of 308 mph (495 km/h).

The Australian-built and -operated Mosquitos were covering the territory as far west as Sourabaya, but a gap of 2,000 miles (3,220 km) of Japanese-occupied territory was outside the range of the Mosquito, making it all the more urgent for the delivery of the increased endurance PR.Mk34s. Despite the limitations, longer-duration flights were achieved, with 2,350 miles (3,220 km) in January 1945 taking 8 hr 20 min. This was soon improved on with a flight of 2,483 miles (4,000 km) through tropical storms with only 20 min of fuel remaining after landing.

Mosquito PR.Mk34s entered service in June 1945 with a special detachment of No. 684 Squadron, based in the Cocos Islands. The first long-range sortie was flown on 3 July in RG185. The remote Cocos Islands are situated about 1,500 miles (2,400 km) from Ceylon (now Sri Lanka) and 1,200 miles (1,900 km) from the coast of Australia. The uninhabited islands had to have space prepared for aircraft to operate, including a coral landing strip. Despite the basic conditions, with all supplies being ferried in by sea, the Mosquitos operated well in the hot climate and salty sea air. By the end of August, seven PR.Mk34s had been delivered to the Cocos Islands. The longest-duration flight was flown by RG210 on 20 August, when the aircraft was airborne for 9 hr 5 min, the target area being Penang and Taiping. Thirteen sorties were flown by VJ-Day, the major hazards being the violent tropical storms, although flak could also be a problem.

The crew who flew the last RAF Mosquito sortie on 15 December 1955 in RG314 were pilot Flg Off 'Collie' Knox, right and navigator Flg Off 'Tommy' Thompson. (RAFM photo)

During the Malayan terrorist emergency, known as Operation Firedog, Mosquito PR.Mk34s of No. 81 Squadron shared photo-reconnaissance operations with Spitfires, commencing in July 1949 for a period of some seven years. The last RAF Mosquito operational flight was with PR.Mk34 RG314 on 15 December 1955, closing a major chapter in the history of the service.

The Mosquito PR.Mk41 had been produced in Australia, and some of the Mk40s were converted to PR work by installing three vertical cameras in the nose and a pair of oblique cameras in the fuselage.

These aircraft were issued to No. 87 (PR) Squadron RAAF for the task of an aerial survey of Australia from 1946 until the squadron was disbanded in 1953, two-thirds of its job having been completed.

The PR Mosquitos had therefore seen the introduction of the type right through to the final retirement, providing the Allies with the vital intelligence they needed in preparation for attacking targets, during the raid itself and afterwards to assess the damage. They had operated unarmed in all climates, bringing pictures back from high and low level, with an acceptable low loss rate for the crews.

10. Fast and Furious: Fighters

Although originally conceived as an unarmed, high-speed bomber, the performance attributes of the Mosquito made it suitable for duties as a long-range escort fighter, and particularly as a night fighter. The Mosquito possessed good endurance, a high load-carrying capability for the heavy airborne interception radar equipment, room for two crew to share the workload, good manoeuvrability and fast top speeds. With the armament of four under-fuselage 20 mm fixed cannons and four .303in fixed machine-guns in the nose, when not displaced by the radar, the Mosquito could provide a very destructive punch against other aircraft.

The Mosquito fighter took early priority over the bomber, the night-fighter prototype making its first flight from the fields adjacent to Salisbury Hall, as already discussed, on 15 May 1941. Following the initial flight-testing to prove the airframe, by the end of July the first AI radar set was installed for development in the night-fighter role. The main radar antenna was of vertical double arrowhead shape in the extreme nose between the two pairs of machine-guns, with short double whip aerials out on the top and bottom wingtips. Later versions with more effective AI radar equipment housed the radar antenna under an electronically transparent radome, replacing the machine-guns. The long-range escort fighter designed for convoy protection did not have the AI radar fitted and was known as the F.MkII. It was later used on intruder operations, which led to the development of the FB.MkVI, an effective fighter-bomber, which is dealt with later.

It was as a night-fighter that the Mosquito gained most prominence in the fighter role. Following the Battle of Britain, the major threat was from enemy bombers making attacks at night on London and the industrial centres of Britain. There was therefore great urgency to defend against these raids and No. 157 Squadron, led by Wg Cdr Gordon Slade, was formed at Debden on 13 December 1941. For training to begin, F.MkII W4073 was delivered on 26 January 1942 to the basic Debden satellite at Castle Camps. Despite the disadvantages of poor accommodation, rudimentary equipment and a bleak, inhospitable and isolated site, particularly in the cold winter weather, No. 157 Squadron made its base there in January. As with any new type of aircraft, particularly one with some revolutionary AI radar equipment fitted, the build-up of the numbers of Mosquitos was slow, many aircraft being delivered to the squadron from the maintenance units with the normal service equipment installed, but without radar sets. By the middle of April, sixteen NF.MkIIs had been delivered, allowing seven crews to be trained. In the light of experience, a number of adjustments were made in the cockpit to ensure that all of the controls were readily available in the dark and, in particular, in the stress of combat. In effect, No. 157 Squadron undertook service trials of the newly equipped aircraft. Once converted to the Mosquito, the crews had to learn how to operate the night-fighter as an effective combat aircraft. The interceptions required an extra team member of the ground-based radar who plotted the targets, whether practice or hostile, vectoring the crew to within range of their own AI equipment, when they could then undertake the night interception.

The next unit to be equipped with Mosquito night-fighters was No. 151 Squadron, led by Wg Cdr Smith. The first NF.MkII was delivered to Wittering on 6 April to begin to replace the outclassed Defiants with A Flight. During the training by the two squadrons, it was found that the flash when the nose-mounted machine-guns were fired destroyed the night vision of the crew, making it impossible for them to make the vital visual identification of a target, although, by the time they had fired, they would have been committed. The engine exhausts were fitted with flame-damping shrouds to avoid visual detection by hostile aircraft. However, not only did these reduce the top speed by around 10 mph (16 km/h) but there were problems with them burning through, requiring about sixty aircraft to be modified to keep enough of them operational. Once the introductory problems had been overcome, the two squadrons developed a healthy rivalry in terms of which would be the first to catch a hostile raider.

No. 157 Squadron made the first operational patrol from Castle Camps on the night of 27 April. Two nights later a Dornier Do.217 was chased, but escaped. No. 151 Squadron became operational with the Mosquito night-fighters on 30 April, but there were a number of frustrations, particularly with the enemy aircraft flying at low altitudes, which gave ground control stations little time to detect the targets and to home the Mosquitos in to them. It meant that the Mosquitos had to be flown on standing patrols and, although they were fast compared with the enemy, the difference in speed was not great, resulting in some long-running chases to catch up with, and identify, the raider, before attempting to shoot it down. Mid-air collisions were also a hazard, even during training, when some crews were killed.

The first claim was an unconfirmed probable by No. 151 Squadron on 29 May. The German bomber was believed to have crashed in the North Sea after a long running fight. The Mosquito flew back to base on one engine, with damage to the other as well as to the wing and tailplane. The next night another inconclusive probable victory against a Do.217 over the English Channel off Dover was claimed by No. 157 Squadron. Subsequent analysis of the records after the war suggested that the first aircraft was only damaged, but the No. 157 Squadron victory was confirmed.

As more aircraft came off the production line, the night-fighter force was able to increase, B Flight of No. 264 Squadron at Colerne beginning to replace its Defiants with the first Mosquito on 3 May. Conversion of the pilots usually started with a few hours on Airspeed Oxfords to gain familiarity with twin engines, but sometimes the pilots transferred to the Mosquito directly. To assist in the conversion training, W4053 was converted to a T.MkIII after development flying with the turret and was issued to No. 264 Squadron. The squadron's first operational night patrol was on 13 June, although there was little enemy activity at the time. No. 157 Squadron also had little success, owing to minimal enemy activity in their sector. By the end of June, however, No. 151 Squadron was able to claim four confirmed victories and three damaged, followed by another five confirmed victories in July. The CO, Wg Cdr Smith, claimed two confirmed victories and a probable in a 30 min period on one night sortie.

The AI radar equipment, still in early operational use, suffered from unserviceability and could be erratic in its operation. The crews were also unfamiliar with the full operation of the equipment, which could be temperamental, depending on its maintenance, production quality and the installation in the aircraft. The high speed of the Mosquito could be a disadvantage when closing in on a hostile

As part of the defence policy of locating the Mosquito night-fighter squadrons around Britain, No. 25 Squadron took delivery of the first Mosquitos at Church Fenton in October 1942. The squadron continued to operate later versions of the Mosquito night-fighters, the ultimate RAF version being the NF.Mk36 when No. 25 Squadron was based at West Malling in 1950. NF.Mk30 RL123 ZK-G was one of the examples before being replaced by Vampire NF.Mk10s. (G.A. Heather photo via Chaz Bowyer)

The Canadian No. 410 Squadron received their first Mosquito MkII at Acklington in December 1942. In the last year of the war the squadron had re-equipped with Mosquito NF.MkXIII, HK429 RA-N having been the mount for Flg Off E. Hermanson and Flt Lt D. Hamm when they scored a triple victory on the night of 23/4 April 1945. (Photo Chaz Bowyer collection)

No. 307(Polish) Squadron received their first Mosquito night-fighter at Exeter in December 1942. By January 1945 they were based at a rather bleak Castle Camps and equipped with NF.MkXXXs. Here NT295/G EW-W is being prepared for starting. (J.B. Cynk photo via Chaz Bowyer)

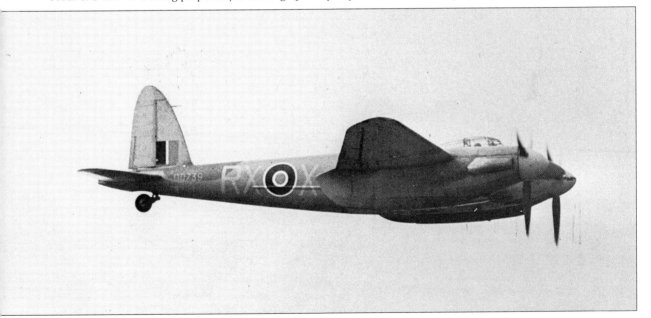

The fourth regional night-fighter unit to be formed was No. 456 Squadron at Valley, commencing operations in January 1943. One of their aircraft was Mosquito NF.MkII DD739 coded RX-X and painted in the modified day camouflage scheme. (Photo Chaz Bowyer collection)

raider, particularly if the enemy aircraft was slower. Although airbrakes had been considered, the most effective way of slowing down was found to be to put the propellers into fine pitch and open the radiator flaps to create some drag. Further drag could be achieved by lowering the undercarriage or flaps, but often the Mosquito was flying above the limiting speed, and this would add delay to the acceleration back to operational speed if the target tried to escape. In the summer months, with the shorter periods of darkness, any raiders flying at higher altitudes could be identified against the background of the Northern Lights. Generally, however, enemy aircraft flew over Britain at lower altitudes to avoid detection by the ground-based radar. During the early operations, the effectiveness of various camouflage finishes were evaluated. Overall, matt black was thought to be the best, particularly against searchlights, but the non-gloss finish reduced the top speed by 15 mph (25 km/h) owing to the extra drag, and it was found that the aircraft showed up in silhouette in moonlight, especially against cloud. A modified day-fighter camouflage was adopted as the most effective.

On 29 July the first Mosquito T.MkIII was delivered to No. 85 Squadron, but the following day it crashed during training, and it was not until 15 August that training could commence with the squadron's first NF.MkII, ready for patrols to start three nights later. Meanwhile, No. 264 Squadron claimed their first victory when a Ju.88 was shot down near Malvern on 30 July. No. 157 Squadron began to achieve some successes when Gordon Slade shot down a Do.217 on 22 August at Worlingworth in Essex, two of the crew parachuting into captivity.

Operations against enemy raiders were not mounted only at night, as a number of hostile bombers used the cover of cloud and poor visibility to try to escape detection. The Mosquito night-fighter squadrons therefore also used their radar at times of poor visibility. The first use of AI radar in daylight combat was on 30 September, when Wg Cdr Clarke of No. 157 Squadron shot down a Ju.88 30 miles (48 km) off the Dutch coast. On 19 October No. 157 Squadron claimed another Ju.88 in daylight and on the same day No. 85 Squadron had some inconclusive results.

Four more squadrons were converted to Mosquito night-fighters towards the end of 1942. These were based strategically around Britain, although some of the sectors were relatively quiet, making contact with the enemy rare. At Church Fenton in Yorkshire, No. 25 Squadron took delivery of the first three NF.MkIIs on 21 October, and following training it commenced operations on 17 December without making contact with the enemy. The Beaufighter-equipped Canadian No. 410 Squadron was suffering from low morale because it had not claimed a single victory after sixteen months of operations. It received Mosquito NF.MkIIs at its Acklington base, ready to start operations on 6 December. At Exeter No. 307 (Polish) Squadron received its first Mosquito night-fighters in December, ready for operations to begin on 14 January 1943, without any contact with hostile aircraft. The fourth unit was No. 456 Squadron, based at Valley in Anglesea. Its first three MkIIs were delivered in December, and operations started from this exposed coastal airfield on 22 January.

Britain therefore had night-fighter squadrons of Mosquitos located around the country to defend against air attack from any direction, and allowing a rapid reaction to any threat. However, the sometimes remote and exposed airfields brought problems with water soakage into the balsa wood sandwich shell of the fuselage. The Mosquitos were dispersed widely for protection from hostile raids and they were normally only taken under cover for major maintenance or repairs. Although all of the cut-outs in the fuselage were doped and covered in fabric for protection, the fabric

Mosquito MkII W4087 was modified at Heston with the fitting of a Turbinlite in the nose as a proposed means of locating hostile aircraft at night. Following trials with nos 151 and 85 squadrons, it was rejected. (GE photo)

often cracked in the hot sun and the rain soaked into the wood underneath. It was not just the deterioration caused to the structure, but also the extra weight and likely change in the centre of gravity that could cause serious handling and performance problems. Constant care and attention was required to keep water soakage to a minimum, and one of the cures was to fit a wooden strip along the starboard side of the rear fuselage, over the rear equipment bay hatch, to deflect the water away from the cut-out.

As a result of the difficulties with the AI radars, an earlier idea involving an airborne searchlight was still being considered. In what was known as a Turbinlite installation, a number of Bostons and Havocs had been fitted with a bright light in the nose. The idea was to

patrol in pairs, one aircraft being fully armed and the other being directed towards the hostile aircraft by ground radar. When the raider had been located, the Turbinlite-equipped aircraft would attempt to illuminate the target while the companion would try to shoot the enemy down. Not only was the enemy aircraft immediately alerted, but any hope of retaining night vision was lost. Mosquito MkII W4087 was modified at Heston by having a Turbinlite installation fitted in the nose at the end of 1941. On 16 January the plane was delivered to No. 151 Squadron for service trials, being flown by a crew from No. 532 Squadron. On 18 February it was passed to No. 85 Squadron for further trials, but was soon returned to 1422 Flight at Heston with an adverse report on its effectiveness.

Wing Commander John Cunningham took command of No. 85 Squadron in January 1943 at Hunsdon. (Photo Chaz Bowyer collection)

Wg Cdr John Cunningham took over as commanding officer of No. 85 Squadron on 27 January 1943, having already gained a significant number of night-fighter victories flying Beaufighters, along with his observer Jimmy Rawnsley. Cunningham had gained the nickname 'Cats Eyes Cunningham' which referred to his outstanding night vision, helped by the vitamin C he gained from eating carrots. Not only is he not particularly fond of carrots, but, although his eyesight has always been good, it was the secret AI radar that led to his outstanding successes. The fact that he was based in a very active sector also played a part in his successes. The move to the Mosquito from the Beaufighter was necessary

for the additional speed, but the water-cooled Merlin engines, with their radiators fitted in the wing leading edge between the fuselage and the engines, were prone to damage from debris from the destruction of enemy aircraft. The air-cooled radial engines in the Beaufighter were much more robust and less prone to damage in this way.

Like the other crews, Cunningham and Rawnsley were vectored on to potential targets by the ground control interception (GCI) radar. Once identified at short range on their own radar, they would take over the chase. Once sighted, Cunningham would fly the Mosquito below the target to identify it visually against cloud or starlit background, in case it was an Allied aircraft. Once identified as hostile, Cunningham would climb to immediately behind the enemy aircraft, in the hope of remaining undetected by a rear gunner, and fire his guns before the raider was able to escape. There were occasions when an alert rear gunner spotted the Mosquito, the enemy aircraft diving away to make an escape while the gunner shot at the Mosquito. On one occasion, Cunningham returned to base with his windscreen shot up, only being saved by the bullet-proof laminated screen. When the new windscreen was fitted, he was given the damaged one as a souvenir. On the night of 3 March, he was close to adding a brace of Dorniers to his total, but an electrical lead had become disconnected and, with the aircraft in his sights, on both occasions the guns failed to fire. There would have been a definite advantage in having upward-firing guns as had been successfully used by the Germans, fitted to the night-fighter Mosquitos, but this idea was never adopted by the RAF.

The first of twelve of the Mosquito NF.MkXIIs began to be delivered to No. 85 Squadron in February 1943 at Hunsdon in Hertfordshire, fitted with the much improved centrimetric radar, situated under a nose-

No. 29 Squadron received their first Mosquito night-fighters in May 1943 and when later based at Hunsdon used Mosquito NF.MkXIIIs, for example HK382 RO-T, on Night Ranger sorties over enemy territory.

mounted radome, thus displacing the machine-guns. However, the greater effectiveness of the radar more than compensated for the loss of the guns, the cannon being far more destructive anyway. John Cunningham found that the bomber-type control wheel gave him better combat manoeuvrability than the fighter-type stick, and the rudder trim control was repositioned to the side of the cockpit to give a better view around the gunsight. During the night of 14 April, No. 85 Squadron claimed its first kills with the MkXII, when two Do.217s were destroyed.

By the spring of 1943, enemy night bombing had decreased significantly, and some of the Mosquito night-fighter squadrons joined their fighter-bomber colleagues on 'Ranger' patrols at night over hostile territory. When still chasing enemy aircraft over Britain, victories were sometimes shared with the anti-aircraft guns on the ground. However, these could be just as hazardous to friendly aircraft as to the enemy, as not only were the ground-based guns less accurate, but they did not always differentiate between the combatants.

A new enemy threat was experienced from mid-April, when high-speed Fw.190s with a single bomb carried beneath the fuselage and wing-mounted fuel drop tanks under the wings were used on nuisance raids on London. The first raid of thirty Fw.190s was not very successful, as only two bombs were dropped on target, one of the aircraft crashed and three landed in error at West Malling. The Fw.190 was almost as fast as the Mosquito, giving little speed advantage, so No. 85 Squadron moved to West Malling to replace No. 29 Squadron, which went to Bradwell Bay to exchange the Beaufighters for Mosquitos in May. No. 157 Squadron moved into Hunsdon to take the place of the departed No. 85 Squadron.

The relocation of No. 85 Squadron proved effective, as on the night of 16 May, out of a raid by some seventeen FW.190s, No. 85 Squadron claimed five victories in the one night, having taken over from some unsuccessful Typhoons. The honour of the first victory against these Fw.190 went to Sqn Ldr Green and Flt Sgt Grimstone, when they destroyed one of these aircraft close to Dover. On 20 May the last two production NF.MkIIs were delivered to 60 OTU for the training of aircrew in the fundamentals of night-fighting, while No. 256 Squadron at Ford received its first MkXIIs in the same month.

On 13 June, Wg Cdr Cunningham achieved his first night-fighter victory in the Mosquito, his seventeenth overall, when he downed one of a pair of Fw.190s flying at 23,000 ft (7,000 m). With the improvement in radar interception techniques, more aircraft fell to Britain's defending fighters, although the German nuisance raids had dropped in frequency. During June, the success of the Fw.190 operations was beginning to wane and a new threat came from the heavily armed and fast Me.410. Its top speed was around 388 mph (624 km/h) and rearward-facing remote-controlled 13 mm guns were mounted for defence on either side of the rear fuselage. Its offensive forward-firing armament consisted of two 20 mm cannons and a pair of machine-guns. The bomb load of the Me.410 could be up to 1,100 lb (500 kg).

The Mosquito was still faster, and this was demonstrated on the night of 13 July, when No. 85 Squadron claimed its first victory flying a MkXII, and shot down another two a few nights later. The success continued against these raiders when No. 256 Squadron claimed a third Me.410 at the end of the month.

The Me.410 units had learned from the experience of the Mosquito operations, and they mingled with the returning RAF heavy bomber streams, shooting down the bombers when the crews were beginning to relax. The Me.410 was similar to the Mosquito in outline, especially in the darkness, and was therefore difficult to detect. While some of the Me.410s bombed the runways of the RAF heavy bomber airfields, keeping the aircraft in the air, other Me.410s picked off the waiting aircraft at their leisure.

During August and September, Mosquito crews claimed a further seventeen victories, including seven Me.410s and six Fw.190s. The Fw.190s, with a bomb under the fuselage and the underwing fuel tanks, slowed the aircraft down sufficiently to make it an ideal target, providing the destruction of the aircraft did not cause the wreckage to damage the Mosquito. Cunningham shot down one of these Fw.190s off Aldeburgh in Suffolk, but had to return to base on one engine after the plane was damaged by debris from the target aircraft. In October a new threat from Germany was a mini-Blitz on London and the Home Counties by Ju.188s. (The Ju.188 was a developed version of the earlier Junkers Ju.88.) Although the German bombers carried a much smaller load than the RAF Lancasters and Halifaxes, they could still cause considerable damage. A number were shot down by Mosquito night-fighters.

The further improved Mosquito NF.MkXIII was issued to No. 488 Squadron and the first victory was claimed on 8 November, when an Me.410 was destroyed off Clacton. The major difference from the MkXII was that the aircraft was fitted with

One of the hazards of stalking enemy aircraft too closely was possible damage to the Mosquito. A Mosquito night-fighter flown by Flg Off E.R. Hedgecoe of No. 85 Squadron had most of the fabric burnt off his aircraft when a Ju.188 was destroyed on the night of 24/5 March 1944.

the universal wing, which provided room for extra fuel tanks to give a patrol endurance of nearly 6 hr. On 9 November, No. 307 Squadron was removed to the comparatively quiet sector based at Drem in Scotland, taking on the role of night-fighting, equipped with MkIIs and MkXIIs. It claimed its first victory on 22 November. During December, No. 29 Squadron began claiming victories with the new NF.MkXII version of the Mosquito.

With the growing capability of the enemy aircraft, there was a constant need for greater performance from the Mosquito night-fighters, particularly at altitudes of more than 20,000 ft (6,000 m). Trials were made by injecting nitrous oxide into the fuel system,

increasing the speed by nearly 50 mph (80 km/h), as well as keeping the aircraft as clean as possible to reduce drag. Using this improvement, Cunningham was able to shoot down an Me.410 at 28,000 ft (8,500 m) off Le Touquet on 2 January 1944. With the higher-performance Mosquitos in service, the last of the MkIIs were phased out from operational flying by the end of January, being relegated to operational training. However, before this happened, a No. 410 Squadron crew claimed a record number of three enemy aircraft in one night when it shot down three Do.217s on 10 December while defending the Chelmsford area against night attack.

On the night of 21 January a large number

No. 96 Squadron were operating the Mosquito NF.MkXIII from West Malling in 1943, HK419 ZJ-B being an example. (Chaz Bowyer collection)

of enemy bombing raids were planned for the London area. However, as a result of the defending Mosquito night-fighters, few reached their target. Nine enemy bombers were shot down by Mosquitos from nos 25, 28, 96, 410, 456, 488, 151 and 85 squadrons, the latter using four MkXVIIs equipped with the improved SCR.720 AI radar. Among the claims was a Heinkel He.177 by No. 151 Squadron, the first of this type to be shot down over Britain. Despite the losses by the enemy on this raid, more attacks were mounted during the succeeding months. On many occasions, efforts were made to jam the British radars by dropping 'Duppel', the German equivalent of the RAF 'Window', which were strips of tin-foil dropped from the attacking aircraft. The SCR.720 radar-equipped aircraft were able to overcome some of the jamming, and additional help in locating the raiders came from using

radar-directed searchlights. The Mosquitos became so effective at defending London that by mid-March the enemy were attacking what they believed might be less-heavily defended targets in East Anglia and further up the east coast. However, their assumption was wrong, as proved by the Mosquitos of nos 25, 307 and 264 squadrons.

The city of Bristol was selected as the target for more than a hundred German bombers on 27 March, eight of which were shot down. One of these, a Ju.88, was claimed by No. 219, a squadron based at Colerne, using a Mosquito MkXVII, on which the squadron had only just become operational after taking first deliveries the previous month. On 18 April the last attack in the series was made with a return to London, but there were enemy losses claimed by nos 96 and 488 squadrons, with the

No. 219 Squadron became operational with Mosquito NF.MkXVIIs at Colerne in March 1944, later equipping with NF.MkXXXs at Wittering, including MM813 and MM806. (E. Gosling photo via Chaz Bowyer)

Hunsdon-based No. 410 Squadron claiming an He.177. The enemy night-bombing activity then gradually decreased with the last major attack on Portsmouth on 15 May.

With the reduction in enemy night-bombing of Britain, the Mosquito night-fighter squadrons were deployed on more offensive operations in support of the preparations for D-Day. Six squadrons were allocated to 85 Group, as part of the 2nd TAF to provide night protection to the invading Allied troops. Seven squadrons and the FIU were initially tasked with the protection of the Allied beach-head, until the V-1 flying bombs were sent over the English Channel, when the Mosquitos were diverted to the new indiscriminate threat against Britain. The

remaining Mosquito night-fighter squadrons were deployed to defend against low-flying He.111s, which were air-launching flying bombs from over the North Sea.

With the D-Day landings starting during the night of 5/6 June 1944, the 85 Group squadrons began their support operations over Normandy. No. 264 Squadron opened the battle with radar jamming and defensive patrols, followed by No. 604 Squadron, which claimed five enemy aircraft destroyed on 7 June and five more the next night. Claims continued at a steady, but reduced, rate as the bad weather conditions, as well as a shortage of fuel and the ever advancing Allied troops, kept the German aircraft on the ground. More effective versions of the

Mosquito NF.MkXVII DZ659 ZQ-H served with the Fighter Interceptor Unit at Ford. The FIU were allocated with seven other squadrons to the protection of the D-Day beach-head, until the V-1 menace started. (RAFM photo)

Mosquito night-fighters were entering service with some units, and No. 604 Squadron received its first MkXIIIs in July, which it retained until being disbanded on 1 September 1945, when hostilities were over.

In mid-June the Germans sent over a new weapons combination, which at night appeared to be a Ju.88 with a glider bomb on top. However, it was found to be an Fw.190 or Bf.109 single-seat fighter guiding an uncrewed Ju.88 loaded with explosives, which was released and allowed to crash, although the precision was inaccurate, making it another revenge weapon. The V-1 flying bomb threat began on 14 June, four out of the ten launched reaching Britain, giving the enemy information on the range settings. These aircraft were first observed in the air by a Mosquito of No. 418 Squadron on a Ranger patrol. Two nights later, 244 V-1s were launched from along the occupied French coast, of which 144 were reported to have crossed the British coast and about half

fell on London. Destroying these small fast targets was not easy, and was often hazardous to the defending fighters, as the target could blow up in front of the Allied aircraft. The first V-1 to be claimed in air-to-air combat succumbed to a Mosquito FB.MkVI of No. 605 Squadron on the night of 15 June. No. 96 Squadron, based at West Malling in Kent, right under the path of the V-1s, claimed its first V-1 on 18 June, and by 23 June it had destroyed twenty-four flying bombs. About half of the V-1s were either crashing prematurely, or being destroyed by the defences, but the remainder were falling indiscriminately over London and the home counties, the weapon falling when the fuel to the pulse jet engine was exhausted.

Nos 219 and 409 squadrons joined nos 96 and 418 on the V-1 'anti-diver' patrols, No. 409 having begun re-equipping with Mosquito MkXIIIs in March as part of 85 Group, gaining its first victory over Normandy on 9 June. With the lack of German aircraft over

No. 604 Squadron began to take delivery of Mosquito NF.MkXIIIs in July 1944 at their base at Hurn, where they were to support the D-Day beach-head.

France, No. 409 Squadron was allocated to the destruction of V-1s, gaining its first victory on 18 June, before rejoining 85 Group in the second half of July. The defence against the flying bombs was layered, the aircraft, including Mosquitos, patrolling above the normal altitude of the V-1s over the English Channel. When a V-1 was spotted, the planes dived down to increase the closing speed, hoping to destroy the target before it reached the English coast. If a V-1 was shot down over the English Channel, it counted as one victory. If it had crossed the coast when it was destroyed, it was half a victory. Once the aircraft were flying over Britain, the anti-aircraft guns also tried to shoot down the V-1s, which added to the hazards of the RAF squadrons. The final layer of defence was the line of barrage balloons around south-east

London, where it was inadvisable for the defending aircraft to fly.

With the build-up of the flying bomb menace, in mid-July nine Mosquito squadrons – not all night-fighters – were committed to the anti-diver patrols, No. 418 Squadron joining the task on 17 June, flying FB.MkVIs. It was accompanied on 24 June by No. 456 Squadron, which developed the technique of flying close to the V-1s so that the slipstream of the Mosquito toppled the gyro in the autopilot of the flying bomb, causing it to crash without the risk of it blowing up in the air. By the end of the threat from the V-1s, the full-time Mosquito anti-diver squadrons had shot down 471 flying bombs. A further 152 were claimed by the part-time units. The top scorer was Canadian Sqn Ldr Russ Bannock, who was credited with 18½.

No. 409 Squadron were allocated to anti-diver patrols in June 1944 until rejoining 85 Group in July.
Mosquito NF.MkXIII MM466 based at a forward airfield in France in January 1945 may have been the
top scoring night-fighter with a total of 11 victories claimed.

Mosquito FB.MkVIs of No. 418 Squadron RCAF joined the night-fighters against the V-1 menace and
NT137 served with the squadron coded TH-H. (Photo Chaz Bowyer collection)

Canadian Sqn Ldr Russ Bannock with Flg Off R. Bruce was the top scoring pilot against V-1s with a total of 18.5 destroyed. He was flying a Mosquito FB.Mk VI. (Photo Chaz Bowyer collection)

Meanwhile, the Mosquitos with 85 Group were gaining victories against the conventional German bombers, 97 being claimed by the end of July and 200 by the end of November. The Mosquito NF.Mk30 was introduced by No. 219 Squadron on 13 June, followed by No. 406 Squadron in August. Although operations were started in the same month, problems were experienced with the exhaust shrouds, which were not fully overcome until November, when satisfactory louvred shrouds were fitted. Seven squadrons were then equipped with the NF.Mk30s by the end of the year, some remaining in RAF service into the late 1940s as part of the peacetime night-fighter force, until replaced by jet fighters.

The He.111 air-launched V-1 combinations began to appear in early July. They flew so low over the North Sea that they were difficult to detect on ground-borne radar. They were also tricky targets for the Mosquitos because they flew so slowly that the Mosquito was close to the stalling speed near the sea, when lining up for shooting at the target. In addition, there was certainly no room to spare to fly under the target for identification. A number of air-launched V-1s were targeted at London, Portsmouth and Southampton during September, and the first victory against these raiders was claimed by No. 409 Squadron on 25 September. To combat this new menace, the squadron were joined by nos 25, 68, 125 and 307 squadrons, the combined victories against these cumbersome combinations being forty-one destroyed. No. 68 Squadron had been operating a mixture of

No. 68 Squadron used Mosquito NF.MkXIXs, some flown by Czech crews against the air launched V-1s in July 1944. (Photo Chaz Bowyer collection)

No. 125 Squadron replaced their Mosquito NF.MkXVIIs with NF.Mk30s in March 1945, one of which was NT585.

Mosquito MkXVIIs and XIXs from July, but began converting to the NF.Mk30 in February 1945. No. 125 Squadron had been flying the MkXVIIs from February, but replaced them with NF.Mk30s in March 1945.

The 85 Group squadrons were able to advance further across Europe as the Allies made their advances, and, when they made contact with the enemy, some impressive numbers of victories were claimed. The Canadian nos 409 (Night Hawks) and 410 (Cougars) squadrons were each able to claim 38 victories between D-Day and the end of November, with No. 488 Squadron not far behind. The Ardennes offensive brought the final period of intense activity, and, despite the poor weather conditions, a further 27 enemy aircraft were claimed destroyed by the time the advance had been halted. No. 85 Group Mosquitos claimed 227 victories from D-Day, with No. 410 Squadron claiming the top score of 46 enemy aircraft destroyed.

The Mosquito lost the speed advantage in December 1944 when the Me.262 jet fighters were encountered for the first time, although the engines of the newer aircraft were unreliable and the endurance of the aircraft short.

Despite the Allied advances across Europe and victory being inevitable, in March 1945 British airfields came under attack from German bombers, the defenders claiming some victories. The ground-launching of the V-1s continued from Holland, keeping the anti-diver squadrons busy fending off some 6,500 flying bombs, the last one falling in Hertfordshire on 29 March. Enemy air activity then began to decrease rapidly, owing to the Allied advances, plus shortages of fuel and aircraft. The main targets were various transport and light observation aircraft, the latter being difficult to locate and destroy. The final total of claims by the Mosquito squadrons in 85 Group came to 299 enemy aircraft, with No. 264 Squadron recording the final victory on 26 April.

Although night-fighter operations were, for

obvious reasons, concentrated over Britain, some modest operations were carried out in the Mediterranean, No. 108 Squadron flying Mosquito NF.MkXIIs in February 1944, but keeping them for only five months. Also both nos 255 and 600 squadrons flew Mosquito NF.MkXIXs and NF.Mk30s from Malta and Italy during the final stages of the war.

As well as mainly taking part in defensive operations and the protection of the advancing Allied armies after D-Day, the Mosquito night-fighters were able to undertake offensive operations over enemy-held territory. Operations within 180 (Bomber Support) Group included intruder, rangers and spoof raids by Mosquito units covered in other chapters. The night-fighters were tasked with providing protection for the RAF heavy bomber formations over Germany, where the enemy night-fighters were a major threat. The heavy bombers did not carry any warning radar of their own, and were therefore vulnerable to attack. The offensive night-fighter operations were organised from 8 November 1943 by 100 Group under the command of Air Cdre E.B. Addison. The main problem was to locate the hostile targets from the air without the assistance of the ground-based radar stations. One of the earliest systems used was 'Serrate'. This was capable of locating and homing in on enemy radio transmissions over ranges of up to 100 miles (160 km), but it only gave a bearing and was not capable of providing range. Once the Mosquito had flown closer to the target aircraft, range was established using AI MkIV radar. Initial service trials had been attempted using Beaufighters of No. 141 Squadron, but they were neither manoeuvrable nor fast enough, so Mosquitos were allocated to the task.

The service trials of 'Serrate' fitted to Mosquito B.MkIVs commenced in November 1942 with 1474 Flight at Feltwell, which was renumbered No. 192 Squadron on 4 January 1943. With the completion of these service

Mosquito night-fighters of No. 141 Squadron joined nos 169 and 239 squadrons in 100 Group to seek out enemy targets over Germany and provide RAF bomber support. Having started with some very worn-out NF.MkIIs they were later equipped with more up-to-date versions and after the war were equipped with Mosquito NF.Mk36s at Coltishall as part of the peacetime night-fighter force. RL239 TW-D is parked in the snow in January 1951. (R.A. Brown photo via Chaz Bowyer)

trials, the squadron was allocated to signals work, detecting enemy radio and radar transmissions with the aim of developing countermeasures or using them as a homing aid as a means of their own destruction. Training for these specialist and demanding duties was protracted, operations not commencing until 11 June 1943, with the Mosquitos sharing their duties with the slower, but more roomy, Wellington and Halifax bombers with the capability of carrying additional specialist equipment.

The FIU at Ford was issued with two Mosquito F.MkIIs fitted with rearward-facing radar for service trials, so that when a target was detected the Mosquito could make a turn through 360°, and approach from behind the unsuspecting aircraft. This equipment installation was codenamed Mahmoud and was issued to nos 605 and 456 squadrons from late 1943, obtaining some encouraging results.

No. 100 Group began its initial period of operations from November 1943 through to April 1944, and nos 169 and 239 squadrons were joined by No. 141 Squadron on 4 December. Once the initial training was completed, they moved to the East Anglian bases of West Raynham and Little Snoring. Here they were equipped with some well-used Mosquito MkIIs fitted with the most rudimentary AI radars in the nose and tail, because the aircraft were operating over enemy territory and it was important not to risk having the latest radar equipment fall into the hands of the Germans. Despite the limitations of this equipment, No. 141 Squadron claimed a Bf.110 as damaged on the first 100 Group operation on 17 December and soon all three squadrons were claiming victories. Mosquito sorties were normally flown during or after bombing attacks, either by escorting the bomber stream over the last 40 miles (65 km), or by flying to known enemy night-fighter rendezvous points. No. 515 Squadron joined 100 Group at Little Snoring on 29 February 1944, with No. 23 Squadron arriving in July. Both were equipped with Mosquito FB.MkVIs for low-level intruder operations over enemy night-fighter bases without the use of radar, allowing them to destroy the hostile night-fighters on the ground before they posed a threat to the Allied bombers.

The withdrawal and replacement of the worn-out MkIIs commenced in mid-1944, when 'Serrate'-equipped MkVIs were issued to No. 141 Squadron on 18 June. All the MkIIs had been replaced by the end of July, allowing 100 Group to claim its hundredth victim on 21 July. The strength of 100 Group was increased in May by the addition of nos 85 and 157 squadrons based at Swannington and equipped with Mosquito NF.MkXIXs. The addition of an advanced long-range night-fighter with much improved AI radar gave an improved capability of destroying enemy night-fighters and was considered worth the risk of the technology falling into enemy hands if a Mosquito was brought down in hostile territory. Rearward-facing radar was not fitted to these aircraft. They began scoring in mid-June, but were transferred to the more threatening 'anti-diver' patrols at the end of the month, leaving the bombers with less protection. In August the Germans developed SN2 radar-jamming equipment, drastically reducing the effectiveness of 'Serrate' and the AI MkIV radar. However, the problem was overcome in January 1945 with the

development of 'Serrate MkIV'. 'Perfectos' was developed from November 1944 to home in on the transmissions of the enemy Identification Friend or Foe (IFF) equipment. The last NF.MkII patrol was flown by No. 239 Squadron on 27 October, the earlier aircraft having been replaced by the more advanced AI.MkX-equipped Mosquito MkXIXs.

The American AI MkXV radar, referred to as ASH, was fitted in the noses of Mosquito FB.MkVIs of nos 23, 141 and 515 squadrons from October for operational trials, while nos 85 and 157 squadrons had the improved rearward-looking 'Monica IV'. No. 85 Squadron also had 'Perfectos II', and No. 157 Squadron had 'Serrate IV'. No. 169 Squadron received its first Mosquito MkXIXs in January 1945 and also had 'Perfectos' fitted. Towards the end of 1944, the German bombing raids on Britain had decreased sufficiently to release the Mosquito NF.Mk30-equipped nos 151, 307 and 406 squadrons from defensive duties to offensive operations. No. 456 Squadron commenced bomber support duties in March, but with no apparent success. ASH-equipped Mosquitos with No. 141 Squadron entered operational service on 21 December, requiring highly trained and skilled operators. The first victory was a Ju.88 claimed on 1 January.

No. 239 Squadron introduced the NF.Mk30 into service on 21 January 1945, claiming its first victim, a Bf.110, on 2 February. The first NF.Mk30s were issued to No. 141 Squadron in March, followed by No. 157 Squadron, while No. 169 Squadron retained its NF.MkXIXs. With the Allied advances across Europe, the Mosquito night-fighters could make much deeper penetrations into enemy territory, although the opposition was waning rapidly. No.100 Group finally disbanded on 3 May, having claimed 249 enemy aircraft shot down, with 18 more destroyed on the ground for the loss of 69 Mosquitos during the seventeen months of operation.

No. 515 Squadron, equipped with Mosquito FB.Mk VIs at Little Snoring, joined 100 Group on 29 February 1944, and their aircraft are lined up on the airfield in 1945. (T. Cushing photo via Chaz Bowyer)

No. 23 Squadron joined 100 Group in July 1944 equipped with Mosquito FB.Mk VIs on low level intruder operations, one example being HJ675 YP-V.

No. 29 Squadron were equipped with Mosquito NF.MkXIIIs in 1944, HK428:K being used to destroy a Ju.88 on 17 June. (de Havilland photo)

With the end of the European war in sight, many of the twenty-seven night-fighter squadrons were disbanded between April and September 1945. However, six were retained to become part of the peacetime night-fighter defence force equipped with Mosquito NF.Mk30s, which were later replaced with NF.Mk36s, while No. 192 Squadron continued on secret signals duties, the Mosquitos eventually being replaced by Canberras. Two additional squadrons continued in operation for a short while after the war: No. 151 at Weston Zoyland, until its disbandment on 10 October 1946, and No. 307, which remained with Fighter Command until it was disbanded at

Horsham St Faith, now Norwich Airport, on 2 January 1947.

The post-war night-fighter force was based in the 11 Group area in the south-east of England, and 12 Group in East Anglia. At West Malling in Kent the night-fighters of nos 25, 29 and 85 squadrons, and nos 23, 141 and 264 squadrons were at Coltishall in Norfolk. No. 23 Squadron had reformed in Fighter Command at Wittering on 11 September 1946, moving to Coltishall the following February. No. 141 Squadron had already reformed at Coltishall on 17 June 1946, with the ultimate RAF Mosquito night-fighter, the Mk36. On 20 November, No. 264 Squadron re-equipped with the same mark at Church Fenton, moving

No. 23 Squadron were part of the RAF peacetime night-fighter force reforming at Wittering on 11 September 1946 and moving to Coltishall the following February with Mosquito NF.Mk36s. This is RL206 YP-S parked at dispersal. (Photo Chaz Bowyer collection)

Mosquito NF.Mk36s, including RL174:E of No. 85 Squadron visiting Coltishall in September 1952. (M.C. Gray photo)

Mosquito NF.Mk36 RL201 YP-C of No. 23 Squadron at Coltishall. (M.C. Gray photo)

Some of the RAuxAF squadrons were equipped with Mosquitos for a short while, and No. 616 Squadron at Finningley operated NF.Mk30s, including NT508 RAW-E in 1947/8. (Photo Chaz Bowyer collection)

Conversion training for the postwar night-fighter squadrons was handled by 204 AFS at Driffield. Leavesden-built T.MkIII RR299 FMO-B was later to be acquired by Hawker Siddeley Aviation. (Photo Chaz Bowyer collection)

to Coltishall in September 1950. With its heavy load of equipment, the NF.Mk36 could be difficult in a climb. The single-engine safety climb speed of 170 kt (315 km/hr) was higher than the normal climb speed of 155 kt (290 km/hr), meaning that, if an engine failed during a climb, the nose would have to be lowered to maintain flying speed.

Typical training for the post-war night-fighter force included Harvards for advanced training, followed by twin engine training on Oxfords. No. 204 Advanced Flying School (AFS) at Driffield, equipped with the light and responsive Mosquito T.MkIIIs, was used for the conversion to type, with about 8 hrs flying, before posting to 228 OCU at Leeming for the introduction to the much

heavier operational NF.Mk36. Once cleared for solo flight on the NF.Mk36, the pilots and navigators were paired up informally, before commencing the task of operational flying as a team in all weathers and at night. In peacetime operations, the Mosquito was normally flown during the day to ensure that everything was serviceable. Following some rest, the crew would often fly a couple of night sorties totalling 4 to 5 hrs. When the OCU course was successfully completed, the crew would be posted to one of the operational squadrons. With the introduction of instrument-rating systems in early 1949, the T.IIIs were issued to each squadron and fitted with cockpit screens when appropriate.

In normal peacetime operations the flying

Mosquito NF.Mk30 NT245 RO-A of No. 29 Squadron ready to taxi at West Malling in August 1947.

consisted of practice interceptions, with a pair of Mosquitos taking it in turn to be the hunted and the hunter. The attacking aircraft was guided by the GCI, starting at a range of around 20 miles (32 km) at various angles of approach. The aircraft usually located the target at 8 to 9 miles (13 to 14 km), when the navigator would call Judy over the RT to signal that he had control. The GCI would normally keep the two aircraft at an altitude separation of 1,000 ft (300 m) as a safety measure until the navigator took over, giving directions by the clock code in relation to the hunter, with range and height above or below. The attacker showed lights, but the target remained in darkness, while the approach was made to within 600 to 800 ft

(180 to 245 m) from the rear, when the attacker would shout 'Murder, Murder' when the target was in the sights. The planes would then change roles for the next practice.

At least one night a week, Bomber Command was flying 600 to 700 heavy bomber formations around Britain for navigation exercises to the bombing ranges. The Mosquito night-fighters were able to use these occasions for target practice, the AI radar being employed to locate targets, as well as to avoid collision. Although the bombers usually flew in darkness, the Mosquitos often had their navigation lights on. When spotted by the bomber crews, they would often try to evade in a rather crowded sky but to no avail, because the Mosquitos

No. 29 Squadron also had T.MkIII VA893 on charge for continuation training at West Malling. On the left is the CO, Sqn Ldr Mike Shaw, talking to Flt Lt Wakeford and a member of the ground crew.

had no trouble following until the bomber crew had had enough.

One of the postwar Mosquito pilots was Don Mortimer, who joined No. 29 Squadron at West Malling as a sergeant pilot in September 1948. In February 1949 he suffered an engine failure on take-off. The drill was to abandon the departure. Mortimer managed to get the tailwheel back on the ground to allow the brakes to be applied, but the boundary fence was approaching rapidly, and the only way left to stop was to retract the undercarriage. The rotating propellers created a hazard as they could come through the cockpit sides, but all went well for

Mortimer and his navigator, because the aircraft went through a fence into a ploughed field, breaking up on the way and absorbing the shock of the crash. The aircraft was a total write-off, with the port engine torn out and the rear fuselage separated.

In November 1950, Mortimer was posted to No. 264 Squadron at Coltishall, gaining his commission and continuing the high-, medium- and low-level training intruder sorties. Live gun firing was done at the Armament Practice Camp (APC) at Acklington, the sleeve targets being towed by Martinets, often at night, when the target was dimly illuminated. Air-to-ground firing was

Mosquito NF.Mk36 RL231 of No. 29 Squadron crashed on departure from West Malling on 8 February 1949, when the port engine failed on take-off.

carried out on the Holbeach ranges, by day and night, the intended pull-up being at 600 ft (180 m). The risk in this situation was from ricocheting shells as the target was overflown.

With the Cold War warming up as a result of the Soviet blockade of Berlin, the Allied defences were brought to a higher level of alert. The Mosquito night-fighters took on the defence against possible Russian bomber approaches to Britain. The major type was the Soviet copy of the B-29, Boeing examples of which were in operation with both the USAF and the RAF, causing an identification problem. One night, Mortimer was given the task of identifying a mystery raider over the English Channel flying along the French coast. The Mosquito was guided by the Isle of Wight-based GCI. Just as it passed out of range of the GCI, the target aircraft was picked up by the AI radar in the Mosquito. Owing to the low speed of the target, Mortimer overshot and flew underneath, turning and re-acquiring the mystery aircraft. In the semi-darkness, he was surprised to identify the aircraft as an all-black Lancaster without any national markings. Mortimer continued to follow the anonymous Lancaster as far as Dover, where he was back in RT range. After calling base, he flew around the aircraft without any signs of acknowledgement or recognition, and after about 10 min he broke away and landed at West Malling for a debriefing. It was later believed that the Lancaster had been one of the RAF aircraft that had bombed targets deep in Germany during the Second World War, and flown on to land in Russia. The aircraft was probably based in East Germany, and was being flown by Russian crew on an intelligence-gathering mission.

The 11 Group squadrons converted from the Mosquito NF.Mk30s to the NF.Mk36s from September 1946 although No. 29 Squadron also flew NF.Mk30s again during the conversion to Meteor night-fighters in October 1950, when it became the first jet night-fighter squadron. Between September and the end of 1951, nos 85, 141 and 264 squadrons also exchanged their Mosquitos for the new Meteor night-fighters, while nos 25 and 23 squadrons re-equipped with Vampire night-fighters in July and October 1951. No. 23 Squadron was the last Mosquito night-fighter squadron in the RAF. The last NF.Mk36 was retired in May 1952 and soon after scrapped.

The Mosquito night-fighters had made a significant contribution to the defence of Britain, pioneering the use of effective AI radar, as well as a number of homing aids, the developed concepts of which are now in common military use. While the basic airframe changed little, the Mosquito was capable of improved performance and payload as a result of the increased power of the Merlin engines. It also proved tough in combat and resilient when damaged, offering welcome protection to its crew.

11. STRIKE HARD: BOMBERS

Although designed as an unarmed, high-speed bomber, it was not until the Mosquito had entered service on its unarmed photo-reconnaissance and night-fighter role that it joined the RAF as intended. It served as a bomber with distinction, particularly against pinpoint targets, which were shared with the fighter-bombers, and later in the demanding Pathfinder duties.

The first Mosquito bombers were introduced into active service by No. 105 Squadron, which was based at Swanton Morley and commanded by Wg Cdr Peter Simmonds. The first aircraft, W4064, was delivered on 15 November 1941 by Geoffrey de Havilland Jnr, announcing the arrival by un-bomber like aerobatics and high-speed fly-pasts. However, the initial enthusiasm was dulled when the aircraft developed hydraulic leaks and had to be returned to Hatfield for rectification the next day. The second Mosquito, W4066, was delivered on 17 November, starting the gradual build-up of equipping the squadron with the potent new aircraft, which was to be used in daylight attacks against heavily defended targets. The initial task of the squadron, while training the aircrew to fly and operate the aircraft, was to evaluate the high speed of the Mosquito as a means of evading enemy fighters. Training in the new aircraft was fairly rudimentary as there was no formal conversion unit and the squadron were responsible for conversion to the Mosquito. Each pilot normally flew for about an hour with a check pilot in the right-hand seat before being sent solo. The operational training included checking the fuel consumption under a variety of operational conditions to ensure an accurate endurance for longer-range operations and flying at high speed over long distances, including some high altitude flying. Both high- and low-altitude practice bombing sorties were included, with mock combat with Spitfires, which were considered outperformed.

One of the early pilots with the squadron during the introductory phase was George Parry, who had flown two tours on the rather more vulnerable Blenheim bombers. His introduction to the Mosquito was to have one pointed out to him at Boscombe Down, where service trials were being undertaken. He climbed into the aircraft and had a good look round the cockpit before starting the engines, taxiing out and taking off for his first sortie. Following this initial period at Boscombe, Parry helped to compile the early version of the Pilots' Notes. He joined No. 105 Squadron at Swanton Morley, although a move was made to Horsham St Faith at the end of November.

By the middle of May 1942, seven Mosquito B.MkIs, mostly still with the short engine nacelles, and one B.MkIV had been delivered to No. 105 Squadron, but Bomber Command were slow to allocate the aircraft to operations as there was a concern about undue risk to the crews, despite their eagerness to begin operations. By the end of May, eight of the more effective MkIVs had been delivered, allowing the first active operation to be flown on 31 May. This operation involved two Mosquitos flying to Cologne to add to the confusion of the previous night's 'Thousand Bomber' raid, when two 500 lb and two 250 lb bombs were dropped, one of the Mosquitos failing to return to base after the raid. No trace of it was ever found.

No. 105 Squadron were the first to receive Mosquito bombers at Swanton Morley in November 1941, moving a month later to Horsham St Faith. By the end of May 1942 the squadron was fully equipped with B.MkIVs, examples being DZ353 GB-E and DZ367 GB-J.

Mosquito B.MkIV, DZ367 GB-J of No. 105 Squadron, being loaded with four 500 lb bombs ready for the next sortie. (Flight photo)

Light flak damage to No. 105 Squadron Mosquito B.MkIV DK337 on 22 September 1942 while based at Horsham St Faith. (de Havilland photo)

Some of the early active sorties supplemented the work of the PR force, which took photographs of the damage inflicted by the heavy bombers the night before to assess the effectiveness of the raid. On these flights, bombs were not normally carried, but when the Mosquitos were used to establish the weather pattern for a forthcoming night raid, they were. They were dropped initially from high altitude, then later from low altitude for greater precision. Before the bombers began their departures, Mosquitos would fly out over enemy-occupied territory during the early evening to update the initial part of the route weather.

They did not normally carry bombs on these shorter-duration flights, the priority being to establish the weather and report back before the bombers took off.

No. 139 Squadron became the second unit to form with bomber Mosquitos when it joined No. 105 Squadron at Horsham St Faith on 8 June 1942. The two squadrons shared aircraft until sufficient were available by the end of the year. On 2 July an offensive operation was carried out against the U-boat yards at Flensburg by four Mosquito bombers, but the defending Fw.190 fighters were able to claim two aircraft, although the other two escaped by pulling away using full boost. As a result of this

On 25 September 1942 the Mosquito made its much-publicised bombing debut when the Gestapo HQ in Oslo was the target of No. 105 Squadron. The target building along Victoria Terrasse with the domes has bombs falling through the roof.

experience it was decided to operate at a high level on clear days and come down to lower altitudes when there was cloud cover, because the Fw.190 was a demanding adversary.

When operations were planned, the day started with an early-morning briefing on the targets available, the expected weather and the anticipated defences. The crews then selected a target out of those available, usually taking into account the weather conditions over the area. The required fuel and bombs would be loaded by the ground-crews during their routine preparation of the aircraft ready for an afternoon take-off,

timed to reach the target around dusk. With the enemy defences alerted, the return was made under cover of darkness. Normal operations were flown with groups of four or six Mosquitos, unless multiple targets were to be attacked, when up to twelve aircraft would be used, splitting into the different elements when approaching closer to the targets. This avoided too many Mosquitos over the target at once, which posed the risk of collision. To confuse the defences routing was never direct to the planned target, with a turn as late as possible on approach to the target selected. The pilot normally kept a lookout for enemy aircraft, and, when flying at low level, also for obstructions in the forward 180°, while the navigator kept an eye out for hazards from the rear. One example of a hazard from the ground was a Danish chimney-pot, which penetrated the nose of a Mosquito and caused the port engine to run roughly. However, the aircraft was flown safely back to base and repaired.

Berlin became a target for the first time on 17 September, when six Mosquitos from Horsham St Faith set out on a high-level raid during daylight. The results were unconfirmed owing to cloud cover over Berlin and the alternative target of Hamburg, and one Mosquito failed to return.

The low-level precision daylight raids began on 25 September, with four Mosquitos led by George Parry from Leuchars to bomb the Gestapo headquarters in Oslo, where incriminating records of the Norwegian Resistance were kept. In preparation for this raid, Parry had to fly to Stockholm in an unmarked, overall grey Mosquito to collect photographs of the target from the British Embassy. He was therefore the first pilot to take a Mosquito to neutral Sweden, before the civil-registered examples were operated regularly by civilian BOAC crews on the 'Ball-bearing Run'. The arrival at Stockholm was just ahead of a German Ju.52/3m on an official visit, and Parry was directed to an isolated apron to await the Embassy staff, who were initially unaware of his arrival. The Gestapo headquarters was located in the centre of Oslo along Victoria Terrasse, in a large building erected in 1899, with a number of domes on the roof helping the identification. The building was a maze of long, dark corridors with many cell-like rooms, and the cellars were ideal for the torture of victims without their being heard from outside. This was the first of a number of precision attacks on Gestapo buildings throughout occupied Europe. Great care had to be taken to limit damage to the target and thereby avoid civilian casualties in the local population. The Mosquito proved the ideal aircraft for these duties.

At 14.00 hrs on 25 September, the crews were ready for their departure from Leuchars with each of the four aircraft carrying a pair of 1,000 lb (455 kg) bombs. The raid was led by Sqn Ldr Parry with his navigator, Plt Off Robson, flying DK296:G. Plt Off Rowlands and Plt Off Reilly supported them in DK313:U. The second pair were Flg Off Bristow and Plt Off Marshall in DK328:V, and Flt Sgt Carter and Sgt Young in DK352:S. After flying as a group across the North Sea, the Mosquitos travelled up the Skagerrak at low level, passing the mouth of the inner Oslo Fiord at Drobak before dropping down to the attack height of 100 ft (30.5 m) over the Oslo rooftops.

As a result of an unrelated Norwegian Nazi conference being organised the same day, and headed by Minister-President Quisling, four Fw.190s were stationed temporarily at Fornebu, although the German pilots did not expect any action, and were therefore not at full readiness. However, only 2 hrs after their arrival, they were scrambled when the Mosquitos were spotted on the approach. Only two of the German fighters took to the air, owing to a shortage of starters. By the time the Fw.190s had the Mosquitos within range, the bombs had already been released, hits being observed on Victoria Terrasse and the surrounding buildings. Hits from the Fw.190s were made on DK296 without serious damage, but the fourth aircraft, DK352, was more seriously damaged, the starboard engine catching fire. Carter radioed that he would attempt to fly the crippled Mosquito to Sweden, but he could not maintain height, hitting trees and crashing into Lake Engervann to the west of Oslo. Despite a rapid rescue attempt by two Norwegians in a rowing-boat to pick up the crew, who had been thrown clear, both were killed.

The other Mosquitos returned safely via Sumburgh in the Shetlands, after flying 1,100 miles (1,170 km) in nearly 5 hrs with adequate fuel remaining in the tanks. It was therefore possible to establish a low level operational range of the Mosquito of 900 miles (1,450 km), and a high-level range of 1,350 miles (2,170 km). With the publicity from this raid, the previously secret Mosquito was revealed to the British public for the first time during a BBC news broadcast the day after the bombing. Subsequent analysis of the success of the damage found that five buildings around the Gestapo headquarters had been hit, with the loss of eight Norwegian lives and a further sixty-seven injured. German casualties were unknown, and the work of the Gestapo continued almost without interruption, although the morale of the people of Oslo was raised. A further raid was to be planned at a future date.

By the end of September, nos 105 and 139 squadrons had nineteen Mosquitos on strength and were working on various ways to raise the top speed. With already good attention to detail, polishing the aircraft only added about 5 mph, but improvements of 10 to 13 mph were achieved by replacing the exhaust shrouds with plain, oval-ended stubs. Defensive armament was again being considered, including fixed or remotely controlled guns firing rearwards from the tail, canopy or engine nacelles, but the increases in speed resulted in these ideas being dropped again.

With priority being given to other Mosquito variants, the equipping of the bomber squadrons was slow, No. 109 Squadron at Wyton beginning to receive its aircraft in September 1942. Meanwhile No. 139 Squadron moved from Swanton Morley to Marham. Training continued, particularly at low level where bird strikes were a hazard and aircraft were known to hit the water when flying over a calm sea with little additional reference. Despite some losses during training, the Mosquitos developed a high level of immunity during the development of the attack procedures in 1942. It was possible to fly at low level in daylight unarmed without undue risk, and to achieve surprise and accuracy in the destruction of medium-sized defended targets in occupied territory, many in built-up areas.

Although in the early operations the Mosquito loss rates of 8 per cent were higher than the 5 per cent on heavy bomber raids, the planes were flying on much more hazardous missions and achieving more accurate and effective levels of destruction. However, with the commitment of Bomber Command to the area bombing by a large force of heavy bombers, the loss rates of these aircraft grew significantly, particularly as they carried a much larger crew than the pilot and navigator in the Mosquito.

No. 139 Squadron started operations, using its own aircraft, with a precision raid on the Philips radio factory at Eindhoven in Holland on 6 December 1942. It was accompanied by No. 105 Squadron, led by their new CO, Wg Cdr Hughie Edwards VC, DFC. Out of the ten Mosquitos which set out, seven reached the target and destroyed it. Wg Cdr Edwards then led a raid of nine Mosquitos against the Burmeister Diesel engine works in Copenhagen on 27 January 1943. These highly accurate tactical raids required a great deal of planning, preparation and training to achieve the best results. The training itself was hazardous because of the realistic conditions required to achieve the desired results.

It was discovered that there was to be a major Nazi rally in Berlin, led by Goering and Goebbels, on 30 January 1943, which was to be broadcast to the German nation. This provided an ideal opportunity to drop bombs on Berlin: not necessarily to hit the site of the rally, but to cause confusion and an interruption to the broadcast. With their speed and range, the Mosquitos were ideal for the task, three arriving over the German capital at 11.00 hrs and dropping their bombs. As a result, Goering's speech was interrupted and the prime minister's speech was delayed. All of the Mosquitos returned safely to Marham. A second group of three Mosquitos dropped their bombs on Berlin at 16.00 hrs, the last aircraft being lost to the defences. These attacks were not only good morale boosters for the Allies, but also established a useful means of collecting data on fuel consumption, routings and timing for future visits to Berlin.

The effective Mosquito precision bomber daylight attacks continued, the armament works at Liège being a target for No. 139 Squadron on 12 February, followed by the locomotive depot at Tours six days later. In the attack against the U-boat stores at Rennes on 26 February, nos 105 and 139 squadrons combined their forces, but, although defences were light, two Mosquitos collided in the target area, killing the CO of No. 105 Squadron, Wg Cdr Langfield. The molybdenum mines at Knaben in Norway, from which Germany obtained four-fifths of its supply for its war effort, was bombed by nine aircraft from No. 139 Squadron, one plane being lost in the successful attack with all of the bombs being placed on the compact target. Among many medium-sized targets that received the attention of the Mosquitos was the locomotive works at Nantes, which was attacked by eleven Mosquitos on 23 March. Not one bomb fell

No. 139 Squadron started operations with their own Mosquitos on 6 December 1942 when they were accompanied by No. 105 Squadron on the first of a number of attacks on the strategically important Philips radio and valve factory at Eindhoven. The target photo was taken from No. 139 Squadron Mosquito DZ314 flying at 800 ft after the raid. (IWM photo)

outside the target area, and only one damaged office building was left standing. Many of these facilities were returned fairly rapidly to production by the Germans, an example being the Philips works at Eindhoven. However, shortly after, four Mosquitos put it out of action again. Although production could not be stopped for long, at least it was possible to create considerable disruption.

The final Mosquito day bomber operations were flown on 27 May 1943, when No. 139 Squadron attacked the Schott optical glass works at Jena, while No. 105 Squadron bombed the Zeiss optical works in the same

town. Although some Mosquitos were lost on this raid, the bombs were placed accurately, many with delayed action, causing a diversion for some time after the raid.

In the year of day bomber operations from 31 May 1942 to 27 May 1943, nos 105 and 139 squadrons flew 193 operations, from which 48 Mosquitos failed to return, although the aircraft proved capable of absorbing punishment. It had established a good reputation, and its qualities rapidly became recognised. It was therefore decided to form a small, skilled force for night attacks, as well as to develop the aircraft and crews for path-

Wg Cdr Hughie Edwards VC, DFC, left, commanded No. 105 Squadron from 1 August 1942 and he and his navigator are about to board Mosquito B.MkIV at Marham for another daylight attack over occupied Europe. (AM press photo)

Sqn Ldr Ralston and his navigator Flt Lt Clayton of No. 105 Squadron bombed both ends of a railway tunnel 40 miles north-west of Paris on 11 December 1942, trapping a train inside. (PNA press photo)

Nine Mosquitos from No. 139 Squadron bombed the molybdenum mines at Knaben in Norway on 3 March 1943, losing one aircraft, but completely destroying the high value target. (AM press photo)

On 17 March 1943 Wg Cdr John Wooldridge DSO, DFC, DFM *became CO of No. 105 Squadron.* (de Havilland photo)

The final Mosquito day bomber raid was by nos 105 and 139 squadrons to Jena on 27 May 1943 where anti-aircraft defences were strong. Mosquito DZ601:Z crewed by Wg Cdr Reynolds, with bandaged hand, and Flt Lt Sismore had their aircraft hit on the propeller blade. (Sport & General photo)

Air Commodore, later AVM, Don Bennett commanded the Pathfinder force. (Photo Chaz Bowyer collection)

No. 139 (Jamaica) Squadron was equipped with Mosquito B.MkIVs and shared the airfield at Marham with No. 105 Squadron. Mosquito DK336 of No. 139 Squadron is having its turn-around maintenance done in the open. (AM press photo)

finding for the heavy bombers. The low-level precision day bomber attacks were taken on by the Mosquito FB.MkVI units, because, with their firepower of four machine-guns and four cannons, as well as their effective load of bombs, the crews could keep the enemy heads down during the attacks. This made them less vulnerable so that they did not have to rely just on speed and surprise.

THE LIGHT NIGHT STRIKING FORCE

On 1 June 1943, nos 105 and 139 squadrons were withdrawn from daylight tactical missions in Group to join the 8 Group Pathfinder Force under the command of Air Cdre Don Bennett. They joined No. 109 Squadron, which had already been part of this force, using the radar aid 'Oboe'. No. 105 Squadron joined No. 109, which was already part of the Pathfinder Force, having developed the use of 'Oboe' for pinpointing the target positions in all weather conditions and at night. However, it was No. 105 Squadron, re-equipped with Mosquito B.MkIXs, which initiated night nuisance raids with an attack on Berlin on the night of 20 April to celebrate Hitler's birthday. The Germans believed that Berlin was under attack by a main bomber force, thus committing their night-fighters to the defence of the capital, while the main RAF heavy bomber force attacked Stettin, without the threat of German night-fighters. The final nuisance raid on Berlin by No. 105 Squadron was on 21 May, when individual bombs fitted with screamers were dropped, both to keep the night shift in the air-raid shelters and the day-shift population awake, disrupting production during the night and the following day. No. 105 Squadron then became part of the Pathfinder Force, leaving No. 139 Squadron to continue with the disruptive night nuisance raids.

As existing squadrons were re-equipping with improved MkIXs, XVIs and XXs, the surplus MkIVs became available to equip new units. No. 627 Squadron formed at Oakington on 21 November, followed by No. 692 Squadron at Graveley near Huntingdon, nominally as part of the Pathfinder Force but involved with the LNSF.

The switch to night operations reduced Mosquito losses drastically, the major threat being anti-aircraft guns, although care had to be taken to avoid any prowling night-fighters. During autumn 1943 Mosquito bomber losses dropped to around 1.75 per cent of sorties flown, and although the damage caused was relatively limited, the disruption and the interruption of the defences was considerable, allowing the heavy bomber raids to continue with less opposition. Diversionary nuisance raids were flown to Hamburg, Duisburg, Cologne, Dusseldorf, Mannheim, Dortmund, Frankfurt and Berlin. The Mosquito MkXIs were used by No. 139 Squadron on operations for the first time on 3 October during a visit to Hanover, as a diversion for the main raid on Kassel by the heavy bombers. The load carried by the squadron was four 500 lb (225 kg) bombs carried internally and two more beneath the wings. The result was very successful, the Mosquitos attracting a number of German night-fighters, all of which were successfully evaded. To add to the confusion, the Mosquitos scattered 'Window' ahead of the main bomber force, and at the spoof target they dropped coloured flares and target markers on the aiming points for the following Mosquitos to aim at and create further diversion and damage.

On 2 December 1943, No. 139 Squadron used the Canadian-built B.MkXX for the first time, flying in three waves to Berlin, dropping 'Window', flares and finally bombs. Four Mosquitos from No. 627 Squadron bombed on the flares, but one of their aircraft was lost, the first from this unit. The first operational use of the 4,000 lb 'Cookie' was shared by nos 627 and 692 squadrons on a raid on Dusseldorf on 23 February, when modified B.MkIVs were used.

Hatfield-built Mosquito B.MkXVI MM156 was sponsored by 'Oporto British' and was delivered to No. 109 Squadron on 13 July 1944, moving to No. 571 Squadron on 13 September. It was eventually delivered to General Aircraft for conversion to a TT.Mk39 and issued to the FAA on 13 August 1947. (de Havilland photo)

Mosquito B.MkIX LR503 with No. 105 Squadron completed a record number of 213 operational sorties with Bomber Command. The crew, Flt Lt Maurice Briggs and navigator John Baker flew the aircraft on a goodwill commemorative tour of Canada, but were both killed when the aircraft crashed at Calgary on 19 May 1945. (de Havilland photo)

A Mosquito B.MkXVI being loaded with a 4,000 lb 'Cookie' blast fragmentation bomb, the heaviest bomb carried by the Mosquito. (de Havilland photo)

Having gained experience with carrying the 4,000 lb bombs, it was decided to develop the B.MkXVI fitted with a pressure cabin, which allowed altitudes of 35,000 ft (10,670 m) to be reached, the additional power being obtained from a pair of two-stage Merlin 72s. The extra altitude was helpful in reducing the danger of flak, which could reach up to 40,000 ft (12,190 m), although the cabin was only pressurised to 2 lb/sq in (0.14 kg/sq cm), reducing cabin altitude by between 5,000 and 6,000 ft (1,500 to 1,830 m), to avoid an explosive decompression if hit by enemy fire. The new B.XVI was introduced into service by No. 692 Squadron on 5 March during a raid on Duisburg.

The effectiveness of the Mosquito bombers was being demonstrated all the time, but there were insufficient aircraft coming off the production lines as a result of the priority of other versions. AVM Bennett urged for priority to be given to at least 200 B.MkXVIs to equip a growing number of bomber squadrons, but still a number were completed as PR.MkXVIs. On 7 April 1944, No. 571 Squadron formed at Downham Market, half-equipped with MkXVIs, some of the crews having been detached to No. 692 Squadron to gain operational experience in advance. As part of a growing sustained night bombing offensive against German cities, No. 692 Squadron

Mosquito B.MkXVI MM220 at the moment of release of a 4,000 lb 'Cookie'. (de Havilland photo)

Mosquito B.MkXVI ML991 P:109 Squadron on 25 April 1944, showing the enlarged bomb-bay doors for the 4,000 lb 'Cookie'. (Photo Chaz Bowyer collection)

No. 627 Squadron formed at Oakington on 21 November 1943 as part of 8 Group, later becoming equipped with Canadian-built Mosquito B.MkXXVs, KB416:AZ-P being one of their aircraft. (Photo D. Garton)

began operations with the MkXVIs on 24 April. It was at about this time that No. 627 Squadron was withdrawn from 8 Group LNSF. In early May, No. 139 Squadron marked the chemical works at Mannheim and Leverkusen for nineteen Mosquitos carrying 'Cookies'.

The Mosquito was not just capable of dropping conventional bombs, but demonstrated its versatility further by No. 692 Squadron seeding the Kiel Canal with mines from a low-level at night in mid-May. The mines were released from heights of 250 to 50 ft (75 to 15 m), as a result of which this important waterway was closed for more than a week. Further mining operations were made in the Baltic the following month. From the beginning of July, the battle-weary B.IVs were withdrawn from use, leaving the LNSF with MkXVIs operated by nos 139, 571 and 692 squadrons. On 1 August, No. 608 Squadron joined 8 Group equipped with B.MkXXs at Downham Market, and the use of H2S ground-mapping radar aid with its clear definition of the target in all weathers helped to improve accuracy. Target indicators could be placed within 1,500 yds (1,370 m) of the aiming point, and an average raid of twenty-five Mosquito MkXVIs carrying 4,000 lb bombs could cause considerable damage and was rather more than just a nuisance. Despite the increasing speeds of enemy defending fighters, including the early, somewhat unreliable, jets, the Mosquito loss rate remained low at 0.9 per cent, equivalent to fifty-nine aircraft lost in 12,517 sorties. From mid-July to mid-August 1944, 336 'Cookies' were dropped on Berlin, compared with 818 V-1 rockets falling on London.

On 12 September, No. 692 Squadron led a day attack on Wanne Eickel, first dropping 'Window' to confuse the radars, and then following with four 4,000 lb bombs. No. 128 Squadron was added to the LNSF on 15 September when it reformed at Wyton, although two crews had bombed Berlin five days before the unit was declared operational. The crews used a pair of B.MkXXs with single-stage Packard Merlins. Without the enlarged bomb bay they could only drop the standard 2,000 lb (907 kg) bomb load. Both nos 139 and 608 squadrons were also using the Canadian-built MkXXVs since the beginning of September, and No. 142 Squadron received its first two Mosquito bombers at Gransden Lodge two days after it reformed on 25 October. The first operation by this squadron was to Berlin on 29 October.

With the cloudier weather of the approaching winter, Mosquitos in forces of twenty-four or more were bombing through cloud cover with the help of Oboe, and the LNSF continued to grow with the formation of more squadrons. No. 162 Squadron reformed at Bourn near Cambridge on 17 December 1944, followed by No. 163 at Wyton on 25 January, both equipped with Mosquito MkXXVs. No. 162 Squadron was allocated to target marking and training on the use of H2S, while No. 163 Squadron concentrated on nuisance raids, often to Berlin. The increasing numbers of Mosquito bombers available was beginning to approach the desired 200 aircraft, allowing a 91-bomber raid on Berlin on 1 February, continuing as a series of night attacks.

The last Mosquito day-bomber operation was by nos 128, 142, 162 and 571 squadrons on 6 March, when Wessel was bombed using 'Oboe' through the cloud cover. Unfortunately the results were inconclusive owing to two of the marker aircraft being lost in a mid-air collision. By this time No. 162 Squadron had only just started operations, as the second H2S unit with only some of the aircraft equipped with this aid.

The largest Mosquito attack on Berlin was at night on 21 March, when 138 sorties were despatched in two waves with only one aircraft being lost. Aircraft were taken from nos 128, 139, 142, 162, 163, 571, 608 and 692 squadrons, with the speed of the

Mosquito B.MkXVI ML963 8K-K of No. 571 Squadron of the Light Night Striking Force, based initially at Graveley near Huntingdon, and then at Oakington. (de Havilland photo)

No. 692 Squadron formed at Graveley as part of the Light Night Striking Force in No. 8 (PFF) Group, and was equipped initially with B.MkIVs modified to carry the 4,000 lb 'Cookie' bomb. DZ637 is being loaded with a 'Cookie' at Graveley.

No. 128 Squadron joined the LNSF at Wyton on 15 September 1944 initially equipped with Canadian Mosquito B.MkXXs which were later replaced with B.MkXVIs. (Photo Chaz Bowyer collection)

Mosquito allowing some of the crews to fly in both waves. The last Berlin raid was by 59 Mosquitos on 20 April. On 2 May, Kiel became the last German Mosquito target when eight squadrons despatched 63 aircraft in the first wave, and 53 more in the second.

In the first four months of 1945, Berlin had been the target for 4,500 tons of bombs from the 8 Group Mosquitos during nearly 4,000 sorties. Overall, the LNSF flew 27,239 sorties for the loss of 108 aircraft, although a further 88 were written off after their return as a result of battle damage. This represented combat losses of 0.4 per cent, which was remarkable for a wooden, unarmed combat aircraft.

PATHFINDER FORCE

Post-raid photo-reconnaissance showed that the Allied heavy bomber formations were scattering their loads indiscriminately and often missing the designated targets by wide margins, resulting in unnecessary losses to the bombers and an unwelcome return to make a further attempt to create the required destruction. There was obviously a need to provide a more accurate means of identifying the target, both at night and during poor weather by day. The Mosquito bomber provided the ideal platform with its speed at about double that of the heavy bombers. By taking the best crews and training them in using the latest aids and accuracy of navigation, the targets could be effectively marked using coloured flares, either on the ground during clear conditions or in the form of sky markers above the clouds. The 'Oboe' bombing aid could be used from high altitudes, with H2S helping to identify the target through cloud. The accurate marking by Mosquitos was the spearhead of Bomber Command and was one of the most vital and demanding tasks of the crews and their aircraft.

The range of 'Oboe' was limited because it was a ground-based aid with development starting in 1941, while H2S was fitted in the aircraft and was therefore more flexible and less prone to jamming by the enemy. 'Oboe' consisted of two ground stations located about 100 miles (160 km) apart and transmitting radio signals to the Mosquito at different frequencies. The function of the 'Cat' station was to measure the range to the target release point accurately, and the 'Mouse' station would signal the moment of release of the bombs. The effectiveness of this aid was limited to the maximum altitude of the aircraft at which it was still able to pick up the beams in a straight line from the transmitters, because they could only be sent on a tangent to the earth in a straight line. Towards the end of 1944 the range was increased by a further 275 miles (440 km) at 28,000 ft (8,500 m) when a repeater unit called 'Oboe II' was developed to be carried in another Mosquito. A further early limitation of 'Oboe' was that each station could only control one Mosquito at a time, reducing the target-marking ability. In April 1944, however, 'Oboe III' came into use, allowing the simultaneous control of up to four Mosquitos and keeping the target markers burning much longer. The Mosquito proved an ideal carrier of this equipment as it required manoeuvrability, as well as stability on the approach to target, altitude and range, and a relative immunity from enemy defences during the vulnerable run to the target.

The overall command of the Pathfinder development, and its later operation, was allocated to Gp Capt. D.C.T. (Don) Bennett. The first Mosquito, DK300, was delivered to No. 109 Squadron at Stradishall on 21 July 1942 for the mission equipment to be installed. The first operational use of 'Oboe' which allowed bombing blind through cloud, was on 20 December 1942, when six Mosquito B.IVs of the squadron attacked the coking plant at Lutterdale in Holland. Post-raid reconnaissance showed that the nearest hit was some 200 yds (180 m) from the aiming point.

Air Vice Marshal Don Bennett led the Pathfinder Force, and is here chairing a briefing at the Wyton HQ before another pathfinding operation. (AM press photo)

Although the early results were often inconclusive, it was believed that the target marking by 'Oboe' was reasonably accurate, so it was decided to attempt a raid on the Krupp works in Essen, which were permanently shrouded in industrial haze and pollution. Led by a force of eight 'Oboe'-equipped Mosquitos, followed by eight H2S-equipped Lancasters from No. 83 Squadron, the target was marked for a force of 442 heavy bombers. Post-raid analysis showed this to have been the most effective RAF heavy bomber raid to date, proving the accuracy of the target marking.

The development of 'Oboe' was obviously sensitive. To reduce the risk of it falling into enemy hands if a Mosquito were shot down over Germany, it was generally only used to mark for the larger attacks from early March. In June 1943, No. 109 Squadron began re-equipping with the more effective Mosquito B.IXs increasing the 'Oboe' range owing to the capability of reaching altitudes of around 30,000 ft (9,140 m). The first 'Oboe'-carrying Mosquito was lost in the North Sea on 26 March, and the first to be lost in Germany fell in flames on 12 May near Essen.

With the major policy change on 1 June 1943, nos 105 and 139 squadrons became part of 8 Group at their base at Marham, with No. 105 Squadron joining No. 109 Squadron on 5 July as the second unit equipped with 'Oboe', using five of No. 109 Squadron's MkIXs to start operations. Taking advantage of the third ground station being commissioned, allowing up to eighteen Mosquitos to be controlled in one attack, nos 105 and 109 squadrons marked the Krupp works for 599 heavy bombers on 25 July. When the targets were beyond the effective range of 'Oboe', the Mosquitos marked more specialised, smaller targets nearer to home, examples being power stations, railway installations and individual industrial complexes.

As experience and skills improved, so did the accuracy of the marking and the subsequent bombing. It became possible to place a load of six 500 lb (227 kg) bombs within 100 yds (91.5 m) of the target around 80 per cent of the time from altitudes of up to 30,000 ft (9,100 m). In one example, a direct hit was made on a lock gate at night from 29,000 ft (8,840 m), a feat that would have been difficult in good visibility and daylight. Once the V-1 launch sites were located in France, the Pathfinder techniques were used to bomb them before the flying bombs could be launched, as well as the German night-fighter bases. Once the invasion of Europe had begun, Pathfinders were used in conjunction with the fighter-bomber units to destroy the rail and other transport network in France and the Low Countries.

To improve the range further with greater altitude, pressurised Mosquito MkXVIs were delivered to No. 109 Squadron on 10 December, although the first operational sortie did not occur until a raid on Deele on 1 March. With the reduced period of darkness during the summer months, Mosquitos undertook daylight target marking on V-1 supply depots, gun emplacements and troop concentrations in support of the Allied advances from Normandy. To put the heavy guns out of action on Westkapelle, five Mosquitos marked for a force of 259 Lancasters on 3 October to flood the low-lying island by breaching the sea wall. However the guns survived, only to be silenced by a further attack at the end of the month.

From the middle of October, the major German cities again began to be marked by Pathfinder Mosquitos, leading the heavy bomber raids as well as Mosquitos of the LNSF. The first time that an 'Oboe' Mosquito was shot down by enemy fighters was on a daylight raid on Cologne on 23 December. The vulnerability of this Mosquito was increased considerably as it was in operation with a force of 'Oboe'-equipped Lancasters at 17,000 ft (5,200 m), despite their unsuitability for the use of the equipment. The Mosquito was shot down by the four defending fighters, with two of the Lancasters being damaged. Another Lancaster was hit and set on fire during the bombing run, and was finally shot down by flak after the bombs had been released.

On 12 March 1945, the biggest raid to date was made on Germany with a thousand or more heavy bombers led by twenty-one Pathfinder Mosquitos against Dortmund. Precision targets were still on the agenda when, two days later, four Mosquitos marked the Bielefeld viaduct for a successful attack by Lancasters of No. 617 Squadron. These planes dropped the Dr Barnes Wallis 22,000 lb (10,000 kg) earthquake bomb, which undermined the foundations, as a direct hit was so difficult to achieve.

With the advances of Allied troops across occupied Europe, it was possible to use 'Oboe' to mark targets further into Germany. On 8 April 1945, two Mosquitos from No. 105 Squadron and three from No. 109 Squadron started a series of marking night attacks on Berlin, often leading other Mosquitos of the LNSF. All major targets gradually became within range of 'Oboe', the contribution by just two Mosquito squadrons being out of all proportion to their numbers, while the loss rate remained remarkably low.

'Oboe' was not the only navigation and

bombing aid used by the Pathfinder Force, although it was generally used against specially selected targets to be hit by the heavy bombers. The usual duties of the Mosquitos with No. 139 Squadron equipped with H2S, previously known as G-H, were to lead the LNSF. They therefore worked as part of that organisation. The H2S was an active radar system, the target positioning being achieved on board the aircraft. Teething troubles with the equipment caused failures on the early raids, but the first successful operation was to Dortmund on 10 October. When first introduced, G-H was based on the Gee navigation aid combined with the H system for bomb release, but this gave range limitations similar to those of 'Oboe'. By fitting the self-contained H2S radar into the Canadian-built Mosquito bombers, all transmissions were to and from the aircraft, without any reliance on ground stations. Gee was still carried in the nose for navigation, with the display on the right of the main instrument panel. The H2S display for target identification was located behind the pilot between the two crew, so the navigator had to turn round to view the system. Although H2S was not as accurate as the other aids, it was ideal for the Mosquito and had no range limitations.

Operational trials with H2S were started by No. 139 Squadron in January 1944 with modified Mosquito B.MkIV DZ476. Berlin was the first target, on 1 February. By this time, No. 139 Squadron was operating a variety of Mosquitos, including Mk IVs, IXs, XVIs and XXs, with H2S and G-H fitted. The MkXVIs were fitted with H2S for the first time in March, and by the end of the month about half of the aircraft were flying with the new equipment. Because the Mosquitos were able to operate at higher altitudes with modest pressurisation, the crews still had to pass a decompression test to the equivalent of 37,000 ft (11,275 m) for a period of 2 hrs, with a 1 hr build up and 1 hr for the descent.

As the cabin altitude was still high, the crew had to use oxygen to remain conscious.

On 18 December 1944, No. 162 Squadron was formed at Bourn, equipped with Canadian bomber Mosquitos specialising in nuisance operations known as Siren Tours. It flew throughout the night, keeping the night shift in the air-raid shelters and the day shift awake. During February it joined No. 139 Squadron working with H2S, commencing with a marker raid on Berlin on 3 March.

The Mosquito was becoming a popular aircraft, probably because of its low attrition rate, and there was a long waiting list of crews wishing to join the slowly growing force. For a navigator, typical training after service on the heavy bombers involved learning the new techniques at an OTU, starting on twin-engine Oxfords before moving on to the faster Mosquito. With its speed about double that of the heavy bombers, the operation was more demanding on both crew members, especially as the workload was greater. Some crews were unable to adapt to the higher speeds. As a result, a number were lost during training. The heavy bomber navigator had the luxury of an illuminated navigation table, with adequate space to spread out the charts. In the Mosquito, the specially prepared Gee charts had to be folded up on the navigator's lap, with great care being taken not to drop any of the instruments, such as pencils and dividers. The draughty heavy bombers were usually cold places of work, while the wooden Mosquito, with the radiators located on either side of the cockpit, often kept the crew too warm. Each crew member had a one-man dinghy issued, but they were too uncomfortable and too warm on long trips, so were often left behind.

Once the OTU course was successfully passed, the crews moved to the Pathfinder Training Unit at Warboys, where the greatest of navigation skills demanded by Don Bennett were acquired. The intensive and demanding course often required up to three

A Mosquito B.Mk35 of No. 139 Squadron in May 1950, soon after the move to Hemswell, being loaded with four 250 lb target indicators for training.

high-level navigation training flights in a day with any errors less than 5 per cent. Despite the role requiring a high level of navigation accuracy at night, the training also included day and dive-bombing attacks.

Flt Lt Reg Davey joined No. 139 Squadron at Upwood on 23 April, within sight of Warboys. He made his first operational flight the next day in Mosquito MkXXV, KB399, to drop a flash target indicator and three 500 lb bombs on Keil. At each turning point the lead Mosquito fired a colour of the day Very Light to guide the following non-H2S-equipped Mosquito force, which then bombed the target indicators. On this particular raid there were eight Pathfinder Mosquitos leading a force of up to a hundred bomber Mosquitos, each carrying a single 'Cookie'.

On the return across the North Sea, Davey wished that he had brought his dinghy, as without warning the starboard engine exploded and started to burn. Despite turning off the fuel and operating the extinguisher, the fire was only put out by diving at high speed. Just then, with the additional loads, the port engine began to cause problems. However, as it kept running, and the alternative was bailing out into an inhospitable sea without dinghies, a safe emergency landing was made at Woodbridge.

The reason for the engine fire was found to be that, on delivery to the production line in Canada, the entire power plant had been packed in grease, which had not been cleaned off. It was this grease that had caught fire.

Once over the target, the pilot pressed the bomb release, while the navigator took a photograph of the H2S screen to identify the target picture for future analysis. By this time the war in Europe was almost over, and there were fewer targets available. Squadron training continued, and a number of low-level 'Cook's Tours' were flown over Europe to view the damage, but they were stopped when some aircraft crashed after hitting high-tension cables strung across valleys. Davey was then posted to No. 627 Squadron at Woodhall Spa in July 1945 to train on H2S-equipped MkXVIs, which were to lead Lincoln heavy bombers against the Japanese. Special H2S charts had to be devised to match the ground features, and the idea of 7 to 8 hr sorties over water were not popular with the crews. The ground crews left for Asia in August, but, before the aircraft and aircrew could follow, the Americans dropped the atomic bombs, ending the war.

Probably the best-known bomber squadron of all time is No. 617 Squadron – the 'Dambusters'. After the famous dams raid, the squadron moved from Scampton to Coningsby. About three months after the raid, with specially adapted Lancasters, No. 617 Squadron received its first Mosquito on 30 August 1943. The aircraft was used operationally for the first time by the squadron, when Gp Capt Leonard Cheshire marked an aircraft factory at Toulouse on 4 April 1944. By 10 April, four Mosquitos had been delivered, and a favoured method of target marking was a dive attack on the target. During a raid on Munich on 24 April led by Cheshire in a Mosquito FB.MkVI, the target was marked by diving from 12,000 to 3,000 ft (3,650 to 910 m). Then Cheshire distracted the defences by flying over the city at below 700 ft (210 m) while the bombs were being dropped. After around 12 min, a departure was necessary owing to the limitations on available fuel, Cheshire returning safely to base. For his courage in this and previous operations Cheshire was awarded the Victoria Cross. This was probably the only occasion that the medal had not been awarded for a single heroic act. No. 617 Squadron retained their Lancaster bombers, but used the Mosquitos to target mark for difficult precision targets such as the Saumur Tunnel and weapons sites, where Tallboy bombs were dropped, one being carried by each Lancaster. The Dambusters were joined by their colleagues of No. 627 Squadron at Woodhall Spa in April 1944, the intention being for No. 627 Squadron to mark for No. 617 Squadron Lancasters. It was found that, by adopting a visual diving attack on the target without bomb-aiming aids, the marking accuracy was as close as 50 yd (45 m), the best results being achieved by diving from 3,000 to 1,000 ft (915 to 300 m). The first of these marking operations by No. 627 Squadron was on La Chappelle marshalling yards on 20 April, a typical target in occupied territory. Many of these targets covered a small area, the technique being to mark both ends of the target area, for the following bombers to bomb in between, avoiding casualties and damage whenever possible in friendly territory. An example of this type of attack is that on Usine Lictard at Tours, which had apparently been left largely undamaged by an American day-bombing attack. The RAF heavy bomber night attack was marked by No. 627 Squadron, the only problem being that the first markers went right through the factory's glass roof, becoming almost obscured from the air. However, the factory was still destroyed totally.

The heavy gun at St Martin Varreville was so well camouflaged that it could not be seen from the air. However, a number of tracks leading to an apparently empty space in the

Airspeed-built Mosquito B.Mk35 VP184 DF-Y of the Central Bomber Establishment.

Mosquito B.Mk35 TA651 fitted with a ventral radome containing H2S radar for assistance in bombing targets obscured by cloud or darkness. (de Havilland photo)

Three Mosquito B.Mk35s of No. 139 Squadron, TK620 XD-L, VP185 XD-N both in overall silver, led by VP194 in black and grey camouflage ready for a formation departure from Hemswell in May 1950.

At the RAF Display held at Farnborough on 7 July 1950, Mosquito B.Mk35s of nos 14 and 98 squadrons commemorated the low level attack on the Amiens prison. (de Havilland photo)

middle of a field were spotted, and by bombing the space the gun was destroyed.

Twenty-six-year-old Wg Cdr Guy Gibson VC, DSO, DFC and leader of the dams raid was the master bomber on a raid at München-Gladbach on 19 September 1944, flying a Mosquito MkXX. Although he left for the return safely, the Mosquito crashed in mysterious circumstances in Holland on the way home, killing the two crew. Target marking continued, examples being the Dortmund–Ems Canal, the Kaiserslautern railway yards and the sea wall at Flushing.

On the last day of 1944, No. 627 Squadron was allocated its own target instead of marking for others. This included a repeat attack on the Gestapo headquarters in Oslo. Despite the time of year, the weather, both on the route and at the target, was bright and clear, although the days are short in Oslo during the winter. Led

by Wg Cdr Curry, the raid consisted of two waves of six aircraft in each, with a mixture of B.MkIVs and B.MkXXs, each loaded with either two 1,000 lb bombs, or four 500 lb bombs. The departure from Woodhall Spa was at around 09.30 hrs to achieve a mid-morning arrival over Oslo, the flight over the North Sea being at around 7,000 ft (2,100 m). For the approach up Oslo Fiord, a descent was made to between 1,500 and 1,000 ft, and the leader's bombs were seen to hit the target. However, the German defences were stronger this time, and the Mosquitos took hits from anti-aircraft guns, the second wave being particularly vulnerable as the element of surprise was lost. Flt Lt P.F. Mullender, the leader of the second wave, found the target shrouded in smoke from the first wave, and ordered the crews to attack only if they could see the target clearly, as there were many civilians in the area who had been unable to take cover in time. As a result, only one bomb aimer in the second wave identified the target and dropped a pair of 1,000 lb bombs into the wreckage. No German fighters were encountered, and all twelve Mosquitos made the return to Peterhead in the North of Scotland, where they were all found to have sustained some damage, two being too badly damaged to fly back to base.

Unfortunately, in the post-raid analysis, the precision of the bombing of this target in the middle of the city centre was not as accurate as had been hoped, the main part of the Victoria Terrasse surviving without too much apparent damage. Although many Germans were killed, including about sixty girls serving in the Luftwaffe when their hostel was hit, a tramload of Norwegians were killed by an almost direct hit, and many more civilians were buried in a collapsed four-storey building about 30 ft (10 m) from the target. This attack did persuade the Germans to move their Gestapo records to the suburbs of Oslo, but did not stop the persecution and atrocities.

No. 627 Squadron returned to Pathfinder operations on 13 February, when Dresden was the target. However, with the gradual reduction in potential targets, the squadron flew reconnaissance operations within 5 Group until the end of the war in Europe.

Mosquitos continued in the bomber role in the early uneasy period of peace until they were replaced by the Canberra jet bomber from August 1952. The final bomber version was the B.Mk35, the first of which had flown from Hatfield on 12 March 1945, but entered service too late to take part in the hostilities. The only Bomber Command squadrons to use this final bomber version of the Mosquito were nos 109 and 139 squadrons which were based at Hemswell on Pathfinder duties. Canberras replaced the Mosquitos in No. 109 Squadron in August 1952, followed by No. 139 Squadron in November 1953. With the Allied forces of occupation in Europe, as part of the 2nd TAF, Mosquito B.Mk35s operated with No. 69 Squadron at the ex-Luftwaffe airfield at Wahn, together with No. 14 Squadron. No. 98 Squadron was based at Celle and staged mock attacks on Farnborough during the RAF display on 8 July 1950, commemorating the Amiens prison raid in February 1944. No. 69 Squadron was disbanded in November 1947 and the other two squadrons exchanged their Mosquitos for Vampire jet fighters in 1950 to 1951.

12. LOW ATTACK: FIGHTER-BOMBERS

The most potent Mosquito version was the fighter-bomber. It remained in service from its conception in May 1942 until after the war, with very little modification. There were more of this version produced than any other type of Mosquito. It combined bombing capability with the additional sting of four fixed, forward-firing machine-guns, as well as four of the even more destructive 20 mm cannons. The only major development was the specialist MkXVIII, in which the four cannons were replaced by a single 37 mm Molins cannon used by No. 618 Squadron against the U-boat menace in the Bay of Biscay. The Mosquito FB.VI squadrons shared the small precision targets with the bombers, often experiencing determined defence from surface-based guns on land and at sea.

Approval for the development of the fighter-bomber version was given in July 1941, and a production B.MkIV, although of a different configuration, became the prototype FB.MkVI HJ662/G. Following delivery to Boscombe Down on 13 June, it was written off on 30 July when an engine failed during take-off and the Mosquito hit two Beaufighters. It was not until February 1943 that the first production aircraft was completed, owing to the priorities with other versions of the Mosquito. Initial deliveries were made to the intruder squadrons, No. 418 Squadron at Ford in May, No. 605 Squadron at Castle Camps in July and No. 23 Squadron in Malta, where the new version replaced the earlier F.MkIIs.

In June 1943 the 2nd TAF was formed, eventually to support the Allied advances across occupied Europe. The initial units were nos 464(RAAF), 487(RNZAF) and 21 squadrons. The two squadrons from the dominions had been operating Lockheed Venturas, but moved from Methwold to Sculthorpe where, on 21 August, they each received their first brace of Mosquito FB.MkVIs. Training commenced by forming a conversion flight, and continued when No. 21 Squadron arrived, to form 140 Wing at Sculthorpe. Within a month, No. 464 Squadron had a dozen Mosquitos operational. By the end of September, 140 Wing had more than seventy Mosquito FB.MkVIs dispersed around the airfield.

The station commander and wing leader was Gp Capt P.C. (Percy) Pickard, who had managed to convert to the new aircraft in 10 hrs flying at Hatfield, signalling his intention to play an active part in the operations by his wing. On 2 October 1943 the wing was declared operational. On the next day, two dozen Mosquitos in two waves attacked the Chateau power station near Nantes. Pickard led No. 487 Squadron in the first wave, followed by No. 464 Squadron led by Wg Cdr Meakin in the second. One of the tail-end aircraft was crewed by 2 Group AOC AVM Basil Embry, with his SASO David Atcherley. Each Mosquito carried four 500 lb bombs with 11 sec delays, the attack being made at tree-top height by the first wave, and

Mosquito FB.MkVI LR335 of No. 487(RNZAF) Squadron at Swanton Morley in April 1944 with bomb trolleys ready for loading.

No. 464 (RAAF) Squadron began re-equipping with Mosquito FB.MkVIs at Sculthorpe in August 1943, soon to become part of 140 Wing. Three of their aircraft visited Hatfield on 2 June 1944. (de Havilland photo)

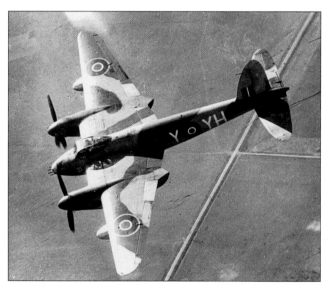

The third member of 140 Wing was No. 21 Squadron who were also equipped with Mosquito FB.MkVIs, PZ306 YH-Y seen flying over France in March 1945. They were the reserve squadron on the Amiens prison raid. (S/L A.F. Carlisle photo)

a shallow dive attack from 2,000 ft (610 m) with the release at 800 ft (245 m) being executed in the second wave. Six of the Mosquitos were damaged, including Pickard's, which returned to Predannack in Cornwall on one engine, while another had shrapnel in its radiator.

Poor weather resulted in a less successful operation six days later, when one of the additional low-level hazards was bird strikes. The target was an aero-engine factory at Woippy near Metz, and only two Mosquito crews, one from each of nos 464 and 487 squadrons, located the target, the remainder of the aircraft losing contact in mist and low cloud. Wg Cdr Wilson, the leader of No. 487 Squadron, was one of the two who attacked, but his navigator was killed by the anti-aircraft defences. Four other Mosquitos were lost on the raid, two of which were brought down when their own bombs were inadvertently released at low level en route. The squadrons were then put on intensive low-level training to improve their skills, and a return was made to operational flying on 5 November. No. 21 Squadron became operational on 10 November, although the attack was aborted owing to poor weather. In October, the crews of No. 464 Squadron were split between No. 418 Squadron at Ford and No. 605 Squadron at Bradwell Bay to allow them to gain experience of the intruder operations at night. They began to use their new skills on 19 November.

With more Mosquito FB.MkVIs coming out of the factories, the formation of another fighter-bomber wing was started at Lasham: 138 Wing on 14 October 1943. The establishment commenced when six crews of No. 613 Squadron were sent to Sculthorpe to gain experience with the Mosquito and the attack techniques. Two days later a Mosquito T.MkIII was delivered to Lasham by a lady pilot of the ATA and Sqn Ldr R.N. (Bob) Bateson arrived on 19 October to take command of the first of the three squadrons to be allocated to

the wing. Training continued throughout November and December, ready for the first operation on 19 December. No. 138 Wing at Lasham was later completed with the arrival of nos 107 and 305 (Polish) squadrons.

Meanwhile, Day Rangers were started by No. 21 Squadron on 25 November, when a pair of Mosquitos attacked a transformer station at Vannes. These attacks, some of which were assisted by Gee as a navigation aid, only continued in this phase until 10 December. At the same time, No. 464 Squadron was operating from Ford and Bradwell Bay on night intruder operations, known as Flowers, against enemy night-fighter airfields.

Then came the offensive against the often well-defended and widely dispersed V-1 flying bomb sites. The Mosquito fighter-bomber attacks began when the Sculthorpe Wing flew twenty-nine aircraft on 21 December 1943 against the installations at St Agathe, but cloud over the target caused the attack to be aborted. These hazardous targets often resulted in damage to the Mosquitos, but, despite this, the aircraft were tough enough to bring the crew home to base. No. 140 Wing took off from Sculthorpe on 31 December to attack a major V-1 weapons site, and made its return to its new base of Hunsdon in Hertfordshire, which brought it nearer to the action. No. 613 Squadron joined 140 Wing for this raid to obtain first-hand experience.

In January 1944 the attacks against the V-1 sites continued, a total of forty-one raids being mounted by nos 21, 487 and 613 squadrons in daylight attacks. The V-1 sites were not only heavily defended but also difficult to locate, and they were sited in occupied territory. Decoy sites were often built to mislead the attackers. The technique for bombing these well-concealed sites was to fly low over the English Channel, pull up to between 5,000 and 6,000 ft (1,520 and 1,830 m) and make a diving attack, with bomb release at 1,500 ft (450 m). It often required

No. 138 Wing at Lasham was completed by nos 107 and 305 (Polish) squadrons. Mosquito FB.MkVI SM-C of No. 305 Squadron is being prepared for its next sortie. (J.B. Cynk photo)

up to 200 Mosquito sorties to destroy such installations. Despite damage being sustained by the aircraft, loss rates were only 1.53 per cent. Meanwhile, No. 464 Squadron commenced Night Rangers on 2 January, attacking enemy-occupied airfields in France.

With the growth of the Lasham Wing, No. 305 (Polish) Squadron had the first Mosquito FB.MkVI delivered on 4 December 1943, as the beginning of the replacement for the Mitchells. Operations started with an attack on a V-weapon site on 25 January, which was aborted, but a more successful mission was achieved three days later. The third unit joined the wing at Lasham when No. 107 Squadron began re-equipping in February, ready to start operations on 15 March. The constant operations to the V-weapon sites delayed the start of the launching of the V-1 flying bombs until June 1944, not only saving many British civilian lives but also resulting in the invading Allied forces reaching the sites in occupied Europe sooner. While two of the squadrons were allocated to V-weapon sites, one

squadron took monthly turns to operate night operations, many against German airfields.

While the Lancaster is probably best remembered for the dams raid, one of the most outstanding raids carried out by the Mosquitos was the Amiens prison raid, known as Operation Jericho. As in the majority of occupied Europe, there was an active Resistance organisation in the Somme area and the plains of Picardy around the French town of Amiens. These groups were supplied and supported by the Allies, in terms of equipment, information and sometimes specialist personnel, while the local people, often at great risk, were able to provide a safe way home for downed aircrew. The group in the Amiens area was led by a very effective trio, the brothers Dominique and Pierre Penchardier, and an ex-communist known simply as Pepe. While the organisation was run efficiently and secretly, some of the members had been caught during acts of sabotage, or were simply betrayed by collaborators, and had been imprisoned in

Mosquito FB.Mk VI TA118 of No. 107 Squadron was the third member of 138 Wing at Lasham. (J.E. Bilbrough photo)

Amiens prison, where the persuasive methods of the Gestapo could put the entire operation at risk.

This Resistance network had started work in October 1940, the major aim being to sabotage the German war effort as much as possible. One of the most effective operatives was twenty-year-old Jean Beaurin, who had led raids that resulted in five major train crashes, killing and injuring many German troops. He was eventually caught and imprisoned at Amiens towards the end of 1943. By December, a dozen members of the Resistance had already faced firing squads, and Beaurin was expecting the same fate with little chance of escape. One of his colleagues was caught with a map of the prison layout while planning a rescue attempt. Another member, Maurice Holleville, was caught trying to obtain documents, including ration cards. So secret was the existence of these members of the Resistance that there were no records of them with the authorities, so they did not qualify for ration coupons.

One of the underlying principles of the Resistance organisations was that, if members were caught, the remainder would attempt to rescue them, even at the risk of their own lives. However, an attack on the prison from their already depleted and infiltrated organisation was clearly impossible, and would effectively have wiped them out. Then it was learned that about a hundred prisoners, including their colleagues, were to be shot on 19 February. The only way to achieve a rescue was by mounting an air attack.

Dominique Penchardier had already been obtaining details of the layout, structure, defences and duty rostas of Amiens prison, and had been passing them on to the Allies, without giving any reason at the time. Another setback was the capture of two Allied intelligence officers, who joined the other inmates of the prison, some of whom were criminals. The deadline for the executions together with the capture of the Allied officers provided the required support

The model of the Amiens prison used to brief the crews for Operation Jericho. (AM press photo)

for a daring air attack, the planning details for which were already in Allied hands. The task was passed to the 2nd TAF, and AVM Basil Embry led the planning for the rescue attempt of up to 700 inmates. It was realised that some Resistance members' lives might be lost in the bombing as the defences had to be neutralised and as many as possible of the guards killed, but it was hoped that many inmates would be able to escape, and some were already condemned to death anyway.

The main prison layout was in the form of a crucifix surrounded by a 20 ft (6 m) high, 3 ft thick wall topped with broken glass, with the guards normally in a separate building within the rectangular compound. The prison

was located by the long, straight road to Albert, and the approaches were unobstructed in the flat countryside. Precise timing was essential, because most of the guards were in their own building at around midday for lunch, which was also the time that most of the prisoners would be out of their cells for food. Great care had to be taken, not only in planning the placement of the bombs but also in ensuring that there were sufficient explosives to breach the walls and spring the doors, while not being so much as to destroy the prison and cause excessive casualties among the inmates.

No. 140 Wing at Hunsdon was selected to undertake the raid led by AVM Embry, with

Gp Capt. Percy Pickard, left, and Flt Lt Bill Broadley prepare for departure to lead the Amiens prison raid, from which they failed to return.

Pickard as his number two, and the operation was ready to go any time from 10 February. Crews were selected from all three squadrons in the wing, and additional support was to be provided by Typhoons of No. 198 Squadron. Because it was a low-level precision operation, good visibility was essential for the greatest effect and success. No. 487 Squadron was allocated the tasks of bombing the German guards' accommodation and breaching the outer walls in two places to allow the prisoners an escape route. No. 464 Squadron was to place its bombs against the prison walls to make holes large enough for the inmates to clear their cell block. Owing to the need for secrecy, only a few knew of the attack; a

message had come from a small number of the inmates that if no prisoners were seen to escape after the first two waves, the prison should be destroyed by bombing. No. 21 Squadron were to carry out this horrifying alternative.

Then came a further setback, when Embry was forbidden to participate in the raid and Pickard took over the leadership, despite the fact that he had had little low-level experience with the Mosquito, his previous low-level operations having been six attacks on V-weapon sites. The weather was also abysmal across Europe, making the low-level training hazardous, and Pickard was one of the crews to sustain damage to his Mosquito. With the force ready to go from 10 February, the weather became even worse, and a forecast improvement for 14 February did not materialise as the deadline for the executions got closer. With the arrival of 18 February any further delay was out of the question, so the decision was made to go. The force consisted of eighteen Mosquito fighter-bombers to be used for the attack and a film production unit Mosquito recording the operation.

The briefing began at Hunsdon at 08.00 hrs, with a high level of security, when a model of the prison was unveiled to the crews to help them to identify the target. If the prisoners were to be saved, surprise and accuracy were essential for success, and Gp Capt. Pickard, with his close friend and navigator Alan Broadley, was to be flying the last Mosquito in the second wave, so that he could assess the success of the raid and call in No. 21 Squadron if necessary. The minimum time possible would be spent in the target area because of the bad weather and to avoid the defences, including German fighters. If Pickard's aircraft was lost over the target, the crew of the film unit Mosquito were to make the decision on whether to call in No. 21 Squadron.

There was no improvement in the weather over southern England, but there were prospects of slightly better conditions over the target area. Since a further postponement would be pointless, Pickard made the decision to go, with only 2 hrs to the deadline. The Mosquitos took off into the gloomy Hertfordshire skies from the humped runway at Hunsdon, and ascended into conditions worse than most of the crews had ever experienced. As a result, four aircraft lost contact with the formation and had to find their way home. However, as had been hoped, the weather improved over the Channel, giving fresh hope that the operation would be achieved. A further Mosquito had to drop out owing to engine problems, leaving nine aircraft in the main attack and four in reserve.

With the free members of the Resistance expecting the attack for some days, they had been walking unobtrusively around the outside of the prison to lend assistance to the escaping prisoners. With no sign of the attacking force at midday, hope was waning for a timely rescue, when at 12.01 the first Mosquitos were seen coming down low through the murk. Three of the No. 487 Squadron aircraft approached the target to drop the eleven 1 sec delay bombs, while two others made a diversionary fake attack on a local railway station, before coming back over the prison. One of the New Zealand pilots saw his bomb knock a hole in the outer wall before exploding. The second wave of No. 464 Squadron were too close and made an orbit to allow the first bombs to explode after the delay, then they made their attack. The first wave had made a direct hit on the guard building, killing or injuring all of the occupants. As expected, a number of the prisoners were killed or wounded, some being trapped by the fallen rubble. Heroic people like Dr Mans tended the wounded and helped many of the others to escape. However, despite these selfless acts, a number of inmates were to die in front of firing squads. Some of the injured were helped to escape and spirited away to recover, their identities having been lost when the bombs destroyed the prison records. Help was given where possible to injured Germans, and the arrival of the occupying forces was delayed for around 2 hrs owing to the successful diversion at the railway station. With them came the Gestapo, to interrogate the survivors to determine what was known of the raid in advance.

Pickard continued to circle over the prison at 500 ft (150 m) watching the prisoners escaping in the snow, and he signalled for No. 21 Squadron to return to base. Meanwhile the film unit Mosquito made a number of runs over the prison to record the damage. The call to No. 21 Squadron was Pickard's last. As he turned for home, he saw another Mosquito

With the outer walls breached, the second wave of Mosquitos bombed the walls of the Amiens prison to allow the prisoners to escape.

make a high-speed crash-landing in open country, the pilot being thrown clear and surviving to be made a prisoner of war, while the navigator was killed. Pickard's aircraft, HX922, EG-F for Freddie, was then attacked by an Fw.190, the bullets cutting through the rear fuselage and severing the tail. With total loss of control, the Mosquito crashed in flames, killing both crew, the rapid attempts by local people to save them being to no avail. It was about two months before the death of the crew was confirmed in Britain.

Of the prison occupants, 87 were killed in the raid, many of them Germans. Some 182 prisoners were recaptured, but 255, half of whom had been awaiting execution, managed to escape, the remaining prison occupants not

being released from their cells. During April, around 260 survivors were shot in reprisal, their bodies being buried in a defensive ditch at Arras, where they were found the following autumn. Despite the loss of Pickard and Broadley, the raid demonstrated what could be achieved with Mosquito fighter-bombers when based on careful planning and attention to detail.

Following this spectacular operation, 140 Wing reverted to medium- and high-level attacks, led by Wg Cdr Iredale, the targets varying from factories to enemy airfields and V-weapon sites, both by day and by night.

The next precision low-level attack was allocated to No. 613 Squadron as part of the 138 Wing, led by Wg Cdr Bateson, and was the Dutch Central Population Registry, which

In addition to the loss of Pickard and Broadley, Mosquito FB.MkVI MM404 SB-T of No. 464 Squadron was also brought down. Sqn Ldr A.I. McRitchie was wounded and taken prisoner, and his navigator Flt Lt R.W. Sampson was killed. (de Havilland photo)

As an indication of the type of punishment a Mosquito could absorb and still bring its crew safely home, FB.MkVI of No. 464 Squadron sustained damage on an operation on 21 February 1944 which not only included the outer portion of the starboard wing missing, but also an unserviceable port engine and the loss of some hydraulics. (Photo Chaz Bowyer collection)

held much of the information useful for the Germans in their control of the people. Six Mosquitos departed from Lasham on 11 April 1944, flying low over the North Sea. The aircraft climbed to 4,000 ft (1,220 m) to cross the Dutch coast before dropping to a low level again, where birds, trees, cables and chimney-pots were among the hazards. The first two Mosquitos placed their 500 lb (225 kg) 30 sec delayed action bombs into the 95 ft (30 m) high, five-storey building. They were followed by the third and fourth planes, carrying incendiaries to set fire to the records. The fifth aircraft carried a mixture of bombs to tidy up any additional damage, but the last aircraft

had a problem and could only take pictures of the damage. These raid photos showed that the building had been totally destroyed without damage to the surrounding property.

In April the two fighter-bomber wings were working in close cooperation. No. 21 Squadron had commenced intruder operations in March. It was joined in early April by the Polish aircrew of No. 305 Squadron, which concentrated on night raids for the time being. On 12 April, nos 107 and 613 squadrons attacked locomotive sheds at Hursan, while nos 464 and 487 squadrons also targeted railway installations. At the end of April, nos 21 and 464 squadrons, led by Pathfinder

No. 613 Squadron made a successful low-level raid on the Dutch Central Population Registry on 11 April 1944 led by Wg Cdr Bateson. (AM press photo)

Mosquitos, made some experimental high-level attacks on V-weapon sites, followed by an attack from 20,000 ft (6,100 m) on Abincourt railway installations, all as part of the preparations for the Allied invasion. In a period of eight months, from October 1943 until May 1944, the Mosquito fighter-bomber wings flew some 1,600 sorties on 155, often well-defended, targets with the loss of 36 aircraft.

With preparations being made for D-Day, the 2nd TAF squadrons rested to build up their strength for the major thrust to support the invasion. Preparations were made to ensure the mobility of the squadrons, as soon as sites became available in France, the fighter-bomber units deploying with support from 511 Forward Repair Unit. To make it easier to identify the Allied aircraft, black and white stripes were painted around the wings and rear fuselages. The attacks by all six Mosquito fighter-bomber squadrons began on the German communications networks during the night of 5/6 June 1944. The Mosquitos concentrated on stopping enemy troop movements at night, while other aircraft in 2nd TAF did the same during the day. Targets were marked by No. 98 Squadron Mosquitos and No. 180 Squadron Mitchells, 500 lb (225 kg) bombs being used, generally backed up by 20 mm cannon shells. The groundcrews worked around the clock to achieve a 93 per cent serviceability in the critical first two weeks, easing off to 85 per cent subsequently. Losses to enemy action were half of the anticipated rate, with 26 Mosquitos being lost during 2,000 sorties. In late July, unguided rocket projectiles were used for the first time. They were launched from underwing rails and proved particularly destructive against trains.

In addition to providing direct tactical support for the Allies during the invasion, the need for the destruction of other targets continued, including the precision attacks on small, high-value installations in occupied territory. Great care was taken to avoid injuries to civilians, and some of the targets were marked under severe risk with white sheets by the members of the Resistance. The Gestapo barracks on a 170 ft by 100 ft (52 m by 30 m) site at Bonneuil Matours was hit by 9 tons (9,000 kg) of bombs on 14 July, and nos 21 and 487 squadrons made a low-level attack on Poitiers barracks on 1 August. The next evening, nos 107 and 305 squadrons destroyed a German saboteur school at Chateau Maulny, and Basil Embry was allowed to lead an attack by No. 613 Squadron on Egletons School, which was being used as an SS barracks, one aircraft being lost over the target. This phase of the operations finished with the destruction on 31 August by No. 487 Squadron of the SS headquarters at Vincey, the base for about 2,000 personnel. Meanwhile, the night offensive continued, disrupting the enemy supplies and retreat across France, and maintaining air superiority. Pinpoint surprise attacks were made by the light of flares on tactical targets, using the Mosquito's speed and manoeuvrability to the best advantage.

Mosquito fighter-bombers were tasked with the support of the disastrous Arnhem operation, but bad weather hampered their capability against well-defended installations. nos 107 and 613 squadrons were both briefed at 07.00 hrs on 10 September 1944, the day the assault began, the initial targets being barracks.

However, owing to heavy flak, two Mosquitos failed to return. One was lost by No. 21 Squadron while bombing Nijmegen, and, although a number of other sorties were flown by day and at night, the result were inconclusive as a result of poor weather. Towards the end of November 138 Wing moved from Lasham to the advanced base at Epinoy, and, despite bad weather conditions, managed to provide little respite for the retreating German army as the Allies liberated occupied Europe.

A Gestapo building gained the attention of the Mosquitos on 31 October when Gp Capt Wykeham-Barnes led two dozen Mosquitos from 140 Wing against the Gestapo headquarters in Jutland. The records of the Danish Resistance were held in two of the buildings of Aarhus University, and the aim was to destroy them. The low-level raid was made in poor weather, until a slight improvement when the target was reached. Despite damage from ground obstructions and blast damage from the bombs during the low-level pass, all crew returned safely.

By this time 140 Wing had moved to Thorney Island. Owing to thick ground fog, the Mosquitos were unable to provide support during the German breakout in the Ardennes offensive. However, with the weather cleared and with the German army in full retreat, the pace became so great that it was difficult to keep up with the position of the lines. No. 140 Wing joined 138 Wing in mainland Europe on 7 February when it moved to Rosière-en-Sauterre, allowing deeper penetrations into hostile territory. Losses were sustained with the more risky day attacks, and, whenever possible, operations were made under cover of darkness.

Then came the need for another daylight precision attack, this time to Copenhagen. No. 140 Wing squadrons moved temporarily back to Britain on 20 March to be based at Fersfield in Essex. Led by Bob Bateson and Basil Embry, who now had much experience of these operations, the target was the Shellhaus

No. 140 Wing bombed the Gestapo HQ in Jutland on 31 October 1944 where the records of the Danish Resistance were housed in two of the Aarhus University buildings. This low-level precision raid was made in poor weather, but all the crews returned safely after a successful destruction of the target. (AM press photo)

No. 140 Wing moved to Thorney Island in November 1944; the fin leading edges of the No. 464 Squadron Mosquitos were treated to the efforts of the wartime censor, for some reason. (Photo Chaz Bowyer collection)

One of the last precision Mosquito fighter attacks was by 140 Wing Mosquitos against the Shellhaus Building in Copenhagen which housed the Gestapo HQ. Regrettably a school was also hit by a crashing Mosquito killing many of the children. (Photo Chaz Bowyer collection)

Building, which housed the Gestapo headquarters. The Gestapo had already arrested some members of the Danish underground movement and were planning further mass arrests, although it was not expected that any of the prisoners would be able to escape in the attack. The building was located in the city, but identification was made easier as it was the only one to be camouflaged, therefore defeating the object. As usual the Mosquitos flew at low level over the North Sea, and then Jutland. The surprise of the attack was so absolute that the covers were not removed from the defending guns. The usual 11 sec delay 500 lb bombs went through the front of the building, killing many of the

Gestapo officials and destroying the records. In fact, many of the prisoners on the top floor managed to escape. One Mosquito hit a flagpole, and Embry pulled up after the target. However, when another aircraft was seen right behind him, he dropped down and flew down a street below rooftop height, hoping that the width was greater than his wingspan.

A tragedy resulted from the raid when one of the Mosquitos in the first wave crashed into a convent school close to the target, killing many of the children. Some following Mosquitos aimed their bombs at the same place owing to the confusion of the smoke and rubble, adding to the death toll, while others abandoned the attack as a result of the same confusion. Eighty-seven children were killed, and many more shocked and injured were found by distraught parents and rescuers wandering in the rubble. Had all of the bombs hit the right target, it would have been totally destroyed, along with all of its occupants, including the members of the Danish Resistance.

In between these special raids, the driving back of the retreating German army was supported by the Mosquito fighter-bombers, bringing Berlin within range. The final daylight precision attack was made by six Mosquitos from 140 Wing on 17 April, when the target was a Gestapo-occupied school building at Odense, completing a distinguished service. With the defeat of Germany certain, and steadily decreasing target opportunities, No. 21 Squadron and all of the squadrons in 138 Wing ceased operations on 26 April 1945. No. 464 Squadron flew its final operation with a night attack on railway targets in the Emden–Bremen area on 3 May, and No. 487 Squadron flew its final operation on the following night.

The squadrons then became part of the British Air Force of Occupation in Germany from 15 July 1945, although a number of the units soon disbanded. The first of these was No. 464 Squadron, allowing its Australian crews to return home, followed by the New Zealand crews of No. 487 Squadron. No. 613 Squadron was renumbered No. 69 Squadron on 8 August 1945 and re-equipped with Mosquito B.MkXVIs in April 1946, before finally disbanding on 6 November 1947. No. 268 Squadron disbanded in March 1946 and the Poles of No. 305 Squadron returned to Britain from Europe in October 1946 to disband. No. 21 Squadron was disbanded on 7 November 1947. No. 107 Squadron was renumbered No. 11 Squadron in October 1948 and continued to operate Mosquitos until August 1950.

The Mosquito FB.MkVI force of the 2nd TAF had made a major contribution against the menace of the V-1 flying bombs, helped to paralyse enemy communications by day and night, and continued to support the various Resistance movements in their effectiveness and maintaining their freedom.

INTRUDERS

In addition to their service in the 2nd TAF, Mosquito MkII fighters initially, followed by fighter-bombers, were involved in intruder operations, the fighters being used for air-to-air and ground attack purposes. The intruder units ranged far and wide over Europe by day and night, attacking enemy aircraft in the air and on the ground, as well as many other targets of opportunity. The fighter Mosquito attacked only with its guns, the 20 mm cannon being fairly destructive against most soft-skin targets. The use of bombs followed later.

The first unit to take delivery of a Mosquito for intruder operations was No. 23 Squadron at Ford, which until then had been using the more vulnerable Bostons. A T.MkIII was delivered for conversion training to start in June 1942, and, on 2 July, DD670 was delivered as the first MkII (Special Intruder) Mosquito, making its first sortie four days later. Although these Mosquitos were not fitted with AI radar, they were flown at night. The commanding officer, Sqn Ldr Sam Hoare, claimed a Dornier Do.217 on 7 July. Two nights later another pilot with the squadron claimed a brace of enemy aircraft as they were preparing to land at their airfields, one being a Do.217 and the other a He.111. To be nearer the action, No. 23 Squadron was moved to Manston. However, because the airfield surface was waterlogged, another move was made to Bradwell Bay. The squadron continued to add to its score of enemy aircraft, catching many of them when they were most vulnerable. It sustained low losses, although care had to be taken not to take the bait of the enemy aircraft with its tail lights on, which would lead the attackers

Intruder Mosquito F.MkII DZ238 was delivered to No. 23 Squadron on 9 December 1942 coded YP-H. It served in Malta, making the last MkII sortie with the squadron on 17 August 1943. (de Havilland photo)

over a concentration of German anti-aircraft guns. With the approach of the poorer winter weather, airborne targets became harder to find, resulting in a greater concentration on ground targets of opportunity, such as trains. To provide an increase in range, additional fuel tanks were installed in the fuselage behind the cameras, giving a further 1.5 hrs endurance for these roving operations.

Despite its success, No. 23 Squadron was prepared for operations in the Middle East and moved to Malta at the end of the year, where it continued intruder operations in the Mediterranean. It commenced operations from Luqa, intruding over Sicilian and mainland Italian airfields, as well as attacking communications installations. Replacements for the older Mosquito F.MkIIs began with FB.MkVI HJ672 on 17 May 1943, the FB.MkVI first being used operationally against Rome on 17 July. By the middle of 1943, many of the major targets were out of range of the Mosquitos, even with a move to the Italian mainland, so a year later the squadron returned to Britain to join No. 515 Squadron at Little Snoring on bomber support duties for Bomber Command, which it continued until the end of the war.

However, the success of No. 23 Squadron had not gone unnoticed. Six Mosquitos in

Mosquito F.MkII DD673 YP-E of No. 23 Squadron had an argument with a steamroller when an engine failed during take-off from Manston on 24 August 1942. Although it looks as if the steamroller won, the Mosquito was repaired and returned to service. (RAF photo)

each of five night-fighter squadrons – nos 25, 85, 151, 157 and 284 – had the AI radar sets removed and were fitted with additional fuel tanks and Gee for improved navigation. In addition their 20 mm cannon armament capacity increased from 175 to 255 rounds per gun, but bombs were still not carried. In October a squadron from 51 OTU at Cranfield was transferred to Twinwood Farm, where Sam Hoare was responsible for the specialist intruder training. With a continual growth in intruder operations, 60 OTU was formed in May 1943 from the nucleus of the

unit at Twinwood Farm to look after all of the special training, eventually being equipped with some fifty Mosquitos.

An adaptation of intruders known as Rangers commenced in February 1943, where Mosquitos made deep penetrations into enemy territory on a freelance basis, attacking any targets that were found. Having departed their airfield, the Ranger Mosquitos would be out of contact with their base, the task being to keep the enemy fighter units at a state of readiness day and night, and, wherever possible, to destroy the aircraft in the air or on the ground, disrupting their training schedules and attacking communications installations. The intruders, however, had clearly defined targets in advance and maintained contact with their base. Another variation, started by Beaufighters and later taken over by Mosquitos, was 'Instep' patrols, which were designated to protect the patrolling Coastal Command aircraft over the Bay of Biscay from hostile fighters. A detachment of No. 264 Squadron was based at Tebalzue in Cornwall from 6 January 1943 to start the Mosquito Insteps, while the remainder of the squadron recommenced intruder operations from Bradwell Bay on 18 January. Wg Cdr Maxwell, the commanding officer of No. 264 Squadron, started the ranger offensive on 4 February by shooting up Lorient harbour. The first Night Ranger mission was flown by nos 25 and 151 squadrons on 16 February, with No. 264 Squadron adding shipping to its list of targets two night later.

Night Rangers were commenced by nos 157 and 456 squadrons on 25 March, and, by the end of the month, Day Ranger operations were under way with nos 151 and 410 squadrons. No. 605 Squadron became fully committed to intruder operations in March when it received Mosquitos, and it was soon joined by No. 418 (City of Edmonton) Squadron RCAF. The two squadrons began a period of friendly rivalry, competing for the highest scores. In early May, nos 25 and 456 squadrons began Day Rangers, and on 14 May a No. 157 Squadron Mosquito managed to shoot down an Fw.190 during a Night Ranger near Eureux. The aircraft was a tough adversary for a Mosquito because under some conditions it could have a speed advantage. Night Rangers were begun on 16 May by No. 307 (Polish) Squadron, which attacked a variety of ground targets during the early stages of the operation. Both nos 418 and 605 squadrons started their high rate of scoring in

Ground crew prepare a battle-worn Mosquito MkII intruder for its next sortie. While Leading Aircraftman T. Hamill of Glasgow cleans the cannon, Leading Aircraftman E. Hurst of Cheadle is loading rounds into one of the .303 in machine-guns. (AM photo)

June, destroying enemy aircraft over Denmark, Holland and France. Detachments from nos 25, 151, 157, 307, 410 and 456 squadrons were allocated to 'Instep' patrols from June. The success of these brought the Fw.190s into the battle, and, on one 'Instep', three out of four Mosquitos were shot down for the loss of one Fw.190. However, No. 151 Squadron did manage to destroy one of the heavily armed Fw.200 Condor four-engine, long-range patrol aircraft about 250 miles west of Bordeaux.

While the fighter squadrons continued on the Ranger and Intruder operations, there was an obvious need for the greater range with

The Mosquito could pack a destructive punch when all four machine-guns and four cannons were fired, as this dusk photo at the gun butts shows. (Photo Chaz Bowyer collection)

underwing fuel tanks and the carriage of bombs of the Mosquito FB.MkVI, thus bringing much of Europe within range. In July 1943 the Mosquito FB.MkVI was introduced to Intruder operations by nos 418, 456 and 605 squadrons, which, with the support of other units, continued to fly Rangers and bomber support duties until the end of the war. Although a variety of targets were allocated, airfields and railway installations were the main priority.

Day Intruder operations could be hazardous with the low flying involved. Also, with aircraft normally operating in pairs, it was not unusual for one to fail to return owing to the enemy defences. In contrast, a crew could complete a tour of thirty-five

sorties on Night Rangers and not be lucky enough to locate a single target. Despite the overall success of these operations, the Germans offered little in retaliation, apart from some night-fighter sorties mixed in with the returning heavy bomber formations.

The night-fighter crews had to adjust their method of operation when transferred to Intruder operations because, with the removal of the radar, the crew had to find its way around hostile Europe, map-reading with the aid of a subdued cycle lamp and keeping an eye out for signs of hostile aircraft. One such crew comprised Henry Morley and his navigator, Reg Fidler. After they had practised over Britain at night, they went on a comparatively

No. 456 Squadron started Night Rangers with No. 157 Squadron on 25 March 1943, one of their aircraft being Mosquito F.MkII DD739 RX-X. (IWM photo)

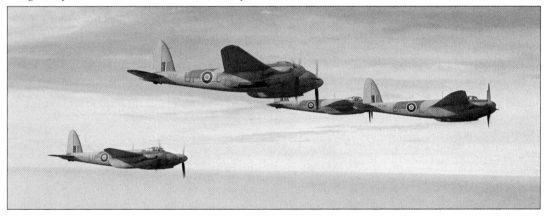

No. 605 Squadron started Intruder operations in March 1943 when their first Mosquitos were delivered. An early aircraft was F.MkII DZ716 UP-L. (IWM photo)

Night Ranger missions were started by nos 25 and 151 squadrons in February 1943. No. 25 Squadron operated FB.MkVI PZ181 YP-E from Little Snoring in 1944 which George Stewart brought back on one engine. (George Stewart photo)

safe sortie over Holland, flying a triangular course to check all of the procedures. Following this the crew were declared operational. Reg was prone to air sickness, but such was his keenness to fly that he took this in his stride. Gee was carried as a navigation aid, but was of little use on the way to the target because the plane was flown at such low level across the Channel that it was soon out of range of the ground station. Gee was, however, a helpful aid for the return at higher altitudes, and Morley and Fidler claim never to have had problems with chimneys and telegraph poles because they did not fly that high.

Railway installations became a speciality of No. 418 Squadron. This was less glamorous than shooting down enemy aircraft but was equally vital in disrupting the transport of war materials and men. Efforts were still made to disrupt the enemy training programme. In August, airfields in Germany came within range owing to the improved endurance of the Mosquitos. Three Mosquitos and crews were detached from

No. 418 Squadron on 15 September 1943 to practise for a week with the Lancasters of No. 617 Squadron, flying at 170 mph (273 km/h) at 150 ft (45 m) altitude in preparation for an attack on the Dortmund–Ems Canal. The duties of the Mosquito crews were to help to defend the Lancasters against the enemy air and ground defences.

During September the top-scoring Mosquito intruder unit was No. 605 Squadron, with claims for ten aircraft destroyed and a further two damaged. Wg Cdr Hoare was appointed commanding officer at the end of the month. He celebrated by shooting down a Do.217 on his first sortie in the new position. On 26 September a No. 410 Squadron Mosquito located a Do.217 over Holland and gave it a 3 sec burst from the cannons from only 100 ft (30 m) away. The enemy aircraft blew up violently, nearly claiming the Mosquito as well. The Mosquito was showered in blazing fuel from nose to tail, burning off much of the fabric covering of the wood. The port engine had to be shut down owing to a loss of oil pressure,

No. 605 Squadron based at Castle Camps were one of the top scoring Intruder Mosquito squadrons.
(Planet News photo)

and control was lost during a 4,000 ft (1,219 m) dive that resulted from the pilot's temporary loss of vision. The dive did, however, extinguish the flames, and, after a difficult return flight, a successful landing was made at Coleby Grange. The aircraft was returned to Hatfield for repair, and, like so many of the repaired Mosquitos, was relegated to training duties.

Both nos 307 and 450 squadrons were tasked with Instep patrols, No. 307 Squadron claiming a Bf.110 and Ju.88 destroyed, plus damage to a further five Bf.110s and four Ju.88s, in September. No. 157 Squadron claimed a giant Ju.290 on 20 November, with damage to four Ju.88s. With the reduced

threat in the spring of 1944, 'Instep' patrols were discontinued in April. On 28 November 1943, No. 418 Squadron was switched to the more hazardous Day Ranger operations, starting with an attack on the well-defended flying-boat base at Lake Biscarosse. The Day Ranger operations depended on the unlikely combination of reasonable visibility and low cloud cover to maintain an element of surprise. The European winter rarely provided such ideal conditions.

Wg Cdr MacDonald, the commanding officer of No. 418 Squadron, led a particularly successful attack with two Mosquitos on 27 January 1944, when two He.177s and an

Wg Cdr Sam Hoare claimed the 100th victory for No. 605 Squadron on 19 January 1944 with the destruction of a Ju.188. The celebration was at the Dorchester Hotel in London on 15 April when Sam Hoare was presented with a silver model of the Mosquito, two days before his final sortie with the squadron. (AM press photo)

Fw.200 were shot down in rapid succession. Another pair of Mosquitos from the same squadron shot down two Ju.88s and two Ju.34s, with damage to a Ju.86. In 8 min of combat, four Mosquitos had been responsible for the destruction of seven enemy aircraft, a record that proved unbeatable.

During February both nos 418 and 605 squadrons were kept busy at night over Germany, seeking out enemy bombers returning from their raids over Britain. The Day Rangers continued, the growing scores reflecting their success. In a period of twenty-two months of operations, No. 418 Squadron had claimed 22½ victories, but in one month of

Day Rangers their score was more than doubled, with twenty-four victories for the loss of one Mosquito. In the following six weeks a further thirty enemy aircraft were claimed as shot down, with another thirty-eight destroyed on the ground by No. 418 Squadron. Wg Cdr Sam Hoare claimed the hundredth victory for No. 605 Squadron on 11 January when he shot down a Ju.188 near Chièvres. In one day, two Mosquitos of No. 418 Squadron shot down four vulnerable minesweeping Ju.52/3ms into the Kattegat, then claimed three more in the air and a pair on the ground. Following this two other Mosquitos destroyed ten enemy training aircraft, thus helping to frustrate the German pilot training effort. By the time Wg Cdr Hoare had completed his tour of duty with No. 605 Squadron on 17 April, his score stood at thirty-three aircraft shot down, two probables, and thirty-five damaged or destroyed on the ground. By early May, No. 418 Squadron had claimed ninety-six enemy aircraft destroyed and were working rapidly towards the century. The next was an He.111Z glider tug, consisting of two He.111s joined together by the wing, but it still only counted as one victory. The century was reached by Bob Kipp, who also scored a hat-trick, by destroying three Fw.190s, giving him the honour of being the top scoring night-fighter pilot in a single sortie, without the use of AI radar.

On 21 May, No. 418 Squadron was mainly withdrawn from Day Rangers, leaving No. 605 Squadron to continue adding to its score, its next victory being during the Allied landings in Normandy. No. 418 Squadron continued to lend support by operating 'Flowers' against a variety of ground targets behind enemy lines, particularly communications installations, similar to the squadrons of 2nd TAF. Intruder operations were taken over by No. 515 Squadron in 100 Group on 16 June, releasing nos 418 and 605 squadrons for operations against V-1 sites. Wg Cdr Hoare had become station commander of Little Snoring where No. 515 Squadron was based, and the commanding officer of the squadron was Canadian Wg Cdr F.F. Lambert. Henry Morley and Reg Fidler were one of the crews with No. 515 Squadron, and they were able to claim one night victory. However, their most rewarding activity was when they were given the task of searching in daylight for a colleague who had bailed out over the North Sea. The pilot was saved quickly, but there was no sign of the navigator, and, although it was August, the sea was rough. The initial search had been completed without success, and Morley and Fidler drew a blank in their allocated area.

Allowing for the high winds, they decided to fly off at a tangent and were delighted to find the missing navigator where the other search services had failed. By this time the survivor had drifted close to the Dutch coast. A Walrus landed in the rough sea by the navigator, the Mosquitos circling overhead as protection. After four attempts, the Walrus managed to get airborne, and even the coastal guns stayed silent while the rescue was being carried out.

During July and August, No. 515 Squadron operated Rangers, claiming a number of victories, and was joined by Mosquitos from nos 29 and 406 squadrons. Ships were an occasional, rather unpopular target, owing to their heavy defences. The gradual move to European bases gave sufficient endurance to reach targets in East Germany and Czechoslovakia.

In September the first of the V-2 rockets fell on Britain, but these were impossible to intercept in flight owing to their speed and trajectory. Nos 418 and 605 squadrons were allocated the task of destroying the launch sites, catching the missiles on the ground. With No. 418 Squadron continuing on Day Rangers, it claimed an unbeatable score. In one day a pair of Mosquitos destroyed, on enemy airfields, seven Ju.88s, a Bf.110, a Bf.109 and a Ju.87, as well as damaging many other aircraft. In one week, No. 605 Squadron claimed sixteen aircraft destroyed, one probable and eleven damaged. Despite the grave risks taken by the crews, the major threat being from ground-based anti-aircraft guns, although flying accidents also played a part, the eventual loss rate was only 2.8 per cent.

The hazards on operations were not only generated as a result of enemy action, as Henry Morley and Reg Fidler were to find out. A pair of No. 515 Squadron Mosquito FB.MkVIs – PZ440 and NS993 – were given the task of a low-level attack on Holzkirchen airfield about 20 miles (32 km) south-east of Munich on 20 September 1944. However,

The wreckage of Mosquito FB.MkVI PZ440 of No. 515 Squadron when it had to crash-land in Switzerland after an attack in the Munich area on 20 September 1944. The crew, Henry Morley and Reg Fidler, escaped with minor injuries, but the Mosquito was written off. (Reg Fidler photo)

both aircraft were damaged by exploding debris from the target as they flew over at low altitude, PZ440 with Henry and Reg on board being in the worst condition. One engine was stopped and some of the fuel tanks were leaking. Both aircraft set course for the comparative safety of neutral Switzerland, but the welcome was far from friendly, with anti-aircraft fire from the ground and attacks by defending fighters, which succeeded in disabling the remaining engine. With no alternative but to make a forced landing, Morley was lucky to be able to locate a reasonably level field, the aircraft disintegrating as it skidded to a halt, throwing Fidler out. Morley put out the smouldering wiring in the cockpit with his gloved hand and released himself from the straps, before dragging Fidler clear. He gave Fidler a morphine injection, which made him feel better in about 30 min, but this only lasted

until the painkiller wore off. As with many Mosquito crashes, the structure absorbed much of the shock and did not burn, although it was a total write-off. The crew were interned, eventually being returned to Britain, but they did not return to flying operations. The other Mosquito also suffered an engine failure, but made a successful emergency landing, joining the growing stock of aircraft from both sides interned in Switzerland.

In the middle of November, both nos 418 and 605 squadrons joined the 2nd TAF. They flew with the other Mosquito FB.MkVI squadrons until the end of the war in Europe. Their success rate had been high, with more than 200 enemy aircraft shot down, and many more destroyed or damaged on the ground. Although 91 Mosquitos failed to return, like that of Morley and Fidler, some of the crews survived. No. 418 Squadron disbanded at Volkel on 7 September 1945, many of the

No. 605 Squadron was renumbered No. 4 Squadron at Volkel in August 1945, moving to Wunstorf and later replacing the Mosquitos with Vampires in July 1950. This line-up at Wunstorf in 1949 includes Mosquito FB.MkVIs PZ165:UP-E, NT181:UP-H, TA639 and RS667. The CO is Sqn Ldr C.P.N. Newman DFC in the white flying suit.

The CO of No. 515 Squadron, Wg Cdr F.F. Lambert DSO, DFC, left, with three crew members in front of Mosquito FB.MkVI PZ338 at Little Snoring shortly before they were supplied with the first ASH-equipped Mosquitos. (AM press photo)

crews returning to their homes in Canada. No. 605 Squadron was renumbered No. 4 Squadron at Volkel on 31 August, retaining Mosquitos until re-equipping with Vampire jet fighters at Wunstorf in July 1950. The fuselage of one of the No. 605/4 Squadron Mosquitos – TA122 – still exists at the de Havilland Heritage at Salisbury Hall, where it will eventually be restored. The port side bears the markings of Gp Capt. Pickard's Mosquito, which was lost during the Amiens prison raid.

No. 515 Squadron was issued with their first ASH radar-equipped Mosquitos in November 1944, gaining its first victory against a Ju.88 on the last day of the year. Intruder operations continued against enemy airfields during the spring, the final operation being on 2 May. The squadron disbanded at Little Snoring on 10 June 1945, the majority of the crews being posted to No. 627 Squadron.

COASTAL STRIKE

Coastal strike operations, even with the high-performance Mosquitos, were hazardous and often spectacular, both for the attacking crews and for the targets. With the priority for the fighter-bombers going to the squadrons of the 2nd TAF and the intruders, coastal strike operations started with Mosquitos using the specially adapted MkXVIII, although no squadron was fully equipped with this version.

The MkXVIII was an adaptation of the basic fighter airframe, with the four underfloor 20 mm cannons replaced with a single six-pounder gun, the fitting of which was designed over a very short period, using a damaged Mosquito fuselage for the trial installation. On 10 May 1943, thirty sets of guns and associated parts were ordered for fitting into a number of the FB.VIs during production, the weapon being a 57 mm Molins anti-tank gun. The prototype

conversion was in Mosquito HJ732. However, a shortage of airframes meant that only three aircraft could be converted initially. An additional 65 gal (295 l) fuel tank was fitted in the fuselage to provide greater endurance for hunting U-boats over the Bay of Biscay. Ground-firing trials at the gun-butts highlighted some shell-feed problems, but these were analysed by the pioneer use of a high-speed camera, which allowed the blockages to be cleared. Air firing trials went well, the airframe absorbing the increased recoil action and blast effect, but the crews reported a momentary slow-down of the Mosquito when the gun was fired.

A few MkXVIIIs were allocated to the anti-shipping units, the plan being to mix the new version with the FB.MkVIs to give the greatest flexibility with dealing with a variety of targets, the Molins gun being particularly effective against submarines. Two FB.MkXVIIIs were allocated to No. 248 Squadron from 22 October 1943 at Predannack, and, because this unit was equipped with Beaufighters, both air and groundcrews were detached from No. 618 Squadron during one of their periods of inactivity for training for 'Highball' operations. This gave the crews of No. 618 Squadron the chance to fly on operations, starting on 24 October, but on their second operation on 4 November they suffered the tragic loss of their commanding officer Sqn Ldr C.F. Rose, whose aircraft was hit by guns on an armed trawler. The plane crashed into the sea. On 7 November the first U-boat was spotted and attacked. It sustained obvious damage before it crash-dived. The Mosquito attacks caused the Germans to provide a greater protection for their submarines in the Bay of Biscay. This did not deter the Mosquito crews but clearly made their lives more risky.

In mid-December 1943, No. 248 Squadron began to convert from Beaufighters to

No. 235 Squadron began anti-shipping operations in June 1944, one of their FB.MkVIs being Standard-built HR118:W-3. (T. Armstrong DFC photo)

Mosquitos using one T.MkIII and a pair of F.MkIIs to train the crews gradually, while operations continued with the Beaufighters and Mosquito MkXVIIIs. The unit's primary role with the Mosquito FB.MkVIs changed to one of fighter reconnaissance, with fighter support for the strike squadrons being a secondary task. The crews were expected to fly regular interception patrols as well as providing escorts for anti-shipping and anti-U-boat operations in the Bay of Biscay. No. 248 Squadron completed its training by 20 February 1944, and the first major action was on 10 March, when four FB.MkVIs and a pair of FB.MkXVIIIs located a German naval force, with Ju.88s providing air cover. The MkXVIIIs concentrated their efforts on the shipping, damaging a destroyer and attacking a U-boat, as well as managing to shoot down a Ju.88 with the machine-guns. Meanwhile, the FB.MkVIs accounted for two Ju.88s and one probable. The heavy defences

of the shipping targets made them hazardous, and a number of Mosquito crews were lost.

A request was made for more Mosquito FB.MkXVIIIs to be delivered to the No. 248 Squadron detachment. However, with the highly effective and simpler rocket-firing FB.VIs entering service, the request was turned down. This version did continue in service for specialised targets until January 1945. The D-Day duties of No. 248 Squadron were to help to protect the invasion fleet from attacks from enemy surface ships and U-boats, help to block the enemy harbours and provide cover for the air-strike forces. As an example, No. 248 Squadron escorted Beaufighters of nos 144 and 404 squadrons on a roving patrol over the Bay of Biscay. Following a number of inconclusive attacks on U-boats, No. 248 Squadron were able to claim a half share with a Liberator on 10 June, when U-821 was sunk. Although not always effective, 500 lb bombs were

Coastal strike was a very hazardous and spectacular operation for the Mosquito crews. Targets were often well-defended enemy shipping off the Norwegian coast where rocket projectiles were particularly effective. (AM press photo)

occasionally dropped on surface shipping. The carriage of underwing mines and depth charges was tested at Boscombe Down in 1944, but only the latter were adopted. In fact, the first operational use of 25 lb (11 kg) depth charges from Mosquito FB.MkVIs was by No. 248 Squadron on 22 June 1944.

The anti-shipping patrols received a boost when No. 235 Squadron joined No. 248 Squadron at Portreath in June 1944, the new arrivals commencing operations on 16 June. By 22 June the Beaufighters with the two squadrons had been entirely replaced by Mosquitos, and the two versions worked together, often with the Beaufighters of nos 144 and 404 squadrons, firing shells, rockets and bombs. During July and August, both squadrons also had aircraft as their targets, each claiming two Do.217s carrying glide bombs. With the Allied advances across Europe, enemy shipping became scarce in the English Channel and Bay of Biscay, the final sorties from the Cornish base being made in the fruitless search for U-boats on 7 September.

A move was then made by both squadrons to Banff in northern Scotland, where they were joined by No. 333 (Norwegian) Squadron to form the Banff Strike Wing. With

Mosquito FB.MkVI HR632 armed with four individual rocket rails under each wing, carrying a single RP on each. (Charles E. Brown photo)

the major target areas along the Norwegian coastline and the Kattegat around Denmark, the duties of the Norwegian crews were to identify and pinpoint targets for the Beaufighters to attack, escorted by the other two Mosquito squadrons at Banff. The PR Mosquitos would usually identify the targets in advance, which was often shipping at anchor, calling in the strike aircraft to destroy the enemy vessels before they could put to sea again and become difficult to locate. The guns on both the Mosquitos and the Beaufighters were used during the attack to try to suppress the many guns fitted to the German ships.

The first combined strike from Banff was on 14 September on an armed reconnaissance along the Norwegian coast. A force of twenty-five Mosquito FB.MkVIs from nos 235 and 248 squadrons and four FB.MkXVIIIs from

No. 248 Squadron escorted nineteen Beaufighters from nos 144 and 404 squadrons, attacking four motor vessels and their two escorts, leaving them burning.

On 26 October, unguided rocket projectiles (RP) were fired from the air for the first time against shipping targets, and they proved far more effective and cheaper than air-launched torpedoes. Studies had started in the autumn of 1943 for carrying RPs under Mosquito wings, and, on 28 September, approval was given for four racks beneath each wing carrying up to eight 60 lb (27 kg) rockets. The RPs gave the Mosquitos a highly effective and mobile punch against all forms of shipping without the recoil or stress of guns, and the ideal dive angle established during trials was 20°. Two versions of RPs were produced, the 25 lb (11 kg) solid armour-piercing type and

Four RP loaded under the wing of a No. 143 Squadron Mosquito FB.Mk VI at Banff.

RAF groundcrew prepare another Mosquito FB.Mk VI of the Banff Strike Wing for its next operation. The RP is already loaded and the guns are being cleaned, while the protective covers are removed from the engines and cockpit.

the 60 lb semi-armour-piercing type with a high-explosive warhead. Although the latter was more destructive, being the equivalent of a broadside from a cruiser, the debris thrown up in the path of the launch Mosquitos created a major hazard, so they were rarely used.

During attacks with RP, the gunsight was depressed by 5 or 6° and aim taken at the ship's waterline below the bridge. The 20 mm cannon were fired in the 20° dive. When hits were seen on the bridge, the range was about 600 yds (550 m) and therefore an ideal distance for the firing of the RP. It was possible to fire the RPs in pairs, but a normal attack fired a complete salvo of all eight rockets. The rocket rails were harmonised for two dry hits on the superstructure, two on the waterline and the other four to fall short in the water. These four would then flatten out and punch a hole through the hull into the engine room. The rocket motors would wreck the boilers and set fire to the fuel and oil pouring out of the fractured pipes, while the ship rapidly started filling with water. As the aircraft flew over the crippled ship, nothing appeared to have happened, but by the time the Mosquitos had climbed to re-form, on looking back the ship would either be rolling over or burning.

As more Mosquito FB.MkVIs became available for the anti-shipping units, No. 143 Squadron was formed at Banff to replace some of the slower Beaufighters. The squadron was formerly a Beaufighter OTU based at North Coates, and had been responsible for working up new crews before their postings to operational squadrons. The unit had therefore not seen any action, although its crews were very experienced. It welcomed the move to be part of the Banff Strike Wing, as well as the conversion to Mosquitos, its main task being the firing of RPs. No. 143 Squadron started operations on 7 November, not carrying bombs but contributing to the overall combined offensive operation with the other squadrons,

using cannons, RP, bombs and the Molins gun. On 21 November the largest anti-shipping strike so far was mounted in Aalesund. Led by a No. 333 Squadron PR Mosquito were thirty-two Mosquito fighter-bombers and forty-two Beaufighters, with top cover provided by a dozen Mustangs.

On 7 December a further major strike came face to face with defending Fw.190 and Bf.109 fighters, the escort Mustangs claiming four Bf.109s, with two of the Fw.190s colliding. Losses to the attacking force were two Mosquitos, a Beaufighter and a Mustang. On 15 January 1945, when attacking a well defended shipping target, nine experienced Fw.190 pilots managed to shoot down some of the six Mosquitos lost, in return for the loss of one of their own aircraft.

With the use of RP becoming so effective, despite the additional drag of the underwing installation, the Mosquito MkXVIIIs were withdrawn from the No. 248 Squadron special detachment and later passed on to No. 254 Squadron. To give increased endurance, fuel tanks were then hung under the wings, displacing the inboard pairs of rocket rails but maintaining the punch by mounting the RP in pairs on the remaining two rails. When committed to the attack, the underwing tanks were jettisoned. However, as they were prone to releasing sideways, a steel barrier was hung in between to stop the tank removing the rockets, adding more weight and drag to the aircraft. On one attack, Wg Cdr Foxley-Norris was the strike leader. When he released his underwing tanks, one of them moved sideways, hitting the fuselage nearby hard enough to break off the tail. With the radio failing simultaneously, one of his colleagues warned him by Aldis lamp signal not to make any violent movements. He suddenly found that, despite being the leader, he was rapidly being overtaken by the other aircraft, which were under attack from some Fw.190s. Avoiding any violent manoeuvres, he flew into the cover of

On 17 March 1945 No. 235 Squadron led No. 248 Squadron on a 31 Mosquito fighter-bomber attack against shipping in Aalesund harbour, firing cannon and RP against six ships, sinking two, and damaging the remainder.

Mosquito FB.MkVI PZ446 of No. 143 Squadron being prepared at Banff for the next anti-shipping strike while the 60 lb solid head rocket projectiles are being loaded. (Illustrated photo)

Mosquito FB.Mk VI RS625 NE-D of No. 143 Squadron shows the revised RP installation when underwing drop fuel tanks were added for increased endurance. A metal frame separates the tank from the RP, to avoid the tank on ejection prematurely removing the rockets. (de Havilland photo)

Mosquito FB.Mk VI HR405 NE-A:143 Squadron attacking shipping in Sandefjord on 2 April 1945. (ACM Sir Christopher Foxley-Norris photo)

cloud and returned to base, where it was found with some surprise that the back of the aircraft had not been broken.

Rocket strikes were begun by No. 235 Squadron in February 1945. In an attack on shipping in the narrow Midgulen Fiord, delayed action bombs were dropped down the 3,000 ft (915 m) cliffs. Although some ships were left burning, it was not possible to assess the total damage because the area was so inaccessible. The following month the Mosquitos began operating without Beaufighters, shipping being the main targets, but from time to time aircraft and land targets were attacked too. On some of the more hazardous over-water operations, rescue preparations were made by flying No. 279 Squadron air–sea rescue Warwicks carrying survival gear for ditched aircrews.

Among the more hazardous and spectacular attacks were those on well-defended shipping in the harbours at Aalesund and Porsgrunn. No. 235 Squadron led No. 248 Squadron on an attack on Aalesund harbour on 17 March, with thirty-one Mosquitos firing cannon and RP against six ships. Despite heavy flak, two of the ships were sunk and the others were damaged. While many of the Allied squadrons were slackening off their activities owing to the lack of targets, Germany still needed supplies to be transported by sea. The coastal strike units were therefore just as busy against enemy shipping. Many of the raids were accompanied by a photographic Mosquito to record the results, because, with the high speed of the Mosquito, it was not possible to gain an accurate visual record and it was usually too hazardous to hang about after a raid.

On 9 April came a major success in the continuing U-boat search, when thirty-seven Mosquitos of nos 143, 235 and 248 squadrons of the Banff Wing were flying an anti-shipping patrol over the Kattegat. No. 143 Squadron was in the rear position, led by Sqn Ldr David Pritchard in Mosquito

FB.MkVI RS625, NE-D, who had been briefed to break away from the formation if any small targets were spotted. Some ships' wakes were seen in the afternoon sun, and No. 143 Squadron turned to port to investigate when U-boats were spotted by the wingman. Nine Mosquitos roared into attack at low level out of the sun, catching the U-boats by surprise. Hearing the activity, the other two squadrons decided to join the attack. All three U-boats attempted to escape by crash-diving, but they were too late, one of them rising up like a cork, exploding violently and taking with it the photo-reconnaisance Mosquito. All three submarines, U-804, U-843 and U-1065, were confirmed as destroyed, and despite the loss of the Mosquito, other camera-carrying aircraft managed to take some dramatic action shots of the attack. On 19 April the U-251 was sunk in the Kattegat, and two days later a formation of forty-five Mosquitos from the Banff Wing were on their way to the Kattegat when they came across a formation of eighteen Junkers torpedo bombers about 150 miles from the Scottish coast, no doubt planning to attack Allied shipping. The Mosquitos accounted for at least nine enemy aircraft, breaking up the raid.

At a late stage in the war, with enemy shipping still posing a threat, No. 404 Squadron converted from Beaufighters to Mosquito FB.VIs, half of the squadron starting conversion at Banff on 24 March, followed by the remainder starting on 3 April. It destroyed a Bv.138 flying-boat at anchor in its first operation. No. 254 Squadron was still operating Beaufighters from North Coates, but there appeared to be a threat of U-boats and midget submarines in the Channel at night. To provide a suitable defence, five Mosquito MkXVIIIs were attached to the squadron in March 1945, with attacks against U-boats beginning on 12 April, with inconclusive results. Meanwhile the Banff Wing continued

Camera gun photo from Mosquito FB.MkVI RS501 NE-Z of No. 143 Squadron crewed by Flt Lt J.
Kedhane and Plt Off A. Fielding during the sinking of U-804, U-843 and U-1065 on 9 April 1945.
(ACM Sir Christopher Foxley-Norris photo)

Although the photo Mosquito was lost in the violent
explosion of one of the U-boats, the cameras located
in the strike Mosquitos were able to capture some
very effective low-level pictures of the action.
(D. Pritchard photo)

The all-Mosquito-equipped Banff Strike Wing in May 1945 consisting of nos 143, 235, 248, 404 and 333 squadrons. The short-term nature of the base is confirmed by the temporary buildings, and a station hack Proctor is parked among the many Mosquitos. (Photo Chaz Bowyer collection)

its patrols of the sea between Norway and Denmark to avoid the enemy making a last stand in Scandinavia. During one of these patrols on 2 May, No. 248 Squadron sunk U-2350 with RP. The final shipping strike came on 4 May when a large, well-defended German convoy was attacked near Kiel. Of forty-eight Mosquitos from the Banff Wing, eight were operated by No. 404 Squadron on their second and last major attack. Top cover was provided by eighteen Mustangs, and three Warwicks were on hand for air–sea rescue. The aircraft flew so low that one of them collected in the nose the top of a ship's mast, complete with German ensign.

Although most of the Allied forces had ceased operations by VE-Day, the Coastal Command squadrons continued flying on the lookout for rogue submarines, which either did not know or did not want to know the war was over. Nos 143 and 248 squadrons flew the final Mosquito anti-shipping operation on 21 May with a pair of aircraft each, but they only located E-boats.

ASIAN OPERATIONS

Although the major use of the Mosquito FB.MkVI was in the European theatre, a significant number were also operated in Asia. Climatic tests of the wooden structure had been made initially to check the effects of temperature, humidity and rain, and also to determine the resistance to insect attack. One of the results of these tests was to change the adhesive from casein glue to formaldehyde, which was more resistant to tropical conditions.

Asian training began in January 1944 at Yellahanka in India, with the formation of 1672 Conversion Unit. The crews of No. 45 Squadron started training on 1 March. This squadron received its first Mosquitos the previous day. The training continued for about three months. No. 82 Squadron commenced training on 4 July at Kobar, followed by No. 47 Squadron on 5 October. The designated targets were enemy communications facilities, such as roads,

Once the Mosquito's structural problems were resolved in Asia, No. 45 Squadron were able to resume operations with Mosquito FB.MkVIs on 9 November 1944. They operated FB.MkVI RF957 OB-B at Santa Cruz in 1946. (RAFM photo)

No. 82 Squadron began Intruder operations on 19 December 1944 against Japanese airfields, railways and road transport by day and night. Standard-built FB.MkVI RF773 UX-P was with the squadron at Madras in 1946. (R.H. Dargue photo)

No. 47 Squadron started operations with Mosquito FB.MkVIs on 23 February 1945, using them for bombing and strafing Japanese positions. (IWM photo)

No. 84 Squadron resumed re-equipping with Mosquito FB.Mk VIs in February 1945, TE616 being one of at least three flying over Java in 1945. (Photo Chaz Bowyer collection)

railways and bridges, and No. 45 Squadron made the first attack on 1 October.

There was a major setback to Mosquito operations in Asia when, on 20 October, during practice shallow-dive bombing on the ranges by a No. 82 Squadron aircraft, there was structural failure in the starboard wing and half of it broke away, killing the crew. All of the Mosquitos in India were grounded, and the investigation soon found serious deterioration in the joints of all of the Mosquitos using casein glue. Fortunately, those with formaldehyde were unaffected, but No. 47 Squadron was one of the units to suffer. On 19 September it was announced that they would be converting from Beaufighters to Mosquitos, and it moved to

Yellahanka in early October, receiving its first Mosquito on 5 October. However, after all the Mosquitos were grounded the Beaufighters were returned by the end of November.

Gen. Slim's 14th Army fighting in Burma urgently needed the enemy railway and communications networks neutralised to allow them to advance against the Japanese. With cleared Mosquitos, No. 45 Squadron was able to resume operations on 9 November, and it attacked Meiktilla airfield with eight aircraft. Intruder operations were commenced by No. 82 Squadron on 19 December, starting a series of 'Rhubarbs' against trains, road transport and airfields by day and night. On 18 February, No. 47 Squadron returned to Mosquitos, joining nos 45 and 82 squadrons, to become 908 Wing. No. 47 Squadron started operations with Mosquitos on 23 February, using them for bombing and strafing, while retaining some Beaufighters for two months for bombing and RP attacks.

No. 84 Squadron began re-equipping with Mosquitos in autumn 1944. However, owing to the structural problems, it did not resume conversion until February 1945. Meanwhile, No. 110 Squadron received its first FB.MkVI at Yellahanka on 28 January, and, after training, the two squadrons joined forces at Joari and commenced operations on 31 March, patrolling roads and rivers.

Meiktila fell to the Allies in April 1945, the enemy retreating rapidly, making targets further away from the Mosquito bases, with attacks on Rangoon starting on 1 May. No. 908 Wing aircraft operated on a cab rank basis, attacking targets when called in by the ground forces. The wing flew its last operations in May, practically completing Mosquito fighter-bomber operations in Asia before VJ-Day. No. 110 Squadron continued, its final sortie being on 20 August.

With about 350 Mosquito FB.MkVIs remaining in Asia, No. 211 Squadron re-equipped in India in June 1945 to help to maintain an uneasy peace in the region. The squadron had expected to be involved in the invasion of Malaya, but this was avoided as a result of the collapse of Japan. In October the squadron moved to Siam, but an order was made to ground the Mosquitos on 20 January 1946 for a main wing-spar inspection, and the squadron was disbanded at Don Muang, Bangkok, in March.

Even with the surrender of the Japanese, peace did not readily come to the Asian region. Rebel forces in the Dutch East Indies proclaimed the independence of Indonesia, and Mosquito FB.MkVIs of nos 84 and 110 squadrons were called in to assist in curbing the restive elements from 9 November. No. 82 Squadron joined in briefly on 15 November, firing RP at ground targets that day, and No. 47 Squadron attacked the Soeramarta radio station on 25 November. The final Mosquito strikes were made during December, although some escort and reconnaissance flights continued until 20 January 1946.

The fighter-bombers had therefore become the major combat version of the Mosquito, combining the unarmed bomber concept with that of the fighter and resulting in an effective aircraft used on a range of combat duties. After the war Ernst Heinkel, the famous German aircraft designer, said of the Mosquito: 'That is the aircraft I would have liked to have designed.' As a reminder, he kept a picture of the aircraft displayed in his boardroom.

13. OTHER DUTIES

The Mosquito proved ideal for its major operational roles of unarmed photo-reconnaissance and bomber duties, as well as a night-fighter and fighter-bomber. In addition, the basic airframe proved easily adaptable to a number of other specialist duties, which could not have been envisioned by the original design team, making the Mosquito a truly multi-role aircraft.

THE MOSQUITO AIRLINER

Probably the most unlikely task for a high-speed tactical bomber was as an airliner, not just for the carriage of urgent freight but also for important passengers. A small number of Mosquitos were converted to civil aircraft for service with BOAC on a single route from Leuchars in Scotland to Stockholm in neutral Sweden. Known as the 'Ball-bearing Run', because one of the most vital cargoes was ball-bearings from Sweden, it not only helped to keep British industry turning but also denied the cargo to Germany. The Mosquitos were unarmed converted bombers and fighter-bombers carrying civil markings and flown by BOAC crews, who used the high speed to attempt to avoid the enemy defences in Germany, Norway and Denmark before reaching the comparative safety of Swedish airspace.

The services started originally in 1942 to bring back Allied aircrew who had managed to escape to Sweden, and also Norwegians who wished to leave their occupied country and carry on the fight against the Germans from Britain. Sweden was trading openly with both sides to maintain its neutrality. When the Schweinfurt ball-bearing factory in Germany was destroyed by the USAAF in mid-1943, the situation became critical for the enemy. To prevent them from getting supplies from Sweden, two Mosquitos were rapidly modified to carry a passenger each in the comparative discomfort of the bomb bay. The two British representatives were able to fly quickly to Stockholm and negotiate for the entire ball-bearing output of the Swedish factories. The facilities on the aircraft were somewhat basic, the passenger lying on a mattress in the rear end of the bomb bay, in full flying kit, including oxygen mask and reading lamp. His only contact with the crew was via the intercom. A parachute was supplied for emergency use and it could drop out of the bomb bay. Despite the discomfort of being sealed in the Mosquito, the trip only took 3 hrs, compared with up to 9 hrs in a more vulnerable, slower aircraft. The slower Hudson and Lodestar flights continued for larger loads, but, to avoid risk, they could only operate under cover of cloud or darkness. In the summer the hours of darkness were too short. During the winter, additional hazards came from icing and navigation difficulties.

The Swedes maintained their own civil airliner links with Britain by flying Dakotas to Leuchars. However, to ensure their neutrality, similar flights were made to Berlin. During the operations to Stockholm's Bromma airport, British Mosquitos were often parked alongside the Lufthansa Ju.52/3m airliners, many of the crews having known each before the war.

BOAC had originally been offered Venturas, Hudson IIIs, Merlin-powered

Whitleys and an Albemarle to replace its original fleet. However, with the successful flight to Stockholm by George Parry in civilian clothes and with the military markings removed from the No. 105 Squadron aircraft, BOAC urged strongly for the higher speed of the Mosquito. Although the aircraft were in short supply, the need was recognised and B.IV DZ411 was delivered to BOAC on 15 December 1942. It was re-registered as G-AGFV and fitted with additional fuel tanks in the bomb bay. Following training of the crews, the first sortie left Leuchars for Stockholm on 4 February. On 12 April, following the successful introduction of this aircraft, confirmation came that a further 6 unarmed FB.MkVIs would be made available to BOAC, the aircraft selected being HJ690, HJ681, HJ718, HJ720, HJ721, and HJ723, which were allocated the civil registrations G-AGGC to G-AGGH. This batch of Mosquitos was delivered to BOAC between 16 April and 2 May 1943, soon entering service, but the slightly faster earlier MkIV was usually favoured by the crews.

The high speed did not always guarantee immunity from enemy attack, as was discovered on the night of 22 April 1943, when the MkIV G-AGFV was attacked and badly damaged by a Fw.190 while flying over the Skagerrak, resulting in a belly-landing in Sweden. Fortunately the FB.MkVIs were just entering service, with all other BOAC aircraft withdrawn from the Stockholm route, and the damaged aircraft was repaired by December. The appearance of the Mosquitos intensified enemy attempts to try to stop them, with an increase in fighters and anti-aircraft guns along the route. During the light summer months, when it never really became dark along the route, the Mosquitos were able to spot the defending fighters in advance and escape after a high-speed chase.

Most of the initial losses were the result of accidents rather than enemy action, the first

loss being on 17 August 1943 of G-AGGF. The aircraft had departed Leuchars, flown by the senior pilot, Capt. Wilkins, when soon after he called on the radio that he was returning. Nothing further was heard of the aircraft and crew until wreckage was found by a gamekeeper on 8 September, the aircraft having hit high ground on the approach to Leuchars in bad weather. Capt. C.N. Pelly was then appointed as chief pilot.

The second loss was of G-AGGG on 25 October, when it crashed about a mile short of Leuchars. It had struggled across the North Sea with the port engine having failed. Both crew, who were ex-Norwegian Air Force officers, and their passenger were killed in the crash.

During the winter months of 1943/4 there was an urgent need to transport 90 tons of machinery and other cargo from Sweden to Britain. As only 35 tons would fit into a Mosquito, BOAC used Dakotas and a Liberator to collect the bulkier items. Delays were experienced owing to bad weather, and without reliable information flights were held up further. It was therefore decided to use the repaired MkIV G-AGFV as a pathfinder, to transmit code back to base to indicate whether the weather was suitable or not, or if there was a threat of enemy activity. The greater endurance of this MkIV allowed the crew to fly within 100 miles (160 km) of Bromma and still have enough fuel to return to Leuchars if necessary.

The Mosquitos again had the Stockholm run to themselves with the coming of the lighter summer months. Three more FB.MkVIs were delivered in April 1944 to replace those lost or damaged. The new aircraft were HJ667, LR296 and HJ792, and these were re-registered G-AGKO, G-AGKP and G-AGKR. Three T.MkIIIs were allocated for crew-training duties, but they retained their RAF identities as they were flown only locally. In June 1944 a record number of forty-two sorties were flown, and between

The Mosquito MkVIs allocated to BOAC for the courier flights from Leuchars to Stockholm had all the armament removed, the RAF roundels replaced by a civil registration underlined in red, white and blue, and had underwing fuel tanks for extra range.

The first Mosquito airliner to be delivered to BOAC at its Leuchars base was MkIV G-AGFV, previously DZ411 with the RAF. It arrived at Leuchars on 15 December, and was damaged near Stockholm on 4 July 1944, as the later MkVIs were entering service. It was repaired and returned to the 'Ball Bearing Run' between Leuchars and Stockholm. (de Havilland photo)

Mosquito MkVI G-AGGD, previously Hatfield-built FB.MkVI HJ681 for the RAF, was delivered to BOAC in April 1943 and is on finals to Leuchars.

Mosquito MkVI G-AGGF was delivered to BOAC at Leuchars in April 1943 and was previously HJ720 with the RAF. About to depart from the Leuchars runway at night, this aircraft was lost when it hit high ground near Leuchars on 7 August 1943, killing the crew. (BOAC photo)

Naval prototype Mosquito FB.MkVI LR359 was the first twin-engined aircraft to be landed on the deck of an aircraft carrier. This landmark was achieved by Commander Eric 'Winkle' Brown on HMS Indefatigable on 25 March 1944. The aircraft did not have folding wings. (de Havilland photo)

Converted from a Hatfield built FB.MkVI, LR387 was the second prototype Mosquito TR.Mk33, and the first to feature folding wings. This aircraft is also seen carrying an underslung torpedo. (de Havilland photo)

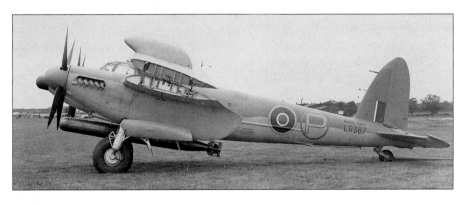

May and August a total of 151 flights were made. Two more Mosquitos, both from the latest deliveries, were lost in August in mysterious circumstances. G-AGKP was lost in the North Sea about 9 miles (14 km) from Leuchars, killing the two crew and Capt. Orton, who was travelling as a passenger. G-AGKR failed to arrive from a trip from Goteburg on the night of 28/9 August. No trace of the crew or wreckage was ever found.

With the Allied armies advancing rapidly across Europe, the need for the Mosquito flights diminished, eight return flights being made in November before they were finally suspended as a regular operation on 30 November 1944. One round trip was flown in February, and then a further series was operated from 12 April until the last operation from Leuchars on 17 May 1945. The BOAC crews then moved south to Croydon, where three of the remaining Mosquitos were handed back to the RAF on 22 June. G-AGGG was retained until 9 January 1946, being stored at maintenance units until it was disposed of as scrap.

The BOAC Mosquitos had flown 520 round trips from Leuchars to Stockholm, which averaged about nine single flights per week for two and a quarter years. The speed of the Mosquito made it possible for several crews and aircraft to make three single sorties in one night. Losses accounted for eight crew members and two passengers. Some of the passengers carried had been quite well-known personalities as well as diplomatic couriers.

NAVAL OPERATIONS

Not only did the Mosquito serve with distinction with the RAF, but it was also the first twin-engined aircraft to land on the deck of an aircraft carrier, later entering service with the Fleet Air Arm of the Royal Navy. This historic first landing was made by Lt Cdr Eric 'Winkle' Brown on HMS *Indefatigable* on 25 March 1944, flying modified Mosquito FB.MkVI LR359. These trials created a number of new problems that had to be overcome before the landing could be attempted safely, including whether the normal landing speed of 125 mph (200 km/h) was too great for practical carrier operations, and whether the traditional swing caused by the powerful Merlin engines would be uncontrollable in the confines of a carrier deck. To allow sufficient clearance of the starboard wingtip from the carrier island, the aircraft had to be landed with the starboard engine over the deck centre line instead of the nose. The modifications included a Fairey Barracuda A-frame-type arrester hook fitted underneath a strengthened rear fuselage, but this aircraft was not fitted with folding wings. Before the deck landing, Winkle Brown flew the aircraft to establish the lowest stalling speed and practised landings on a runway marked out to represent a carrier deck. Final practice approaches were made at Arbroath and the nearby East Haven airfield, prior to the attempts on the carrier at sea.

On 25 March, HMS *Indefatigable* was steaming in ideal conditions off the Scottish coast, crowded with VIPs and other observers for the epic event. Cdr Brown turned for his approach about 1½ miles astern of the ship and had an excellent view of the approaching deck. He planned to touch down at 85 mph (136 km/h). The approach was made with flaps and hook down, engines at full power, but propellers in fine pitch, to allow for a quick overshoot if necessary. With expert guidance from the batsman on the deck, Cdr Brown reduced power over the roundown, caught the second arrester wire and came gently to a halt. On analysis, it was found that, at a weight of 16,000 lb (7,260 kg) the Mosquito touched down at a speed of 78 mph (125 km/h). Following a thorough check, the Mosquito took off from the carrier, the speed of the wind over the deck helped by the forward speed of the ship giving the rudder enough power to counter the expected swing.

The next day a further three landings and take-offs were made, gradually increasing the landing weight, first to 16,800 lb (7,620 kg), and then 17,000 lb (7,710 kg) and finally 18,000 lb (8,165 kg). The first two landings went as planned, but the increased weight on the third created a considerable deceleration on picking up the wire and the aircraft suddenly lurched violently forward. Cdr Brown had to decide quickly whether it was the arrester wire or the hook which had broken, or, worse, if the rear fuselage had fractured. If it was one of the first or second, he would be better opening up the engines and making an overshoot for the flight back to base for repairs to be made. If it was the latter, he should try to stop on board, because any effort to fly would be disastrous. With some feel for control, he decided to open up the engines rapidly, which started an almost uncontrollable swing to port, fortunately away from the ship's island. The Mosquito soon began to leave the side of the deck. It sank towards the water, but recovered about 10 ft above the waves, climbing away with a somewhat shocked crew to make a safe landing at Macrihanish. It was found that the claw at the end of the hook had failed, so a strengthened version was fitted by de Havilland at Hatfield. During a further series of deck trials, a different pilot missed all of the arrester wires and managed to stop the aircraft just before going over the bows with his brakes completely burned out.

The naval requirement was outlined in Specification N.15/44 and resulted in the Mosquito TR.Mk33, which was based on the RAF FB.MkVI. The naval aircraft was fitted with manually folding wings outboard of the flaps and an A-frame arrester hook fitted to a strengthened fuselage. Merlin engines drove four-blade propellers with the diameter increased to 12.5 ft (3.8 m). The partially navalised prototype conversion was carried out

on FB.MkVI LR359, which retained its fixed wings. The second prototype, LR387, was fitted with upward-folding wings. Although folding the wings manually was labour intensive, much time, weight and cost was saved in what would have been the complete redesign of the hydraulic system, which was simple in the basic aircraft. However, the rubber in the compression main undercarriage was quite unsuitable for the high vertical loads during deck landing, causing the aircraft to bounce on touchdown. In its place a Lockheed-designed pneumatic undercarriage was substituted from the fourteenth production aircraft onwards to give improved damping.

Other modifications included replacement of the four nose-mounted machine-guns by an American ASH radar located under a thimble radome. The four-cannon armament was retained. Two 500 lb bombs could be carried internally, with the usual FB.MkVI external loads under the wings. Alternative underfuselage war loads were an 18 in torpedo, a 2,000 lb bomb and an anti-shipping mine. With all of this additional weight to fly off a carrier deck, there was provision for jettisonable Rocket-Assisted Take-off Gear (RATOG) to be attached to the rear fuselage. Two more development TR.Mk33s – TS444 and TS449 – were built at Leavesden, followed by fifty production aircraft. A further batch of fifty were ordered, but later cancelled, because none of the naval aircraft would have been ready before the war finished.

The first Mosquitos to enter service with a first-line squadron of the FAA were a batch of 15 FB.MkVIs, when No. 811 Squadron reformed at Ford on 15 September 1945. The replacement by TR.33s began in April 1946, and in January 1947 a move was made to Brawdy in South Wales, followed by Eglinton in Northern Ireland, where the only first-line navy Mosquito squadron disbanded on 1 July.

Other second-line and training FAA units flew Mosquitos, including No. 700 Squadron

A demonstration of the labour-intensive Mosquito TR.Mk33 wing folding, requiring seven men for each side. The Mosquito had insufficient hydraulic power for power lifting, and to install it would have been an expensive and major operation. (de Havilland photo)

which operated FB.MkVIs at Middle Wallop and Yeovilton as a maintenance test pilots' school. No. 703 Squadron provided the naval flight of the RAF's Air–Sea Warfare Development Unit, and flew Mosquito FB.MkVIs, PR.MkXVIs, TR.Mk33s and TR.Mk37s at Lee on Solent, Thorney Island and Ford between June 1945 and October 1950. The naval OTU for the Mosquito was operated by No. 704 Squadron at Zeals from April 1945 until the end of the year flying T.MkIII, FB.MkVI and B.MkXXV. No. 728 Squadron was a Fleet Requirements Unit (FRU) based in Malta, mainly at Hal Far, with a variety of aircraft, including Mosquito

T.MkIII from October 1945, and B.MkXXV, which arrived from September 1945, replacing the T.MkIIIs by mid-1946. With the arrival of PR.MkXVIs in May 1948, the MkXXVs were phased out in November of the same year, the MkXVIs continuing in service with No. 728 Squadron until September 1952. No. 739 Squadron flew TR.Mk33s at Culham for the Photographic Development Unit from 1 May 1947 until disbandment on 12 July 1950. No. 762 Squadron started with Mosquito FB.MkVIs in August 1945 at Halesworth as the conversion unit, adding T.MkIIIs in February 1946, having moved to Ford on 1 January

TS449 was the second of two development Mosquito TR.Mk33s produced at Leavesden, followed by 50 production aircraft. It could be fitted with rocket-assisted take-off gear (RATOG) for overweight take-off from confined airfields or carrier decks. (de Havilland photo)

The first and only FAA Mosquito first-line squadron was 811NAS who reformed at Ford in September 1945 with FB.MkVIs, TE723 FD-4F being an example. (FAAM photo)

1946 when it became the Heavy Twin Conversion Unit. Mosquito TR.Mk33s began to join the other aircraft in November 1947, and a further move was made to Culdrose on 1 May 1948, No. 762 Squadron disbanding there on 8 December 1949. No. 770 Squadron operated Mosquito PR.MkXVIs and B.MkXXVs as a FRU at Drem briefly from July to September 1945, until it was absorbed by No. 772 Squadron on 1 October.

No. 771 Squadron was equipped with a variety of Mosquitos, including FB.MkVIs, PR.MkXVIs, B.MkXXVs, TR.Mk33s, PR.Mk34s and TR.Mk37s, at Ford as an FRU from August 1945 until August 1952. No. 772 Squadron was the northern FRU based at Ayr, Burscough, Anthorn and Arbroath from May 1945, with PR.MkXVIs, B.MkXXV and PR.Mk34s, until disbanded on 13 October 1948. No. 777 Squadron operated as a trials unit on HMS *Pretoria Castle* with Mosquito B.MkXXVs from October 1945 until the end of the year. No. 778 Squadron was responsible for Mosquito service trials at Arbroath, Ford and Tangmere from November 1944, starting with the FB.MkVI and including PR.MkXVI and B.MkXXV, and finishing with the TR.Mk33 from April 1946 until 1948. No. 780 Squadron operated Mosquito T.MkIIIs and FB.MkVIs from Hinstock during the last three months of 1946 as an advanced Flying Training Unit. No. 787 Squadron was part of the Air Fighting Development Unit (AFDU) at West Raynham, using TR.Mk33s from March until December 1946, when they were replaced by FB.MkVIs, which were withdrawn in May 1948.

Airwork was awarded a contract to undertake heavy twin conversion training at Brawdy and St Davids, starting in January 1950 with T.MkIIIs and TR.Mk33s, until September 1956. The Airwork FRU was also formed at Hurn on 1 September 1952, and it operated Mosquito PR.MkXVIs and TR.Mk33s as part of a varied fleet until they were withdrawn in September 1953.

Two of the TR.33s were used in post-war 'Highball' bouncing bomb trials. In the mid-1950s, fourteen of the surplus stored TR.Mk33s were overhauled and denavalised for the Israel Air Force. The wing of one of these, TW233, which some years ago was returned to Britain, is currently being restored at the de Havilland Heritage at Salisbury Hall, eventually to be attached to the fuselage of FB.VI TA122.

One TR.Mk33, TW240, was fitted with a British-designed ASV MkXII radar under a larger nose-mounted radome, with a modified front fuselage to accommodate it. This version was designated the TR.Mk37, and fourteen were built at the Chester factory for use mainly by No. 703 Squadron. Although not used in combat with the FAA, the Mosquitos served in a variety of roles for the Royal Navy, mainly in second-line duties.

Signals Duties

A classified, little-known duty of the Mosquito was in early Electronic Counter Measures (ECM) work, starting with the Blind Approach Training and Development Unit (BATDU), which was formed on 13 June 1940. Its duties were to locate and interfere with the German *Knickebein* radio beams, which were used to guide the enemy bombers, along similar lines to the RAF Gee. If the beams could be bent, the Luftwaffe would miss its intended target. The BATDU was originally equipped with Ansons and Whitleys, and in October 1940 it was renamed the Wireless Intelligence Development Unit (WIDU).

On 10 December 1940 the unit became part of No. 109 Squadron, which was later equipped with 'Oboe' Mosquitos. Before the squadron started operations, the Mosquitos were used for 'Ferret' flights, establishing enemy radar frequencies and noting radio traffic. The squadron also tested 'Window' and helped with the development of 'Oboe'.

The cockpit of the Sea Mosquito TR.Mk37 with the observer's scope on the right-hand side and the fighter type control column for the pilot. (de Havilland photo)

When No. 109 Squadron became operational, its A Flight was renumbered 1473 Flight on 7 October 1942 to continue with the trials work operating from Upper Heyford. Moves were made to Finmere, Feltwell, Little Snoring and Foulsham, one of the Mosquitos on strength being DZ377. No. 1473 Flight is believed to have been absorbed by No. 192 Squadron in February 1944, No. 192 having been formed from 1474 Flight on 4 January 1943 with three Mosquito MkIVs. Equipment was installed in the aircraft to detect enemy radio and radar transmissions to frequencies of more than 3,000 m/cycles. After a lengthy training period the crews began operations with DZ410 from Feltwell on 11 June 1943, flying over enemy territory during the next 18 months, collecting data without dropping a bomb. Once the frequencies were known, counter-measures were devised, allowing No. 192 Squadron to jam the enemy transmissions, including their AI radar, which continued to the end of the war.

After the end of the war, No. 192 Squadron continued its intelligence-gathering duties from Watten together with other units, this time obtaining data about Soviet-developed systems during the Cold War. As part of this

A Mosquito TR.Mk33 on approach to landing on deck. (FAAM photo)

A total of 14 Sea Mosquito TR.Mk37s were built at Chester in 1948 for issue to No. 703 Squadron FAA. VT724, the first production aircraft, at Hatfield in March 1948 prior to delivery to the FAA. (de Havilland photo)

A small number of Mosquito NF.Mk36s were issued to No. 199 Squadron at Watton for Radio Counter-Measures duties, RL239 being an example. (R.C.B. Ashworth photo)

effort, No. 751 Squadron FAA was based at Watten and used Mosquito FB.MkVIs, PR.Mk34s and TR.Mk33s from March 1952, until the last PR.Mk34 was replaced in November 1954. No. 751 Squadron was the Radio Warfare Unit, as the Royal Navy part of the Central Signals Establishment.

WEATHER RECONNAISSANCE

Whenever contemplating any form of flying, one of the most important prior activities is to know what the weather is going to be like in the areas in which the aircraft is to be flown. A knowledge of the winds is essential for accurate navigation and, in wartime, the visibility along the route, and at the target, can make the difference between success and failure. Modern technology makes weather forecasting a little closer to a science, but, during the Second World War, detailed information over enemy territory was not readily available. The knowledge of the weather situation was critical to avoid large formations of aircraft wandering around in a hostile sky attempting to locate the target, or having to abort the mission at a late stage, increasing the risks unnecessarily. Meteorological flights were therefore essential to gather and bring back the vital weather information along a route, shortly before a planned raid was scheduled to depart, but without alerting the defences.

No. 1401 Flight was formed at Bircham Newton in August 1941 as part of Coastal Command, the initial equipment being a pair of Spitfires. In April 1942 these were replaced by a pair of more suitable Mosquito MkIVs. The first 'Pampa', the codename for the weather flights, was flown by a Mosquito on 2 July, and on 1 August the flight was renumbered No. 521 Squadron. Most of the flights involved deep penetration into enemy skies to determine the expected weather for that night's heavy bomber raid, especially over the target area. In November

1942 the first of the weather flights under the codename 'Rhombus' was flown out over the North Sea to gather information on the weather approaching the target area. Because the flights were principally for the benefit of the night bombers, it was logical that No. 521 Squadron should be transferred to Bomber Command in early 1943, but it was disbanded on 31 March, to be replaced the next day by 1409 Flight at Oakington. Weather flights using the MkIV Mosquitos continued from 2 April, the replacement by MkIXs beginning on 21 May, when the first was delivered to Oakington. Despite the high speed of the Mosquito, there were some unexplained losses, either to enemy action or, more likely, as a result of the hazardous weather conditions that were often experienced by the crews. A move was made to Wyton on 8 January 1944 to locate the unit closer to the group headquarters, when Mosquito MkXVIs started to replace the MkIXs.

Over a period of nearly three years the Mosquitos were flown on the unglamorous, but hazardous and vital task, of determining the conditions ahead of each bomber raid and helping the decision of whether to go or not. The Mosquitos flew in conditions that would seem almost impossible, and without the advantage of knowing in advance what might be encountered. They reported back on cloud bases, visibility and wind velocities, and often had to fly deliberately into icing conditions to bring back full data. In addition to their normal training, the crews were taught about meteorological theory. As well as special instrumentation, a number of cameras were also carried. The aircraft were always kept on standby, and, as well as helping with the planning of raids, they flew ahead of VIP flights, such as when King George VI or Winston Churchill were travelling.

A knowledge of the weather conditions was required not just in Europe, but also to cover operations in other parts of the world. There was a need to have reliable weather reports for transport aircraft flying across the Bay of Bengal between India and Asia. Derek Smith was a young pilot officer who had learned to fly in South Africa on Tiger Moths and Harvards in the Empire Air Training Scheme. On returning to Europe he had to adapt to flying in the less hospitable weather conditions, and was posted to 13 OTU at Middleton St George to train on Mosquito FB.MkVIs for service in the 2nd TAF. However, when a chance of a posting to Asia on unspecified duties was offered, he accepted it. On arrival in Singapore, the choice between flying Beaufighters and Mosquitos was offered, and Smith chose the latter. He joined four other crews at Mingaladon, near Rangoon, where he found that he was to fly on weather patrols. A number of the crews had not flown for some time and therefore had to use the restricted and narrow runway for familiarisation with the Mosquito before beginning the regular patrols. One of the new pilots managed to write off three Mosquitos in as many days by swinging into the monsoon ditches down the side of the runway, and he was posted away before they ran out of Mosquitos.

The duties involved flying a 3 hr sortie on a triangular course, taking off at dawn each day. Messages were transmitted three times an hour using Morse code, giving details of the wind, cloud level, temperature and humidity. The normal operating height of the unpressurised transport aircraft, and therefore the Mosquitos, was 8,000 ft (2,440 m), but at each turning point a descent was made to sea level followed by a climb to 20,000 ft (6,100 m), before a return to 8,000 ft. The main hazard to aircraft were the inter-tropical fronts associated with the monsoon. The monsoon season was normally between March and September in the area of Rangoon, but for the remainder of the year it moved south, the squadron then transferring to Butterworth in Malaya. The crews therefore experienced almost continual monsoon conditions.

Despite the use of improved adhesives, the constant high humidity and temperature conditions caused the aircraft to deteriorate, and monthly inspections were carried out, when panels were opened up in the wings to check the main spars. If a feeler gauge could be pushed between the joints, the Mosquito was scrapped, as there were plentiful stocks of low-hour Mosquitos available in storage in the Asian maintenance units.

Weather hazards were not uncommon during these Asian operations, Smith suffering an engine failure on a met flight from Butterworth. On returning to the vicinity of his base in the usual bad weather, there was a violent thunderstorm over the airfield. He made an overflight at 300 ft (90 m) but was unable to see the runway, and therefore decided to fly back out to sea to wait for the storm to clear. The safety height for a Mosquito on one engine was 1,500 ft (450 m) and the flaps were to be lowered at the last moment. Derek was only able to achieve 800 ft (245 m) because, if he had increased power on the good engine, it would have caused directional control difficulties. With the fuel running low, he decided to make another attempt to land and was advised from air traffic to try to approach from the landward end of the runway. However, as he still could not see the runway, he opted for a wheels-up landing on the seashore. With his speed having dropped dangerously low, he was committed to land immediately. With the seaward end of the runway appearing out of the storm, he dropped down on to it with the wheels up, the aircraft later being repaired to fly again.

The strength of the Mosquito was inadvertently demonstrated in front of cameras for a safety film. The pilot misjudged the approach, unintentionally crashing in front of the cameras, the aircraft being smashed to pieces by rocks and trees, leaving the cockpit section intact with a shaken, but safe, crew.

After the war, 1409 Flight continued in operation on weather patrols with Mosquitos. As the flights in peacetime were mainly for the benefit of transport aircraft, the flight was transferred to Transport Command and moved to Lyneham. A Mosquito PR.Mk34 served with the Meteorological Research Flight from 1952 to 1955, and in 1952 Mosquitos replaced Spitfires at the civilian-operated THUM (Temperature and Humidity) Unit at Woodvale. Each flight flew to a regular position over Worcester at 09.00 hrs GMT daily, collecting data at various altitudes. Information was recorded about cloud formation, visibility, icing level, contrails, isotherms and the prevailing weather conditions. Not long after the Mosquitos arrived at Woodvale, the flights were stopped and the aircraft were retired.

TARGET TUGS

Probably the most mundane and unglamorous task, although not without hazard, is for an aircraft to be used for the towing of targets to be shot at by other aircraft or surface-based guns. This duty was not only performed well by the Mosquito in two basic forms, but it was also the final task in military service. The major specialist version for target towing was the TT.Mk39: a conversion of the B.MkXVIs by General Aircraft to Specification Q.19/45 for the Royal Navy. The rather inelegant conversion with an upward curved, glazed, nose was added for a camera operator, and a perspex dorsal turret was added above the wing trailing edge for a winch operator, increasing the crew to four. Power came from two Merlin 72/73 engines giving a towing speed of around 300 mph (480 km/h). The diameter of the propeller blades was reduced to give adequate clearance from the wider nose. This version was designed not only for towing targets but also as a gunnery target for naval guns, the camera operator recording the predicted miss distance.

The aircraft could be used for the calibration of ground radar systems.

Two prototype conversions were made by General Aircraft followed by twenty-four production conversions, serving with home-based FRUs and in Malta. Mosquito TT.Mk39 PF576 was used by No. 703 Squadron, as NASWDU at Ford for trials from October 1948, and others entered service with No. 771 Squadron at the same base from January 1950 for two years. In Malta, No. 728 Squadron operated TT.Mk39s at Hal Far from March 1949 until they were retired from service in May 1952. The FAA also used No. 790 Squadron on target-towing duties, but it was equipped with Mosquito FB.MkVIs, B.MkXXVs and TT.Mk33s at Dale from July 1946. A move was made to Culdrose in December 1947 and the unit disbanded on 15 November 1949.

The RAF had similar target-towing requirements to those of the Royal Navy. With plentiful stocks of low life late marks of Mosquitos stored at maintenance units, owing to the entry into service of the Canberra jet bomber, it was decided to use conversions of some of these aircraft for target work. Some of the B.Mk35s were converted by Brooklands Aviation to TT.Mk35 target tugs, with a winch installed under the bomb bay, and tubular metal guards around the rear fuselage to avoid the cable becoming tangled around the tail. A number of these aircraft were used on the ranges in Germany and the Mediterranean, one being ferried from Benson to Akrotiri by Flt Sgt Maurice Lachman. Flt Sgt Lachman was used to delivering a variety of aircraft for RAF Ferry Command. He recalled flying a quick check involving a couple of circuits, one with an engine cut, and then he was ready to depart for Cyprus via Malta.

The main user of the Mosquito TT.Mk35 in Britain was the civilian-crewed 3 Civil Anti-

PF606 *was the initial production conversion Mosquito TT.Mk39 and among the modifications was a dorsal turret, strengthened rear fuselage with the removal of the normal equipment bay access to under the rear fuselage, and wire guards around the tail to avoid the drogue cables fouling the control surfaces or tailwheel. (MOS press photo)*

The ultimate service variant of the Mosquito was in the mundane role of target towing. The conversions were undertaken by Brooklands Aviation at Sywell, Mosquito B(TT).Mk35 RS718 serving with 3 CAACU, and seen at Aldergrove in September 1958. (Tom Crossett photo)

Mosquito TT.Mk35s operated with a number of training units at home and overseas, RV365 coded 6 being on the strength of 233 OCU. (J.D.R. Rawlings photo, via Chaz Bowyer)

RAF Mosquito
TT.Mk35 TA722
landing at Woodvale.
The aircraft was silver
overall with yellow
and black diagonal
stripes under the
wings and fuselage.

Mosquito
B(TT).Mk35 VP191
of 3 CAACU was the
subject of some
interest in the Biggin
Hill Battle of Britain
Display static line-up
on 13 September
1958. A winch pod is
fitted below the
bomb-bay doors.
(Philip Birtles photo)

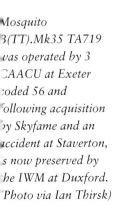

Mosquito
B(TT).Mk35 TA719
was operated by 3
CAACU at Exeter
coded 56 and
following acquisition
by Skyfame and an
accident at Staverton,
is now preserved by
the IWM at Duxford.
(Photo via Ian Thirsk)

The final flight of Mosquitos from 3 CAACU in May 1963 led by T.MkIII TW117:Z and including TT.Mk35s RS712:50, TA634:53 and RS709:47. The Mosquito TT.Mk35s had first entered service with 3 CAACU in January 1953. (Western Times photo)

A trio of Mosquito Mk35s at Bovingdon for the making of the film 633 Squadron. They were all disguised as FB.MkVIs by painting over the nose perspex and sticking on mock machine guns. (Philip Birtles photo)

No. 751 NAS were based at RAF Watton as the Radio Warfare Unit, the RN element of the Central Signals Establishment. One of the aircraft on strength was TR.Mk33 TW250. (FAAM photo)

Aircraft Co-operation Unit (CAACU) based at Exeter, the organisation being under contract to the Air Ministry to provide targets for the Army and Navy gunners at the coastal ranges around the south coast of Britain, from Portland to Cardigan Bay. Operations with the Mosquitos started in January 1953, and the 4½ to 5 hr endurance of the Mosquitos provided a better service than the jet-powered Meteors which replaced them, with an endurance of only about 1 hr. The final Mosquitos in military service were retired in the summer of 1963, some of the survivors flying to Bovingdon to star in the film *633 Squadron*. Three were destroyed by the film makers, but four survived to be preserved. A sequel, *Mosquito Squadron*, was made at Bovingdon five years later, when three of the surviving B.Mk35s were used, together with T.MkIII RR299, the crash sequences being taken from the previous movie, allowing all of the remaining aircraft to survive.

14. EXPORTS AND CIVIL OPERATIONS

OVERSEAS AIR FORCES

With the factories busy producing Mosquitos for RAF use during the Second World War, there was little capacity for exports, except for limited numbers to the Allies, such as South Africa, the USA and the USSR, which shared the common goal of defeating the German war machine. Once hostilities were over, there were sufficient numbers of surplus Mosquitos in storage with low hours, and ideal as an interim combat aircraft for air arms needing to equip in an uncertain world before the availability of jet fighters and bombers. The use of the Mosquito by Russia is not recorded, but a batch of ex-RAF B.MkIVs were withdrawn from storage towards the end of 1943 and prepared for acceptance in August 1944. Mosquito operations by the USAAF were mainly concerned with photo-reconnaissance duties from D-Day onwards, the aircraft being based mainly at Watton.

The Australian-built Mosquitos equipped RAAF units to help in the defence against the Japanese in Asia. Locally produced FB.Mk40s were used by No. 1 Squadron, together with British-supplied FB.MkVIs from airfields in the Halmaheras, with a move to Borneo as the enemy retreated. The final operational task of No. 1 Squadron was to share in the escort of Japanese Gen. Yomanura when he was flown to sign the surrender with the Allies. Among other RAAF units to operate the Mosquito were

nos 87 and 94 squadrons, the last of their aircraft being retired from service in 1954.

The RNZAF ordered 80 Mosquito T.MkIIIs and FB.MkVIs from Britain, and the first batch of 10 aircraft left on 10 December 1946. The 11,800 mile (19,000 km) flight was in twelve stages, totalling about 60 flying hours. Thirty of the Mosquitos were newly built and the remainder were refurbished ex-RAF stored aircraft. When the RAAF finally retired their Mosquitos, four FB.Mk40s and T.Mk43s were transferred to the RNZAF.

In its fight against the Communists, the Chinese Nationalist Government in December 1947 ordered up to 205 Mosquito T.Mk27s and FB.Mk26s from surplus Canadian-stored aircraft. Security surrounded this order worth between $10 million and $12 million, the aircraft being overhauled, test-flown and then dismantled at the de Havilland factory at Downsview during 1948. They were then transported to the most convenient Canadian east coast port for shipment by sea to Shanghai, where they were handed over to the Chinese Air Force. The de Havilland technical team responsible for the reassembly and testing of the aircraft arrived in China in December 1947, soon after the contract had been signed, and the first batch of 4 T.Mk27s arrived in February 1948. The second batch of 30 mixed trainers and FB.Mk26s followed in March, but, on unpacking, the condition of some of the aircraft had deteriorated so badly, owing to exposure to the elements on the ship's decks, that they were only suitable for cannibalisation for spares. Although there were problems and delays with the initial aircraft, ten months from the start of deliveries one aircraft per day was being produced. The different languages did not appear to cause major problems, apart from a lack of understanding of the more technical terms.

A small number of Chinese instructors started training at Downsview in early 1948, to undertake flight training in China for the three planned squadrons. However, the Chinese pilots found difficulty with the swing on take-off, as well as the snow-lined runways, and seven of the Mosquitos were wrecked during take-off and landing. As a result the training effort was moved to China, although the pilots who had difficulty with the aircraft in Canada wrecked nine more in China, largely as a result of a fear of the aircraft, which was probably larger, and certainly more powerful, than anything they had flown before. The new training base in China was Hankow, about 400 miles (645 km) inland from Shanghai alongside the Yangtse River. There was a single 5,400 ft (1,645 m) runway with rough ground on one side and a taxi strip along the other, which was usually crowded with aircraft. Surrounding the field at either end was a 15 to 20 ft (4.5 to 6 m) high dyke wall, and the runway usually experienced a 90° crosswind, making it a rather unsuitable site to train novice crews on such a powerful and high-performance aircraft, which could be a handful on take-off and landing, even in the best conditions.

An additional training team flew out from Canada on 22 March 1948, and the first of the three squadrons to begin conversion was No. 4 Squadron, which had flown tricycle undercarriage Mitchells up to nine months earlier. Even they were somewhat daunted by the Mosquito. The younger and more recent crews from nos 1 and 3 squadrons adapted more easily, some of the pilots going solo

after 5 to 10 hrs dual and others taking nearly 20 hrs, but still becoming competent pilots by the end of the training. Some pilots were obviously never going to manage to fly the Mosquito and were removed from the course. However, despite some fifty training accidents at Hankow, the majority of the crews were able to walk away from the wreckage. Maintenance was made difficult by the relative inexperience of the personnel, a shortage of spares and equipment, and the extreme climate, which was very hot in the summer and very cold in the winter.

The Communist forces were advancing from the north, and it was planned to complete the basic conversion training by December. However, the advances became more rapid and the Canadian training team decided to depart urgently on 17 December, leaving the Chinese to operate the aircraft on their own. It is thought unlikely that many of them continued to fly for long.

Although the original contract was for 160 Mosquitos, records suggest that 181 were assembled, of which 144 had been test-flown by 4 December. About 60 were written off in accidents and a further 40 were grounded owing to maintenance difficulties. Despite the losses from crashes, the accident rate was comparable to some British and Canadian OTUs, and No. 3 Squadron at Peiping did not damage a single Mosquito during training or early operations. No. 1 Squadron was based at Hsuchow and No. 4 Squadron at Hankow, continuing operations until the surviving aircraft were withdrawn to Formosa, where they were used for a while on anti-shipping duties.

In Europe a number of the newly liberated Allied air forces were in urgent need of combat aircraft, No. 333 (Norwegian) Squadron returning home in 1945 with 5 T.MkIIIs and 18 FB.MkVIs, being renumbered No. 334 Squadron for service in peacetime Norway, and adding a further 24 FB.MkVIs in 1947.

Mosquito B.MkIV DK296 was originally delivered to No. 105 Squadron in June 1942. After withdrawal and storage at 10 MU, it was part of a batch of MkIVs allocated to Russia and was ready for delivery at Errol in December 1943. It was finally accepted by the Russians on 31 August 1944, the major external change being to cover the RAF markings with the red star. (de Havilland photo)

Mosquito FB.MkVI A52-525 was one of 46 supplied from surplus RAF stocks to supplement those built in Australia, and served with No. 1 Squadron RAAF coded NA-J. (RAAF photo)

A Mosquito PR.MkXV of No. 87 Squadron RAAF used on mapping survey flights of Australia making a low level pass with the port engine shut down and propeller feathered. (RAAF photo)

The RNZAF ordered 80 Mosquito T.MkIIIs and FB.MkVIs in 1946. FB.MkVI NZ2328 had been built for the RAF as TE758 and was issued to No. 75 Squadron RNZAF. It was configured for anti-shipping operations with RP rails, and the underwing fuel tanks were obviously intended to be retained. (RNZAF photo)

In December 1947 the Chinese Nationalist Government ordered up to 205 Mosquitos, including T.Mk27s from de Havilland Canada, B-M008 being one of a pair ready for shipping. (DHC photo)

Mosquito FB.MkVI RS650 AK-F:334 Squadron R Norwegian AF was one of a number supplied from surplus RAF stocks at the end of the war. The initial equipment was ten MkVIs and eight more FB.MkVIs and three T.MkIIIs were later added, all the survivors remaining in service until early 1952.

The French Air Force was equipped with a mixture of FB.MkVIs and PR.MkXVIs, totalling more than 100 aircraft for the use of 50e Escadre based at Dijon from 1946. The French Mosquitos were also deployed in Indo-China from January 1947, the FB.MkVIs being used against the Communist forces, until the Mosquitos were withdrawn in July 1949. Additional French colonial use of the Mosquitos was with 19e Escadre in Algeria.

On 1 October 1946 the Belgian Air Force officially reformed and 22 NF.Mk30s were supplied, equipping 1 Wing at Beauvechain and being somewhat combat-weary ex-RAF aircraft. One NF.MkXVII, one NF.MkXIX and two NF.Mk30s were also acquired for ground instructional duties. The first Belgian night-fighter unit was No. 10 Squadron, which formed on 28 January 1948, the first aircraft being delivered to the squadron on 25 May and operational status being achieved in November 1949. Economic restrictions, as well as a short supply of spare parts and the generally poor condition of the aircraft, restricted the flying hours of the crews, particularly at night, but efforts were made to participate in all the major NATO exercises. The second Belgian Mosquito night-fighter squadron to form was No. 11 Squadron on 1 July 1951, still as part of the Beauvechain Wing, the normal complement being 8 Mosquitos in each squadron. Meanwhile, 6 aircraft had been lost by No. 10 Squadron in accidents and two more NF.Mk30s were ordered in October 1951, only one reaching Belgium in airworthy condition in 1953. However, by then the selection process had started for a more modern jet-powered replacement night-fighter. With the arrival of Meteor NF.11s in mid-1952, all of the surviving 12 Mosquitos were allocated to No. 10 Squadron until they were withdrawn from service in 1956, the latter duties being targets for the Meteors, or beacons for the ground-based radar stations. All of the Mosquitos, apart from one, were grounded on 18 August 1955, MB24 continuing to operate until all of the remaining Mosquitos were struck off charge on 17 October 1956. In addition 4 Mosquito T.MkIIIs were delivered during the second half of 1947, with 3 more arriving the next year. One of the T.MkIIIs was used for conversion of the pilots for the night-fighter units, and the other 6 were fitted with a wind-driven target towing pods under the fuselage for duties from Koksijde. Three years later a further 3 FB.MkVIs were bought from surplus RAF stocks and converted by Fairey at Ringway to the TT.6 configuration, joining the towing flight in October 1951.

On 10 January 1947 the first of 10 Mosquito T.MkIIIs and 96 FB.MkVIs were handed over by Fairey at Ringway to the Turkish Air Force, where they had been prepared from surplus RAF aircraft, but there were difficulties with continuing serviceability in Turkey. Fairey also supplied a batch of 6 ex-RAF FB.MkVIs to the Dominican Military Aviation Corps in 1948. The Royal Swedish Air Force ordered 60 Mosquito NF.MkXIXs on 19 July 1948 from de Havilland at £11,500 each to equip the F.1 Wing at Vasteras, all being ex-RAF aircraft and overhauled by Fairey Aviation. Deliveries were scheduled from July 1948 until July 1949, and the aircraft was designated J 30 in Swedish service. They remained in operation until the final ones were withdrawn in March 1954. The Czechoslovakian Air Force purchased 26 surplus RAF FB.MkVIs in 1947 for service with the 'Atlantic' Squadron based at Pilsen. Yugoslavia acquired 46 surplus FB.MkVIs, 60 NF.Mk38s and a batch of T.MkIIIs for conversion training.

From 1948 the new nation of Israel acquired about 300 Mosquitos of various marks from France, Britain and other sources, many of which were in poor condition. They were used as a source of spares for the remainder. At the start of the Israel War of

In January 1947 the first of ten Mosquito T.MkIIIs was handed over to the Turkish Air Force, and 542 is on a pre-delivery test flight from Hatfield. (de Havilland photo)

Independence, only one Mosquito PR.MkXVI was available to the air force, but it was soon followed by a couple of ex-USAAF aircraft, only one of which reached its destination. The first major purchase was on 17 February 1952, when 59 Mosquitos of four different marks were ordered from France. A batch of 14 TR.Mk33s were acquired from the FAA, as already noted, in 1954 to 1956, together with some PR.MkXVIs. The most plentiful version was the versatile FB.MkVI which was used by two squadrons until the Sinai Campaign in October 1956, the loss rate being nil and the serviceability often reaching 100 per cent. The final military export was a flight of Mosquitos to the newly formed Burma Air Force in 1955.

CIVIL OPERATIONS

Spartan Air Services of Canada ordered 10 ex-RAF Mosquito Mk35s, comprising nine B.Mk35s and one PR.Mk35, in 1955 for air survey duties across the continent. The aircraft were in storage at Silloth and were air-tested before being ferried to the small grass airfield of Burnaston near Derby. While two aircraft at a time were converted in the Derby Aviation hangar, the remainder were stored out on the airfield. As aircraft were completed, they were flown to Prestwick for Scottish Aviation to prepare for the transatlantic delivery flight. A further B.Mk35 was taken out of storage at Shawbury and flown to Burnaston, when it

Swedish A F Mosquito NF.MkXIX (J30) 30041 'Red H' at an F 16 Wing open day in September 1949 with red spinners and entrance hatch. (Photo Sture Mattsson via Mikael Forslund)

Standard Motors-built Mosquito FB.MkVI PF823 was one of a batch of 26 aircraft ordered by the Czech Air Force in 1947, coded IY-5. (Philip Jarrett photo)

Mosquito PR.MkXVI G-AOCN was one of six ex-FAA Mosquitos which arrived at Thruxton in August 1956. Previously TA614 it was sold to the Israeli Air Force as 4XFDL-92, departing Hurn after overhaul on 1 December 1957 on its delivery flight. (Photo via Ian Thirsk)

Mosquito Mk35 CF-HMT was one of ten converted by Derby Aviation at Burnaston for Spartan Air Services to use for aerial survey and mapping in Canada. This aircraft, previously RS711, was the last to be delivered, and departed Prestwick on 9 April 1956. (Flight photo)

was registered G-AOSS for a planned record attempt to South Africa. Despite work on the conversion starting, progress payments ceased, and work stopped, the remains being used for a 5 November bonfire. Before delivery of the Mosquitos to Spartan, Kenting Aviation had based a pair of ex-Canadian-built T.Mk29 trainers, KA202 and KA244 at Toronto, also for photo-survey and mapping work. The aircraft were re-registered as CF-GKK and C-FGKL, the latter later being acquired by Spartan.

A number of Australian and Canadian Mosquitos found their way on to the civil register, mostly for long-range air racing.

Australian PR.Mk41 VH-KLG was entered for the London to Christchurch, New Zealand, air race in 1953, but it was written off in a forced landing in Burma on 3 October while flying to Britain for the start of the race. Another PR.Mk41, VH-WAD, was also entered for the same race, but subsequently withdrawn, and became derelict at Perth, Western Australia. A pair of surplus Canadian B.Mk25s were acquired by World Wide Aviation Agency in Montreal for air racing. KB377, registered CF-FZG, was entered in the Bendix Trophy Race in 1948, but had to make a forced landing with engine trouble on the way to the start of the race in California. KB985, registered

Mosquito PR.Mk34 G-AJZE was one of a pair operated by BEA from Cranfield on gust research from mid-1948. (BEA photo)

N66313, was entered for the same race, but the aircraft arrived in last place with a single-engine landing at Cleveland.

In addition to the wartime operations by BOAC from Leuchars, the newly post-war-formed sister company, British European Airways (BEA), operated a pair of Mosquito PR.Mk34s from Cranfield on flights in 1948 and 1949 with the Gust Research Unit (GRU). With the new modern airliners being designed capable of operating at higher speeds and altitudes, there was a need to know the effects of clear-air turbulence and how it might affect structural integrity. The two Mosquitos were allocated in June 1947, and following the calibration of the equipment at Farnborough they were delivered to Cranfield in September. Additional equipment was installed and the aircraft prepared for certificates of airworthiness, which were awarded on 1 March and 3 June 1948 to G-AJZE and G-AJZF.

The Mosquitos were flown on two basic tasks: one to collect data on the intensity and location of clear-air turbulence to assist meteorologists in forecasting, and the other to record the strength of the gusts, to allow aircraft to be designed to withstand the loads without adding too much weight. Over a period of two years, these aircraft were flown more than 90,000 miles at altitudes of above

15,000 ft in search of this often elusive phenomenon. The operations ranged from the Swiss Alps and Spain in the south, to Scotland and Scandinavia in the north, the long endurance of the PR.Mk34 being particularly useful. In the search for clear-air turbulence, which could be found at any altitude above 15,000 ft, the Mosquitos were flown at varying altitudes up to 37,000 ft, and the results were of great benefit to the emerging commercial jet age. However, clear-air turbulence is still of concern to aircraft operators, particularly in tropical regions, where it can be much more violent.

APPENDICES

I – SPECIFICATION AND PERFORMANCE

(Changes are only noted after MkI)

Type	Engine	Span	Length	Wing area	Tare wt/Auw	Cruise speed	Climb	Ceiling	Max. range
PR.I	Merlin 21/23	54 ft 2 in 16.5 m	40 ft 6 in 12.35 m	454 sq ft 42.1sq m	12,824 lb/19,670 lb 5,817 kg/8,922 kg	255 mph 410 km/h	2,850 ft/m 14.5 m/sec	35,000 ft 10,668 m	2,180 miles 3,508 km
.II			41 ft 2 in 12.54 km		13,431 lb/18,547 lb 6,092 kg/8,413 kg	360 mph 418 km/h	3,000 ft/m 15.2 m/sec	36,000 ft 10,973m	1,705 miles 2,744 km
T.III					13,104 lb/20,319 lb 5,944 kg/9,216 kg	260 mph 418 km/h	2,500 ft/m 12.7 m/sec	37,500 ft 11,430 m	1,560 miles 2,510 km
B.IV			40 ft 9.5 in 12.41 m		13,400 lb/21,462 lb 6,531 kg/9,734 kg	265 mph 426 km/h		34,000 ft 10,363 m	2,040 miles 3,283 km
FB.VI	Merlin 25				13,797 lb/21,804 lb 6,258 kg/9,436 kg	255 mph 410 km/h	2,850 ft/m 14.5 m/sec	33,000 ft 10,058 m	1,855 miles 2,985 km
B.VII	Merlin 31								
PR.VIII	Merlin 61				14,800 lb/21,395 lb 6,713 kg/9,704 kg	258 mph 459 km/h	2,500 ft/m 12.7 m/sec	38,000 ft 11,582 m	2,550 miles 4,104 km
PR & B.IX	Merlin 72		44 ft 6 in 13.5 m		14,569 lb/24,865 lb 6,608 kg/11,278 kg	250 mph 402 km/h	2,850 ft/m 14.5 m/sec	38,000 ft 11,582 m	2,450 miles 3,943 km
NF.XII	Merlin 21/23		40 ft 5 in 12.3 m		13,696 lb/20,297 lb 6,213 kg/9,206 kg	255 mph 410 km/h	3,000 ft/m 15.2 m/sec	36,000 ft 10,973 m	1,705 miles 2,744 km
NF.XIII			40 ft 6 in 12.34 m		13,948 lb/20,278 lb 6,327 kg/9,198 kg	255 mph 410 km/h		34,500 ft 10,516 m	1,860 miles 2,993 km
NF.XV	Merlin 72/73, 76/77	62 ft 6 in 19m	44 ft 6 in 13.5 m	479 sq ft 44.4 sq m	13,746 lb/17,600 lb 6,235 kg/7,983 kg	230 mph 370 km/h	3,500 ft/m 17.8 m/sec	43,000 ft 13,106 m	1,030 miles 1,657 km
PR & B.XVI	Merlin 72/73, 76/77	54 ft 2 in 16.5 m		454 sq ft 43 sq m	14,635 lb/25,917 lb 6,638 kg/11,756 kg	245 mph 394 km/h	2,800 ft/m 14.2 m/sec	37,000 ft 11,277 m	1,485 miles 2,390 km

Type	Engine	Span	Length	Wing area	Tare wt/Auw	Cruise speed	Climb	Ceiling	Max. range
NF.XVII	Merlin 21/23		40 ft 6 in 12.3 m		13,224 lb/20,393 lb 5,998 kg/9,250 kg	255 mph 410 km/h	3,000 ft/m 15.2 m/sec	36,000 ft 10,972 m	1,705 miles 2,744 km
FB.XVIII	Merlin 25				14,756 lb/23,274 lb 6,693 kg/10,557 kg	255 mph 410 km/h	2,850 ft/m 14.5 m/sec	33,000 ft 10,058 m	1,855 miles 2,985 km
NF.XIX	Merlin 25		40 ft 6 in 12.3 m		14,471 lb/21,750 lb 6563.5 kg/9,865 kg	255 mph 410 km/h	3,000 ft/m 15.2 m/sec	36,000 ft 10,972 m	1,705 miles 2,744 km
B.XX	Packard Merlin 31/33		40 ft 9.5 in 12.41 m		13,400 lb/21,462 lb 6,531 kg/9,734 kg	265 mph 426 km/h		34,000 ft 10,363 m	2,040 miles 3,283 km
FB.21	Packard Merlin 31		41 ft 2 in 12.54 m		13,797 lb/20,804 lb 6,258 kg/9,436 kg	255 mph 410 km/h	2,850 ft/m 14.5 m/sec	33,000 ft 10,058 m	1,855 miles 2,985 km
T.22	Packard Merlin 33				13,104 lb/20,319 lb 5,944 kg/9,216 kg	260 mph 418 km/h	2,500 ft/m 12.7 m/sec	37,500 ft 11,430 m	1,560 miles 2,510 km
B.25	Packard Merlin 225		44 ft 6 in 13.5 m		14,569 lb/24,865 lb 6,608 kg/11,278 kg	250 mph 402 km/h	2,850 ft/m 14.5 m/sec	38,000 ft 11,582 m	2,450 miles 3,943 km
FB.26	Packard Merlin 225		41 ft 2 in 12.54 m		13,797 lb/21,473 lb 6,258 kg/9,739 kg	255 mph 410 km/h	2,850 ft/m 14.5 m/sec	33,000 ft 10,058 m	1,855 miles 2,985 km
T.27	Packard Merlin 225				13,797 lb/21,473 lb 6,258 kg/9,739 kg	260 mph 418 km/h	2,850 ft/m 14.5 m/sec	37,500 ft 11,430 m	1,855 miles 2,985 km
T.29	Packard Merlin 225		41 ft 2 in 12.54 m		13,797 lb/21,473 lb 6,258 kg/9,739 kg	260 mph 418 km/h	2,850 ft/m 14.5 m/sec	37,500 ft 11,430 m	1,855 miles 2,985 km
NF.30	Merlin 72, 76 or 113		44 ft 6 in 13.5 m		13,400 lb/21,600 lb 6,078 kg/9,797 kg	250 mph 402 km/h	2,850 ft/m 14.5 m/sec	38,000 ft 11,582 m	1,300 miles 2,092 km
PR.32	Merlin 113/114	59 ft 2 in 18 m	40 ft 6 in 12.35 m	465 sq ft 43.1 sq m	14,281 lb/22,122 lb 6,477 kg/10,034 kg			43,000 ft 13,106 m	
TR.33	Merlin 25	54 ft 2 in 16.5 m	42 ft 3 in 12.8 m		14,850 lb/23,850 lb 6,735.5 kg/10,819 kg	262 mph 421 km/h	1,820 ft/m 9.2 m/sec	30,100 ft 9,714 m	1,265 miles 2,036 km
PR.34	Merlin 114				14,180 lb/25,500 lb 6,431 kg/11,567 kg	300 mph 483 km/h	2,000 ft/m 10.1 m/sec	43,000 ft 13,106 m	3,340 miles 5,375 km
B.35	Merlin 114A				14,635 lb/25,200 lb 6,638 kg/11,431 kg	276 mph 444 km/h	2,700 ft/m 13.7 m/sec	42,000 ft 12,801 m	1,955 miles 3,146 km
NF.36	Merlin 113/114		41 ft 2 in 12.5 m	454 sq ft 42 sq m	18,229 lb/21,400 lb 8,269 kg/9,706 kg	250 mph 402 km/h		36,000 ft 10,973 m	
TF.37	Merlin 25	54 ft 2 in 16.5 m	42 ft 3 in 12.8 m		14,850 lb/23,850 lb 6,735.5 kg/10,819 kg	265 mph 426 km/h	1,820 ft/m 9.2 m/sec	30,100 ft 9,714 m	1,100 miles 1,770 km

Type	Engine	Span	Length	Wing area	Tare wt/Auw	Cruise speed	Climb	Ceiling	Max. range
NF.38	Merlin 114A		41 ft 5 in	454 sq ft	18,229 lb/21,400 lb	250 mph		36,000 ft	
			12.6 m	42 sq m	8,269 kg/9,706 kg	402 km/h		9,714 m	
TT.39	Merlin72/73		43 ft 4 in	454 sq ft	15,980 lb/23,000 lb	245 mph	2,800 ft/m	36,000 ft	1,485 miles
			13.1 m	42 sq m	7,249 kg/10,433 kg	394 km/h	14.2 m/sec	10,973 m	2,390 km
F.40	Packard				14,344 lb/22,258 lb	255 mph	2,400 ft/m	33,000 ft	1,855 miles
	Merlin 31				6,506 kg/10.096 kg	410 km/h	12.1 m/sec	10,058 m	2,985 km
PR.41	Packard		44 ft 6 in		14,569 lb/24,865 lb	250 mph	2,850 ft/m	38,000 ft	2,450 miles
	Merlin 69		13.5 m		6,608 kg/11,278 kg	402 km/h	14.5 m/sec	11,582 m	3,943 km
T.43	Packard				13,104 lb/20,319 lb	260 mph	2,500 ft/m	37,500 ft	1,560 miles
	Merlin 33				5,944 kg/9,216 kg	418 km/h	12.7 m/sec	11,430 m	2,510 km

B.MkV   Unbuilt bomber project with empty weight of 12,881 lb (5,843 kg) and AUW 18,994 lb (8,616 kg)
B. MkVII   Used in North America only.
NF.MkX   Two-stage Merlin powered night-fighter project.
FB.MkXI   Two-stage Merlin powered fighter-bomber project similar to FB.VI.
NF.MkXIV   Two-stage Merlin powered night-fighter project based on MkXIII, superseded by MkXIX and NF.30.
B.Mk23   Packard Merlin 69 powered Canadian project version of B.IX.
FB.Mk24   Packard Merlin 301 powered Canadian fighter-bomber project based on FB.21.
Mk28   Not used.
NF.Mk31   Packard Merlin 69 powered night-fighter project.
FB.Mk42   Packard Merlin 69 powered Australian fighter-bomber prototype.

Rolls-Royce engine power ratings

Merlin 21/23	1,460 hp
Merlin 25	1,635 hp
Packard Merlin 31/33	1,460 hp
Merlin 61	1,565 hp
Merlin 72/73	1,680 hp
Merlin 76/77	1,710 hp
Packard Merlin 69	1,750 hp
Packard Merlin 301	1,620 hp
Packard Merlin 225	1,620 hp
Merlin 113/114	1,690 hp
Merlin 114A	1,710 hp

During the early deck trials with Mosquito FB.MkVI LR359 a landing was made at high weight, the loads broke the arrested hook, and Commander Brown had to make a rapid decision to overshoot and return to land. (FAAM photo)

Mosquito TR.Mk33 LR387, the first with folding wings, was used for the more representative deck trials. (FAAM photo)

II – Manufacturers and Production

de Havilland Aircraft Company, Hatfield, Hertfordshire
de Havilland Aircraft Company, Leavesden, Watford
de Havilland Aircraft Company, Hawarden, Chester
Airspeed Ltd, Christchurch, Bournemouth, Hampshire
The Standard Motor Company, Coventry, Warwickshire
Percival Aircraft Ltd, Luton, Bedfordshire
de Havilland Aircraft of Canada Ltd, Downsview, Toronto, Canada
de Havilland Aircraft Pty, Bankstown, Sydney, NSW, Australia

Production

de Havilland, Hatfield

W4050–W4059	50 PR.Mk1, F..MkII, T..MkIII & B.MkIV
DD600–644, DD659–691, DD712–759, DD777–800.	150 F.MkII
DK284–303, DK308–333, DK336–339	50 B.MkIV
DZ228–272, DZ286–310	70 F.MkII
DZ311–320, DZ340–388, DZ404–442, DZ458–497, DZ515–559, DZ575–618, DZ630–652	250 B.MkIV
DZ653–661, DZ680–727, DZ739–761	80 F.MkII
HJ642–661, HJ699–715	37 NF.MkII
HJ662–682, HJ716–743, HJ755–792, HJ808–833	113 FB.MkVI
HX802–835, HX849–869, HX896–922, HX937–984	130 FB.MkVI
(HX902–904 converted to FB.MkXVIII)	
LR248–276, LR289–313, LR327–340, LR343–389, LR402–404	118 FB.MkVI
LR405–446, LR459–474, LR478–481	60 PR.MkIX
LR475–477, LR495 –513	22 B.MkIX
ML896–924	29 B.MkIX
ML925–942, ML959–999, MM112–156, MM169–205, MM219–226	152 B.MkXVI
MM227–257	PR.MkIX/B.MkIX
MM258, MM271–314, MM327–371, MM384–397	104 PR.MkXVI
MM398–423, MM426–431	32 FB.MkVI
MM424–425	2 FB.MkXVIII
MP469	1 NF.MkXV
NS496–538, NS551–596, NS619–660, NS673–712, NS725–758, NS772–816	250 PR.MkXVI
(NS586–589 4 PR.Mk32)	
NS819–859, NS873–914, NS926–965, NS977–999, NT112–156, NT169–207, NT219–238	250 FB.MkVI
(NT220, NT224, NT225 3FB.MkXVIII)	
PZ161–203, PZ217–259, PZ273- 316, PZ330–358, PZ371–419, PZ435–476	250 FB.VI
(including 9 FB.MkXVIII)	
RF969–999, RG113–158, RG171 -175	82 PR.XVI
RG176–215, RG228–269, RG283–318	118 PR.Mk34
RS501–535, RS548–580, RS593–633	109 FB.MkVI
RV295–326, RV340–363	56 B.MkXVI
(RV348–350 B.Mk35)	
RV364–367	4 B.Mk35
SZ958 -999, TA113–122	52 FB.MkVI
TA123–156, TA169–198, TA215–249, TA263–308, TA323–357	180 NF.MkXIX
TA369–388	20 FB.MkVI
TA389–413, TA425–449	50 NF.MkXIX
TA469–508, TA523–560, TA575–603	107 FB.MkVI
(TA604–613 cancelled)	
TA614–616	3 PR.MkXVI
TA617–618, TA633–670, TA685–724	80 B.Mk35

TH976–999, TK113–158	70 B.Mk35
TK591–635, TK648–656	54 B.Mk35
(TK657–679, TK691–707 41 cancelled)	
(VL557–583, VL586–599, VL602–610 50 cancelled B.Mk35)	
VL613–625	13 PR.Mk34
(VL678–697, VL714–723 30 cancelled PR.Mk34)	
VP342–355, VP330–349	34 T.Mk3
VT581–596, VT604–631	44 T.Mk3
VT651–669	19 NF.Mk38

de Havilland, Leavesden

HJ851–899, HJ958–999	91 T.MkIII
HJ911–944	34 F.MkII
HJ945–946, HK107–141, HK159–204, HK222–235	97 F.MkII
(converted to NF.MkXII by Marshall of Cambridge)	
HK363–382, HK396–437, HK453–481, HK499–536	129 NF.MkXIII
(HK535–536 renumbered SM700–701)	
LR516–541, LR553–585	59 T.MkIII
MM436–479, MM491–534, MM547–590, MM615–623.141	NF.MkXIII
MM624–656, MM669–685	50 NF.MkXIX
MM686–710, MM726–769, MM783–822	109 NF.MkXXX
MT456–500, MV521–570	95 NF.MkXXX
NT241–283, NT295–336, NT349–393, NT415–458, NT471–513, NT526–568, NT582–621	300 NF.MkXXX
RK929–954	26 NF.MkXXX
RK955–960, RK972–999, RL113–158, RL171–175	82 PR.MkXVI
(RL269–273, RL288–329, RL345–390 93 cancelled)	
RR270–319	50 T.MkIII
(TN466–497, TN510–530, TN542–590, TN608–640, TN652–674, TN690–736, TN750–789, TN802–838, TN850–864 297 cancelled)	
TS444 & 449 (prototypes)	2 TR.Mk33
TN954–984, TW101–119	50 T.Mk3
TW227–257, TW277–295	50 TR.Mk33
(TW240 TR.Mk37 protoype)	
VA871–894, VA923–928	30 T.Mk3
(VA929–948 cancelled)	

de Havilland, Hawarden

VT670–683, VT691–707	31 NF.Mk38
(VT670 1st flight 30 Sept. 1948)	
VT724–737	14 TR.Mk37
VX860–879, VX886–916	51 NF.Mk38
(last completed Nov. 1950)	

Airspeed, Christchurch

RS637–680, RS693–698	50 FB.MkVI
RS699–723	25 B.Mk35
(RS724–725, RS739–779, RS795–836, RS849–893, RS913–948, RS960–999, RT105–123 225 cancelled)	
VL726–732	7 FB.MkVI
VP178–202	25 B.Mk35
VR792–806	15 B.Mk35

Standard Motor Company, Coventry

HP848–888, HP904–942, HP967–989, HR113–162, HR175–220, HR236–262, HR279–312,	
HR331–375, HR387–415, HR432–465, HR485–527, HR539–580, HR603–649	500 FB.MkVI
RF580–625, RF639–681, RF695–736, RF749–753, RF818–859, RF873–915, RF928–966	300 FB.MkVI
TE587–628, TE640–669, TE683–725, TE738–780, TE793–830, TE848–889, TE905–932	266 FB.MkVI
(TE933–944, TE958–999 cancelled)	

Percival Aircraft, Luton

PF379–415, PF428–469, PF481–526, PF538–579, PF592–619	195 B.MkXVI
PF620–635, PF647–680	50 PR.Mk34

de Havilland Canada, Toronto

KA100–102	3 FB.MkXXI
KA103–450	348 FB.MkXXVI/T.MkXXIX
(KA451–773 cancelled)	
KA873–876, KA896–897	6 T.MkXII
KA977–895, KA898–929	49 T.MkXXVII
(KA928–929 cancelled)	
KA930–999, KB370–699	400 B.MkXXV
KB100–299 (9 to USAAF), KB325–369	245 B.MkXX
KB300–324 (6 to USAAF)	25 B.MkVII

de Havilland Australia, Sydney

A52-1–A52-212 (6 PR.Mk40)	212 FB.Mk40
A52-300–A52-327 (A52-300 converted to FB.Mk42)	28 converted PR.Mk41
A52-1050–A52-1071	22 converted T.Mk43

Overseas sales

Australia	46 FB.MkVI and 29 PR.MkXVI
Belgium	24 NF.Mk30 MB1–MB24
	7 T.Mk3 MA1–MA7
	3 FB.MkVI MC1–MC3, plus 3 TT.Mk6
Burma	6 FB.MkVI
China	200 plus FB.Mk26 and T.Mk27
Czechoslovakia	26 FB.MkVI
Dominica	6 FB.VI
France	57 FB.MkVI, 29 PR.MkXVI and 23 NF.Mk30
Israel	300 approximately of various marks
Norway	24 FB.MkVI
RNZAF (New Zealand)	6 T.MkIII and 74 FB.MkVI
SAAF (South Africa)	2 F.MkII and 14 PR.MkXVI
Sweden	60 NF.MkXIX(J30) 30001–30060
Turkey	10 T.MkIII and 96 FB.MkVI
Yugoslavia	46 FB.MkVI, 60 NF.Mk38 and T.MkIIIs

III – Mosquito Squadrons

Squadron No.	Code	Main Role	Period of Use	Bases
4	UP	Fighter	1.44–5.44	Sawbridgeworth
		Bomber	31.8.45–7.50	Gatwick
8	HV	Bomber	1.9.46–5.47	Khormaksar, Aden
11	OM	Fighter-bomber	4.10.48–11.8.50	Wahn, Germany
13		Photo-reconnaissance	1.9.46–2.52	Ein Shemer, Palestine
14	CX	Shipping strike	1.6.45–31.3.46	Banff
		Bomber	1.4.46–2.51	Wahn, Germany
16	EG	Fighter	19.9.45–10.45	Epinoy
18	WV	Fighter-bomber	15.3.47–4.47	Kabrit, Suez
21	YH	Fighter-bomber	7.43–	Sculthorpe
			9.43 –	Hunsdon
			12.43 –	Gravesend
			4.44 –	Thorney Island
			6.44 –	Rosières-en-Santerre
			2.45 –	Melsbroek, Belgium
			4.45–7.11.47	Gutersloh, Germany
22		Fighter	1.5.46–15.8.46	Seletar, Singapore
23	YP	Intruder & night-fighter	2.7.42–	Bradwell Bay
			12.42–	Luqa, Malta
			9.43–	Sigonella, Italy
			6.44–25.9.45	Little Snoring
			11.9.46	Wittering
			2.47–5.52	Coltishall
25	ZK	Night-fighter	21.10.42–	Church Fenton
			12.43–	Acklington
			2.44–	Coltishall
			10.44–	Castle Camps
			7.45–	Bradwell Bay
			8.45–	Castle Camps
			6.46–	Boxted
			9.46–7.51	West Malling
27		Fighter-bomber	11.4.43–9.3.44	Agartala, India
29	RO	Night-fighter	6.43–	Bradwell Bay
			9.43–	Ford

Squadron No.	Code	Main Role	Period of Use	Bases
29 (cont.)			3.44– 6.44– 4.45– 10.45– 10.50–1.51	Drem Hunsdon Manston West Malling Tangmere
36	DM	Shipping strike	1.10.46–14.10.47	Thorney Island
39		Night-fighter	1949–11.52	Fayid, Egypt
45	OB	Fighter-bomber	29.2.44–12.12.45	Yelahanka, Imdia
47	KU	Fighter-bomber	18.2.45 1.46–21.1.46	Kinmagon, Burma Butterworth, Malaya
55		Fighter-bomber	7.46–1.11.46	Hassani, Greece
58	OT	Photo-reconnaissance	1.10.46 1.53–6.53	Benson Wyton
60(SAAF)		Photo-reconnaissance	1.43– 12.43–15.7.45	Castel Benito, Tripoli San Severo
68	WM	Night-fighter	7.44– 10.44– 3.45–20.4.45	Castle Camps Coltishall Church Fenton
69	WI	Fighter-bomber	8.8.45– 4.46–6.11.47	Cambrai/Epinoy Wahn
81		Photo-reconnaissance	1.9.46–15.12.55	Seletar, Singapore
82	UX	Intruder	4.7.44– 10.45–15.3.46	Kolar, India St Thomas Mount
84	PY	Fighter-bomber	2.45– 9.46–12.46	Chharra, India Seletar
85	VY	Night-fighter	8.42– 5.43– 5.44– 6.45– 10.45– 4.47–10.51	Hunsdon West Malling Swannington Castle Camps Tangmere West Malling
89		Fighter-bomber & night-fighter	2.45– 9.45–30.4.46	Baigachi, Ceylon Seletar, Singapore
96	ZJ	Night-fighter	6.43– 9.44–12.12.44	Church Fenton Odiham
98	VO	Bomber	18.9.45– 3.46–	Melsbroek Wahn, Germany

Squadron No.	Code	Main Role	Period of Use	Bases
98 (cont.)			9.49–	Celle, Germany
			11.50–2.51	Fassberg, Germany
105	GB	Bomber	11.41–	Swanton Morley
			12.41–	Horsham St Faith
			9.42–	Marham
			3.44–	Bourn
			6.45–1.2.46	Upwood
107	OM	Fighter-bomber	1.2.44–	Lasham
			11.45–	Epinoy, France
			11.46–	Gutersloh, Germany
			12.47–4.10.48	Wahn, Germany
108		Night-fighter	16.2.44–24.7.44	Luqa, Malta
109	HS	Bomber	7.42–	Wyton
			7.43–	Marham
			4.44–	Little Staughton
			11.45–	Hemswell
			11.46–	Coningsby
			3.50–7.52	Hemswell
110	VE	Fighter-bomber	1.11.44–	Yelahanka, India
			3.45–	Joari, India
			10.45–	Selatar, Singapore
			12.45–15.4.46	Labuan
114	RT	Fighter-bomber	9.45–1.5.46	Khormaksar, Aden
125	VA	Night-fighter	2.44–	Hurn
			7.44–	Middle Wallop
			10.44–	Coltishall
			4.45–20.11.45	Church Fenton
128	M5	Pathfinder	8.9.44–	Wyton
			6.45–	Warboys
			10.45–	Melsbroek
			3.46–1.4.46	Wahn
139	XD	Bomber	8.6.42–	Horsham St Faith
			9.42–	Marham
			7.43–	Wyton
			2.44–	Upwood
			11.46–	Coningsby
			3.50–11.53	Hemswell
140		Photo-reconnaissance	11.43–	Hartford Bridge
			4.44–	Northolt
			9.44–	Amiens, France

Squadron No.	Code	Main Role	Period of Use	Bases
140 (cont.)			2.45– 9.45–10.11.45	Eindhoven, Holland Fersfield
141	TW	Night-fighter	16.10.43– 12.43– 7.45– 6.46–9.51	Wittering West Raynham Little Snoring Coltishall
142	4H	Bomber	25.10.44–28.9.45	Gransden Lodge
143	NE	Shipping strike	10.44–25.5.45	Banff
151	DZ	Night-fighter	6.4.42– 4.43– 3.44– 9.46– 10.46–10.10.46	Wittering Colerne Predannack Colerne Weston Zoyland
157	RS	Night-fighter	13.12.41– 12.41– 3.43– 3.44– 8.44–16.8.45	Debden Castle Camps Bradwell Bay Valley Swannington
162	CR	Bomber	1.44–25.9.44 8.12.44–14.7.46	Kabrit, Egypt Bourn
163		Bomber	25.1.45–10.8.45	Wyton
169	VI	Night-fighter	2.10.43– 12.43– 6.44–10.8.45	Ayr Little Snoring Great Massingham
176		Night-fighter	14.7.45–31.5.46	Baigachi, India
180	EV	Bomber	9.45–1.4.46	Wahn, Germany
192	DT	Bomber	4.1.42– 4.43– 11.43–22.8.45	Gransden Lodge Feltwell Foulsham
199		Signals	1.52–3.53	Watton
211		Fighter-bomber	6.45–22.2.46	Yelahanka
219	FK	Night-fighter	27.2.44– 5.44– 10.44– 8.45–1.9.46	Honiley Bradwell Bay Amiens Acklington
235	LA	Shipping strike	6.44– 9.44–10.7.45	Portreath Banff

Squadron No.	Code	Main Role	Period of Use	Bases
239	HB	Intruder	11.12.43–1.7.45	West Raynham
248	QM	Shipping strike	10.43– 2.44– 9.44– 7.45– 5.46–30.9.46	Predannack Portreath Banff Chivenor Thorney Island
249	GN	Bomber	2.46–6.46	Eastleigh, Kenya
254	QM	Shipping strike	3.45–5.45	North Coates
255	YD	Night-fighter	1.45– 9.45– 1.46–31.3.46	Rosignano, Italy Hal Far, Malta Gianaclis, Egypt
256	JT	Night-fighter	5.43– 10.43– 4.44– 12.45–5.46	Ford Luqa, Malta La Senia, Italia Deversoir, Iraq
264	PS	Night-fighter	3.5.42– 4.43– 12.43– 5.44– 8.44– 6.45– 11.45– 8.51–12.51	Colerne Predannack Church Fenton Hartford Bridge A8, France Twente Church Fenton Linton-on-Ouse
305(Polish)	SM	Fighter bomber	12.43– 11.44– 3.46– 10.46–6.1.47	Lasham Epinoy/Cambrai Wahn Faldingworth
307(Polish)	EW	Night-fighter	12.42– 8.43– 11.43– 1.45– 8.45–2.1.47	Exeter Predannack Drem Castle Camps Horsham St Faith
333 (Norway)	KK	Photo-reconnaissance	10.5.43–21.11.45	Leuchars
334 (Norway)	AK	Fighter bomber	22.6.45–1952	Oslo, Norway
400		Photo-reconnaissance	12.43– 7.44– 4.45– 7.45– 8.45–7.8.45	Kenley France Germany Copenhagen Luneberg

Squadron No.	Code	Main Role	Period of Use	Bases
404 (RCAF)	EO	Shipping strike	4.4.45–25.5.45	Banff
406 (RCAF)	HU	Night-fighter Intruders	4.44– 9.44– 11.44– 6.45–31.8.45	Winkleigh Colerne Manston Predannack
409 (RCAF)	KP	Night-fighter	3.44– 8.44– 5.45– 6.45–1.7.45	Acklington France Gilze-Rijen, Holland Twente
410(RCAF)	RA	Night-fighter	11.42– 21.2.43– 20.10.43– 9.44– 4.45–9.6.45	Acklington Coleby Grange West Malling France Gilze-Rijen, Holland
418 (RCAF)	TH	Intruder	5.43– 4.44– 8.44– 3.45– 4.45–7.9.45	Ford Holmsley South Hunsdon Coxyde Volkel
456 (RAAF)	RX	Night-fighter	12.42– 3.43– 2.44– 12.44– 3.45–31.5.45	Valley Middle Wallop Ford Church Fenton Bradwell Bay
464 (RAAF)	SB	Fighter-bomber	21.8.43– 12.43 6.44– 2.45– 4.45–25.9.45	Sculthorpe Hunsdon Thorney Island France Melsbroek
487 (RNZAF)	EG	Fighter-bomber	21.8.43– 12.43– 6.44– 2.45– 4.45– 7.45–19.9.45	Sculthorpe Hunsdon Thorney Island France Melsbroek Epinoy
488	ME	Night-fighter	30.6.43– 3.9.43– 5.44– 7.44– 10.44– 11.44– 4.45–26.4.45	Drem Bradwell Bay Zeals Colerne Hunsdon Glisy Gilze-Rijen

Squadron No.	Code	Main Role	Period of Use	Bases
489	P6	Shipping strike	6.45–1.8.45	Banff
500 (Aux.)	RAA	Night-fighter	10.5.47–14.8.48	West Malling
502 (Aux.)	RAC	Bomber Night-fighter	17.7.46–12.47 17.12.47–8.48	Aldergrove
504 (Aux.)	RAD	Night-fighter	5.47– 11.46–7.48	Syerston Hucknall
515	3P	Fighter-bomber	29.2.44–10.6.45	Little Snoring
521		Photo-reconnaissance	19.3.43–31.3.43	Oakington
540	DH	Photo-reconnaissance	19.10.42– 2.44–30.9.46 1.12.47–3.53	Leuchars Benson Benson
544		Photo-reconnaissance	4.43–13.10.45	Benson
571	8K	Bomber	7.4.44– 20.7.45–20.9.45	Oakington Warboys
600 (Aux)	BQ	Night-fighter	1.45– 5.45–21.8.45	Cesanatico, Italy Campoformido
604 (Aux)	NG	Night-fighter	26.4.44– 2.5.44– 13.7.44– 5.8.44– 9.44– 12.44–18.4.45	Church Fenton Hurn Colerne France Predannack Venderville
605 (Aux)	UP	Intruder	3.2.43– 3.43– 10.43– 4.44– 11.44– 3.45– 5.46–7.48	Ford Castle Camps Bradwell Bay Manston Hartford Bridge Belgium Honiley
608 (Aux)	6T	Bomber Night-fighter	1.8.44–24.8.45 1947–8.48	Downham Market Thornaby-on-Tees
609 (Aux.)	RAP	Night-fighter	10.5.46–4.48	Yeadon
613 (Aux)	SY	Fighter-bomber	10.43– 10.44– 11.44–8.8.45	Lasham Hartford Bridge Epinoy
616 (Aux.)	RAW	Night-fighter	11.46–12.48	Finningley

Squadron No.	Code	Main Role	Period of Use	Bases
617		Bomber	30.8.43– 1.44–3.45	Coningsby Woodhall Spa
618	SI	Fighter-bomber	1.4.43– 9.43– 6.44– 12.44–8.45	Skitten Benson Wick Australia
627	AZ	Bomber	12.11.43– 4.44–30.9.45	Oakington Woodhall Spa
680		Photo-reconnaissance	16.2.44– 8.44– 2.45– 8.46–1.9.46	Matariya San Severo, Italy Deversoir, Egypt Ein Shemer, Palestine
681		Photo-reconnaissance	8.43–11.43	Dum Dum, India
684		Photo-reconnaissance	29.9.43– 5.44– 10.45– 1.46–1.9.46	Dum Dum, India Alipore Saigon Don Muang, Bangkok
692	P3	Bomber	1.1.44– 6.45–20.9.45	Graveley Gransden Lodge
1 PRU	LY	Photo-reconnaissance	13.7.41–19.10.42	Benson

Principal Mosquito Training and Support Units

204 AFS	Bomber & fighter-bomber – Cottesmore, Driffield, Brize Norton, Swinderby & Bassingbourn–1953, code FMO
226 OCU	Target towing–4.53 – 8.55
228 OCU	Night-fighter – Leeming 1.5.47 – 1954
229 OCU	Target towing – Chivenor 12.54 – 6.56
231 OCU	Bomber – Bassingbourn 5.47 – 1.50
233 OCU	Target towing 6.55 – 8.56
236 OCU	Target towing 9.52 – 9.54
237 OCU	PR – Leuchars and Benson 7.47 – 8.51
238 OCU	Target towing 10.53 – 2.54
8 OTU	PR – Fraserburgh 11.42, Dyce, Haverfordwest, Benson. Became 237 OCU 31.7.47
13 OTU	Bicester/Finmere 1.44, Harwell, Middleton St George. To 54 OTU 1.5.47
16 OTU	Fighter-bomber & bomber – Upper Heyford/Barford 31.12.44, Cottesmore, code GA. To 204 AFS 3.48
51 OTU	Night-fighter – Cranfield 7.44 to 14.6.45
54 OTU	Night-fighter – Charter Hall 8.44, East Moor. To 13 OTU 1.5.47
60 OTU	Night-fighter & fighter-bomber – High Ercall 17.5.43. To 13 OTU 11.3.45
132 OTU	East Fortune 15.5.44, Haverfordwest, East Fortune code 9Y to 1947 Pathfinder Navigational Training Unit, Upwood and Warboys 6.43 – 1945 Mosquito Conversion Unit, Horsham St Faith 30.8.42. Became 1655 Mosquito Training Unit Marham, Finmere, Marham, Warboys. Became 16 OTU 31.12.44.
1653 HCU	Night-fighter – 3.46 – 12.48

1655 MTU   Bomber – 10.42 – 9.45
1672 MCU   Fighter-bomber – Yellahanka 1.2 44, Kolar, Yellahanka, disbanded 31.8.45
1692 Bomber Support Training Flight, Great Massingham, 17.6.44, code 4X Fighter Interception Unit, code ZQ
1300 Met Flight
1317 Met Flight
1401 Flight 1942
1409 Bomber Flight 1.4.43 – 11.44
CBE Marham – Bomber 9.45 – 3.48
1 CAACU   6.56 – 7.56
3 CAACU   9.52 – 5.57
3/4 CAACU   Exeter 1.53 – 30.11.63
5 CAACU   3.54 – 9.56
APS   Sylt, target towing 9.53 – 4.58

FAA

Squadron	Codes	Main Role	Period of Use	Bases
700		Maintenance	2.46–	Middle Wallop
		Test Pilots' School	1.4.46–5.46	Yeovilton
703	001–045,	Naval Flt of RAF	6.45–	Thorney Island
	031–099	Air-Sea Warfare	25.5.48–	Lee-on-Solent
		Development Unit	19.4.50–10.50	Ford
704		Naval OTU for	11.4.45–	Zeals
		Mosquito	4.9.45–2.12.45	Thorney Island
721		Trials	11–12.45	Archerfield
728	500–535	FRU	9.45–9.52	Hal Far, Malta
733		FRU	11.45–12.45	Ceylon
739	701	Photo Dev. Unit	1.5.47–12.7.50	Culham
751		Radio Warfare Unit	3.52–11.54	Watton
762	450–466	Conversion Unit	8.45–	Halesworth
	470–476		15.1.46–	Ford
		Heavy Twin C.U	1.5.48–8.12.49	Culdrose
770		FRU	7.45–1.10.45	Drem
771	542–545	FRU	20.9.45–1.9.52	Ford, detached from Lee-on-Solent
	550–599			
772	501–509	Northern FRU	5.45–	Ayr
			10.1.46–	Burscough
			3.5.46–	Anthorne
			26.6.47–13.10.48	Arbroath
773		FRU	1.50–3.50	Lee-on-Solent

Squadron	Codes	Main Role	Period of Use	Bases
777		Trials Unit	10.45–12.45	Ford
778	000–042	Service Trials	11.44– 3.1.46– 18.7.47–16.8.48	Arbroath Ford Tangmere
780		Advanced FTU	9.46–12.46	Hinstock
787		Air Fighting Development Unit	3.46–5.48	West Raynham
790	402–414	Target towing	7.46– 13.12.47–15.11.49	Dale Culdrose
811		Naval strike	15.9.45– 6.12.46– 31.3.47–1.7.47	Ford Brawdy Eglinton
Airwork	411–450	Heavy Twin C.U	1.50–9.56	Brawdy
Airwork	418–425	FRU	1.9.52–9.53	Hurn

Mark	Prototype
Identity	W4050
Country	Britain
Location	Salisbury Hall, Herts
Status	Public viewing since 1959

Built at Salisbury Hall in 1940, the aircraft was dismantled and moved to Hatfield by road on 3 November 1940. It was painted yellow overall for easy identification and carried the class B markings E0234, in which form it was flown for the first time by Geoffrey de Havilland Jnr on 25 November. Following initial trials at Hatfield, it was delivered to Boscombe Down on 19 February with camouflaged top surfaces, and by now officially adopted as W4050. Following a ground accident on 24 February, the fuselage was changed for the one built for W4051, the PR prototype. On completion of the change, W4050 was flown back to Hatfield for some adjustments on 14 March, returning to Boscombe Down four days later with the extended engine nacelles fitted for handling trials. Returning to Hatfield on 23 March, and on its 100th flight on 4 May, it flew back to Boscombe Down. The maximum level speed achieved was 392 mph at 22,000 ft with an all-up weight of 16,000 lb, but during further handling tests at Boscombe Down, the fuselage was fractured again in a heavy landing. This time the damage was repaired with an irregular patch on the port side just behind the wing trailing edge, and is still visible today. Service trials were completed on the prototype on 23 May 1941, to be continued on more representative production aircraft.

On return to Hatfield, the prototype was used by de Havilland for stall tests in a number of configurations, and in late October it was grounded for the fitting of the more powerful Merlin 61 engines, flying again in this form on 20 June 1942, attaining an altitude of 40,000 ft on its second flight. Merlin 77s were then fitted with flight trials recommencing on 8 October, and a top speed of 439 mph was achieved in November, the highest by any Mosquito. Development flying of the prototype reduced during 1943, but it did spend a short period with Rolls-Royce from 1 March until 10 June. In 1944 the prototype was grounded and allocated to apprentice ground training. It was then restored statically for the SBAC displays at Radlett in 1946 and 1947, surrounded by a selection of the typical weapons loads. W4050 was declared Cat. E and struck off charge on 21 June 1947 and was stored in various locations until a permanent home was found back at Salisbury Hall, where it was put on public display on 15 May 1959.

Mark	NF.MkII
Identity	HJ711
Country	Britain
Location	Yorkshire Air Museum
Status	Composite rebuild

HJ711 was a NF.MkII built at Hatfield in May 1943 and issued to No. 169 Squadron at Little Snoring coded VI, from where it achieved the first victory for the squadron when a Bf.110 was shot down near Berlin on 30 January 1944. Following only three months' service with the RAF, the aircraft was struck off charge and virtually scrapped. However, the cockpit section was acquired on 29 April 1972 from Blackpool by Tony Agar. Tony started restoring the aircraft single-handed initially, obtaining additional parts from many sources, including the rear fuselage from B.35 RS715 from the MGM Studio store at Borehamwood, a wing from B.XVI PF498/6607M previously used by the civil defence at Chorley, additional wing parts from T.III VA878 at St Davids and engines from NF.30 NT616 which had been scrapped at Cosford. When the restoration task became too large for Tony's domestic garage, it was moved to Elvington in 1986, the home of the Yorkshire Air Museum, and a small team led by Tony continued the work. The latest landmark in this lifelong static restoration was the roll-out from the new hangar at Elvington on 6 September 1996 when it was assembled with the wing to the fuselage, the engines hung and tail fitted, including a tailplane on loan from the de Havilland Heritage. Much detailed work continues, but now the aircraft is structurally complete and standing on its own undercarriage.

on 17 May 1947 before going to 22 MU on 20 September 1950 for maintenance and storage. It was then issued to 204 AFS on 15 July 1951, but went into storage again at 27 MU Shawbury until 15 May 1952 when it was issued to the Home Command Examination Unit (HCEU). After periods at 49 MU from 20 August 1953 and 27 MU from 16 November 1954, it returned to HCEU on 16 December 1955. Its final service duties were with 3 CAACU at Exeter coded Y from 30 April 1959, until it was struck off charge on 31 May 1963 and allocated to the Imperial War Museum for preservation. In order to fit it into the restricted space at South Lambeth, the starboard wing outboard of the engine was sawn off, but retained. In recent years the aircraft has been moved to Duxford where The Fighter Collection plan to return it to flying condition on a long-term basis. However, the re-attachment of the wing will be a challenging repair scheme.

Mark	T.Mk.III
Identity	TW117
Country	Norway
Location	Air Force Museum, Bodo
Status	Public viewing

Mark	T.MkIII
Identity	TV959
Country	Britain
Location	Duxford
Status	Under restoration

T.MkIII TV959 was built at Leavesden in 1945 and delivered to 13 OTU on 29 August 1945. The aircraft then had a varied career, going to No. 266 Squadron on 31 October 1946, 54 OTU on 24 April 1947, 228 OCU

Mosquito T.MkIII TW117 was built at Leavesden in 1946 and delivered to 15 MU at Wroughton on 30 May. It was issued to APS Acklington on 22 July 1947, moving to the Linton-on-Ouse Station Flight on 26 October 1949 where it was coded MS-A. A move was made to 204 AFS on 31 July 1951 and then to No. 58 Squadron at Benson on 28 February 1953 where it was coded OT. TW117 was stored at 48 MU at Hawarden from 30 April 1954, followed by moves to 5 MU at Kemble on 30 September 1956, return to 48 MU on 30 November 1956, and finally 27 MU on 31 July 1958 from where it was issued to 3 CAACU at Exeter on 31 March 1960, coded Z. TW117 was retired to the CFS at Little Rissington, Bucks., on 31 May 1963, where it was flown until being grounded as 7805M. TW117 was dismantled and stored at Henlow, and was moved to the RAF Museum at Hendon for the opening in 1972, but was donated to Norway in October 1991, when B.Mk35 TJ138 replaced TW117 in the Bomber Command Museum display.

Mark	FB.MkVI
Identity	HR621
Country	Australia
Location	Camden Air Museum
Status	Under restoration

Mosquito FB.MkVI HR621 was built by Standard Motors in 1944, and following modification to carry a pair of 'Highball' weapons, including the fitting of an arrester hook, it left by ship to Australia on 31 October 1944, arriving in Melbourne on 23 December. Following preparation for service, HR621 was flown to RAAF Narrowmine near Sydney for training to begin with No. 618 Squadron. However, by May 1945 it was obvious that the squadron would not be needed for operational service, and it was officially disbanded on 21 July, although some personnel and aircraft remained until August while the classified equipment was removed. The remaining aircraft and equipment were disposed of as scrap on site, and HR621 was bought by farmer J. Cutmore, who left it in the open for 25 years, allowing it to deteriorate. The remains were acquired in the early 1970s by G.H. Thomas, who runs the Camden Air Museum, but little more than the cockpit floor, wing centre-section and the metal components had survived. Mr Thomas has now been joined by some enthusiastic and skilled volunteers and considerable progress has been made on a scratch-built fuselage towards an eventual complete static restoration.

* * *

Mark	FB.MkVI
Identity	PZ474
Country	USA
Location	Placentia, California
Status	Restoration

Mosquito FB.MkVI PZ474 was built at Hatfield in early 1945 and delivered to 19 MU at St Athan on 19 April for issue to 80 OTU on 5 May, moving to 132 OTU at East Fortune on 13 June. It was put into storage at 15 MU Wroughton on 18 February 1946, and became part of the batch of Mosquitos sold to the RNZAF on 23 January 1948, arriving at its destination on 15 April. It became NZ2384, but was mostly stored until declared surplus and bought by Aircraft Supplies (NZ) who registered it ZK-BCV for sale overseas. In February 1955 it was flown to the USA, becoming N9909F with the Insurance Finance Corporation, which based PZ474 at Whiteman Park airfield for many years. It was finally cancelled from the register in December 1970, and allowed to deteriorate, the fuselage being cut in two. The remains were bought by James Merizan, who is undertaking a long-term restoration of the aircraft possibly to flying condition.

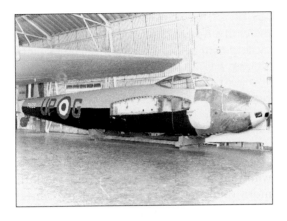

Mark   FB.MkVI
Identity   TA122
Country   Britain
Location   Salisbury Hall, Herts
Status   Fuselage awaiting restoration

FB.MkVI TA122 was built at Hatfield and delivered to 44 MU on 10 March 1945, and issued to 49 ARF ten days later. It was issued to No. 605 Squadron at Coxyde in Belgium on 3 April, moving to Volkel in Holland on 25 April, where No. 605 was renumbered No. 4 Squadron on 31 August, becoming part of 140 Wing based at Gutersloh in November 1946. TA122 was held in 1 BR & SD Pool from 25 November 1948, from where it was reissued to No. 4 Squadron on 13 January 1949 at Wahn and later Celle in Germany. The aircraft was struck off charge on 30 June 1950, and after being used for spares, the fuselage was donated to Delft University in Holland as a training aid. The fuselage was then moved to the Royal Netherlands AF Base at Gilze-Rijen from where it was presented to the Mosquito Aircraft Museum in November 1975, with delivery on 26 February 1978, still carrying the markings UP-G of No. 605/4 Squadron. The plan is to complete the restoration of the ex-Israeli wing of TR.Mk33 TW233 and assemble it to the fuselage of TA122, which will then be restored to represent Gp Capt. Pickard's aircraft lost on the Amiens prison raid on the port side, and TA122 UP-G on the starboard side.

Mark   FB.MkVI
Identity   TE758
Country   New Zealand
Location   Ferrymead Aviation Society, Christchurch
Status   Composite restoration

The basis for this restoration is Mosquito FB.MkVI TE758 with many parts from FB.MkVI HR339, both of which were built by Standard Motors at Coventry. TE758 was delivered to 19 MU at St Athan on 26 August 1945, but was sold to the RNZAF and flown to Pershore for delivery preparations in February 1947. TE758 departed for delivery on 6 March and served with No. 75 Squadron as NZ2328 coded YC-C until retirement in 1956. HR339 had served with nos 487 and 16 squadrons in the RAF before becoming part of the RNZAF order. It departed for its new home on 16 October 1947 to become NZ2382, but there is no record of its service with the RNZAF. The condition of both aircraft was poor when acquired by the Ferrymead Aviation Society, whose members are undertaking this long-term restoration at Harewood airport near Christchurch.

* * *

Mark   FB.MkVI
Identity   TE863
Country   New Zealand
Location   RNZAF Museum, Christchurch
Status   Restoration

Mosquito FB.MkVI TE863 was built by Standard Motors at Coventry and delivered to 27 MU at Shawbury on 22 October 1945. It was issued briefly to the Empire Central Flying School at Hullavington from 17 March to 9 May 1947, before being flown to Pershore for preparation for delivery to the RNZAF. It departed for New Zealand on 22 July to become NZ2355 and was stored until disposed of in the mid-1950s. The remains were acquired by Ted Packer, and using parts from a number of Mosquitos including RF597 he commenced the static restoration. The aircraft then passed to the RNZAF Museum at Wigram in 1985, where the restoration continues.

Mark   FB.MkVI
Identity   NZ2336
Country   New Zealand
Location   Mapua
Status   Privately owned

Mosquito FB.MkVI TE910 was built by Standard Motors in October 1945 and delivered to 27 MU on 19 November where it was put into storage. It was then one of the batch of Mosquitos bought by the RNZAF and flown to Pershore on 12 December 1946 for preparation for delivery, departing on 19 December as NZ2336. Flying at a leisurely pace, NZ2336 reached New Zealand on 3 April 1947, and was delivered to No. 75 Squadron as YC-B on 28 April. It was finally retired in June 1955 and acquired by John Smith, who keeps this original Mosquito in good condition by covering it with a built-on wood and corrugated iron structure.

* * *

Mark   PR.MkIX
Identity   LR480
Country   South Africa
Location   Johannesburg
Status   Public display

Mosquito PR.MkIX LR480 was built at Hatfield and delivered to Benson on 10 November 1943. On 8 June 1944 it was delivered to No. 60 Squadron (SAAF) at Foggia in Italy, its duties being to fly unarmed high altitude photo sorties over the Balkans and Austria. In December 1944 a

record attempt was made to South Africa, but was unsuccessful because damage was incurred en route. The aircraft was later repaired and donated to the South African National Museum of Military History at Saxonwold, where it was displayed elevated in the hangar roof as there was insufficient floor space. Recent inspections have shown that although it has been kept under cover, the high temperatures have caused some deterioration to the wooden structure.

Mark   PR.MkXVI
Identity   A52-600
Country   Australia
Location   RAAF Richmond NSW
Status   Restoration to fly

Mosquito PR.MkXVI NS631 was built at Hatfield in late 1944 and shipped to Australia where it became A52-600. It was issued to No. 87 Squadron, coded SU-A on 1 March 1945 and flew 20 missions. It had completed a total of 321 hr 50 min when it was retired to the Air & Ground Radio School at Ballarat, Victoria, on 21 July 1947. It was disposed of in 1954 and stored in the open for 12 years until acquired by the Warbirds Aviation Museum for restoration. A52-600 was then acquired by the RAAF Museum and the aircraft is currently under a demanding restoration programme to flying condition.

Mark	B.MkXX
Identity	KB336
Country	Canada
Location	National Aeronautical Collection
Status	Public viewing

Mosquito B.MkXX KB336 was built by de Havilland Aircraft of Canada at Downsview for operation in Britain, but was transferred to the RCAF in June 1944 for service with 36 OTU in the training and conversion role. It was retired to the Service Repair Depot at Moncton on 22 June 1945, and became ground instruction airframe A535 on 8 October 1946. KB336 was moved to Calgary on 7 September 1961, and was allocated to the National Aeronautical Collection on 6 February 1964, where it is now on public display.

* * *

Mark	FB.Mk26
Identity	KA114
Country	Canada
Location	Richmond, BC
Status	Stored

Mosquito FB.Mk26 KA114 was built by de Havilland Canada at Downsview and delivered to the RCAF on 22 February 1945 for service with 7 OTU at Digby, Nova Scotia. It was struck off charge on 13 April 1948 and later discovered on a farm in Alberta with the fuselage in very poor condition but a good wing. It was recovered and is in long-term store with the Canadian Museum of Flight and Transportation.

Mark	NF.Mk30
Identity	MB24
Country	Belgium
Location	Musée de l'Armée
Status	Public viewing

This rare night-fighter version of the Mosquito was built at Leavesden in early 1945 as NF.30 RK952. It was delivered to 218 MU on 25 May 1945 and moved to 10 MU on 11 July for storage, never serving with the RAF. It was sold to Belgium in October 1951 as an attrition replacement aircraft, and was delivered in mid-1953 as MB24. This Mosquito was issued to No. 10 Squadron coded ND-N until 18 August 1955 when all Mosquitos except MB24 were grounded at Beauvechain. MB24 continued to fly until all the Belgian Mosquito night-fighters were struck off charge on 17 October 1956, and MB24 was allocated for preservation in the Brussels Air Museum. Restoration work is currently under way to try and re-equip the cockpit, which was stripped out some years ago in an abortive restoration, and many of the parts lost.

* * *

Mark	PR.Mk34
Identity	RG300
Country	USA
Location	Confederate Air Force
Status	Stored

Parts of a Mosquito consisting of engine nacelles and undercarriage, possibly RG300, are believed to have been with the CAF since the late 1970s.

Mark　　PR.Mk35
Identity　RS700
Country　Canada
Location　Calgary Aerospace Museum, Alberta
Status　　Stored

Mosquito B.Mk35 RS700 was built by Airspeed at Christchurch and delivered to 37 MU on 25 November 1946. Following moves to 9 and 19 MUs, RS700 was delivered to Leavesden for conversion to the PR.Mk35 configuration and delivered to No. 58 Squadron at Benson in early 1952. It was withdrawn to 22 MU at Silloth on 30 April 1954 and sold to Spartan Air Services in December. RS700 was delivered to Burnaston for conversion by Derby Aviation for photo survey, and flown to Canada in late 1955 as CF-HMS. Following its service on aerial survey work it was retired and in 1972 was acquired by the Centennial Planetarium for restoration, possibly to flying condition. It was transferred to No. 410 Squadron at Cold Lake for the restoration to start, but it is believed little progress has been made.

Mark　　B.Mk35
Identity　RS709
Country　USA
Location　USAF Museum, Dayton, Ohio
Status　　Public viewing

RS709 was built as a B.Mk35 by Airspeed at Christchurch in early 1946 and delivered to 15 MU at Wroughton near Swindon for storage until May 1952. It was then flown to Sywell for Brooklands Aviation to undertake the conversion to a TT.Mk35. Following this conversion, the

aircraft was delivered to 236 OCU in September 1952, and two years later it was flown to 27 MU at Shawbury for storage and maintenance. It was issued to 3 CAACU at Exeter on 7 June 1956 and coded 47. RS709 was declared surplus in May 1963, and bought by the Mirisch Film Corporation on 11 July for use in the film *633 Squadron* being made at Bovingdon. It was registered G-ASKA and camouflaged, with the fictitious squadron code HT-B. On completion of the filming, RS709 was acquired by Peter Thomas for his Skyfame Museum at Staverton. He later sold the aircraft to Ed Jurist of New York who flew it to Harlingen in Texas, the home of the Confederate Air Force. However, due to engine problems RS709 did not fly in Texas and was bought by Yesterday's Air Force in California, which in turn sold it to the late Doug Arnold. It was returned to Britain and based at Blackbushe. It was not long before this much-travelled Mosquito was crossing the North Atlantic again, this time on its last journey. It was bought from Doug Arnold by the USAF Museum and delivered to Wright-Patterson AFB in February 1985. RS709 has been restored to represent a PR.MkXVI used for weather reconnaissance in advance of bombing attacks, and is in the markings of the 653rd Bomb Squadron, 25th Bomb Group, who were based at RAF Watton from 1944 to 1945.

Mark　　B.Mk35
Identity　RS712
Country　USA
Location　EAA Museum, Oshkosh, Wisconsin
Status　　Public access

Mosquito B.Mk35 RS712 was built by Airspeed at Christchurch, and following storage with the RAF it was delivered to Sywell on 30 November

1951 for conversion to a TT.Mk35 by Brooklands Aviation, which was completed in May 1952. It was then delivered to 27 MU at Shawbury for storage, until issued to 1 CAACU at Hornchurch on 31 December 1953. In March 1958 a move was made to the Armament Practice School at Schleswigland followed by delivery to 3 CAACU at Exeter on 29 April 1958. RS712 was transferred to Flying Training Command on 30 June 1961 and was then retired to 27 MU, from where it was bought by Mirisch Films as G-ASKB on 31 July 1961. It was one of the stars in both *633 Squadron* and the later *Mosquito Squadron*, both made at Bovingdon, and on completion it was stored at Henlow and West Malling, where it was maintained by Short Bros. With its filming career over, RS712 was bought for the Strathallan Museum in September 1972, and flown there on 8 November 1975. However, with the closure of that collection, RS712 was put up for sale and acquired by Kermit Weeks of Florida. The aircraft was flown to Booker for maintenance, and following some airshow appearances around Britain, including in formation with T.MkIII RR299, the delivery to America took place in September 1987, where it is registered N35MK. It is believed that the aircraft has not flown since mid-1990 and therefore is not currently airworthy.

Mark   B.Mk35
Identity TA634
Country   Britain
Location Salisbury Hall, Herts
Status   Public viewing

Mosquito B.Mk35 TA634 was one of the last to be built at Hatfield in 1945 and was originally delivered into storage at 27 MU on 14 April. It was later modified to the B(TT) Mk35 configuration at Sywell for target towing, entering service with 4 CAACU in November 1953. A move was made to the HQ 2nd TAF in March 1956 and its final service was with 3 CAACU at Exeter from September 1959 until its retirement flight to Speke Airport at Liverpool on 6 November 1963. The Mosquito was stored in a hangar pending its incorporation in a new terminal building, but this never happened, and TA634 was flown in the making of the film *Mosquito Squadron* at Bovingdon during June and July 1968. It was returned to Liverpool on 16 July, making its last flight, and bringing total flying time to 742 hrs 50 min. The Mosquito was kindly donated to the Mosquito Aircraft Museum by the Liverpool Corporation, the formal handover being on 15 May 1971. The aircraft was kept outside for a number of years, but suffered from the British climate, and with the construction of the new hangar was brought under cover for a ten-year restoration programme to start. It has been completed to represent a Mosquito B.MkXVI of the Light Night Striking Force in the markings carried by ML963 with No. 571 Squadron at Oakington.

Mark   B.Mk35
Identity TA639
Country   Britain
Location Cosford Aerospace Museum
Status   Public viewing

Mosquito B.Mk35 TA639 was built at Hatfield in 1945 and delivered to 27 MU on 16 April for storage. It was flown to Sywell in May 1952 for conversion to target towing by Brooklands Aviation, following which it was issued to the Aldergrove TT Flight in September 1954. A return was made to 27 MU in June 1958 for storage until issued to 3 CAACU on 30 September 1959, coded 50. On retirement

TA639 was flown to the Central Flying School on 7 June 1963 and was later allocated maintenance number 7806M. The aircraft was moved to the RAF Museum store at Henlow on 5 July 1967, and later transferred for public display at the Aerospace Museum at Cosford, where it is well looked after by local volunteers.

* * *

Mark	B.Mk35
Identity	TA717
Country	Canada
Location	Mission, BC
Status	Stored pending restoration

Mosquito B.Mk 35 TA717 was built at Hatfield in 1945 and delivered to 44 MU at Edzell on 7 July for storage. It was delivered to Martin Hearn in February 1948 and then moved to 15 MU Wroughton on 27 April. TA717 was bought by Cloux Clan Imports of the USA in May 1956, following which it was used for photo survey work in Mexico as XB-TOX. It was later abandoned near Mexico City airport and left to rot in the damaging climate; it was also accessible to vandals. Eventually the deterioration caused the fuselage to break. In the late 1970s the remains were acquired by Mike Meaker and taken to Canada for eventual rebuild, but to date there does not appear to have been any progress with the restoration of this aircraft.

Mark	B.Mk35
Identity	TA719
Country	Britain
Location	IWM, Duxford
Status	Public viewing

Mosquito B.Mk35 TA719 was built at Hatfield in 1945, and stored at various maintenance units until delivered to Sywell on 15 August

1953 for conversion by Brooklands Aviation to a TT.Mk35. On completion it was delivered to 22 MU, from where it was issued to 3 CAACU on 30 June 1954, coded 56. TA719 continued in service at Exeter until it was retired on 31 March 1963. It was flown to Bovingdon for the film *633 Squadron*, following which it was acquired by the Skyfame Museum on 31 July 1963. The plan was to keep this aircraft airworthy, but it was badly damaged in a deadstick landing at Staverton on 27 July 1964. TA719 was abandoned on the airfield, with the arrival of RS709, but when the latter aircraft was sold in the USA, TA719 was brought inside and repaired for static display. With the closure of the Skyfame Museum the Mosquito was moved to Duxford in 1978, where some further restoration has taken place.

* * *

Mark	B.Mk35
Identity	TH998
Country	USA
Location	Silver Hill, Maryland
Status	Stored

Mosquito B.Mk35 was built at Hatfield in 1945 and delivered to 27 MU for storage on 26 August. On 14 May 1952 it was flown to Brooklands Aviation for conversion to a TT.Mk35, and after completion was delivered to 3 CAACU on 30 September. After nearly ten years of target towing, TH998 was withdrawn from service and delivered to 60 MU at Leconfield on 31 May 1962. On 31 August it was declared surplus and donated to the National Air & Space Museum in Washington DC, where it is stored pending the availability of suitable display space.

* * *

Mark	B.Mk35
Identity	TJ118
Country	Britain
Location	Salisbury Hall, Herts
Status	Nose under restoration

Mosquito B.Mk35 TJ118 was built at Hatfield in mid-1945 and was delivered for storage at

27 MU Shawbury on 7 September, where it remained until delivered to Brooklands Aviation on 3 April 1952 for conversion to the target tug configuration. Following completion as a TT.Mk35 on 28 August, the aircraft was delivered to 3 CAACU at Exeter on 30 September, with whom it continued to operate until a return to 27 MU on 31 May 1957. TJ118 was reissued to 3 CAACU on 31 October 1959 but was written off in an accident and struck off charge on 18 September 1961 for use as spares. The fuselage was acquired for film work with *633 Squadron* in 1963, the nose being cut off and sectioned for close-up cockpit scenes. The nose was rescued in 1973 for the Mosquito Aircraft Museum, and after a number of attempts at restoration to a mobile exhibit, work is expected to start off-site soon to complete this long-term restoration.

Mark	B.Mk35
Identity	TJ138
Country	Britain
Location	RAF Museum, Hendon
Status	Public display

Mosquito B.Mk35 TJ138 was built at Hatfield in 1945 and delivered to 27 MU for storage on 28 August 1945. It was flown to Martlesham Heath on 11 February 1948, but returned to 27 MU on 24 May. TJ138 was then delivered to No. 98 Squadron on 31 October 1950 with the code VO, the only preserved Mk35 to serve in the bombing role before conversion to TT.Mk35. It was withdrawn from No. 98 Squadron to 38 MU on 28 February 1951 for storage, and was

then delivered to Sywell on 15 July 1953 for conversion to the target-towing configuration by Brooklands Aviation. On completion TJ138 was delivered to 5 CAACU on 16 March 1954, where it remained until flying to 27 MU on 15 June 1959, where it was retired on 5 July, to become 7607M at 71 MU Bicester. It was then earmarked for preservation and taken into the care of the enthusiastic volunteers at RAF Colerne. When that museum closed, TJ138 was moved to the RAF Finningley collection, until that also was closed, and then to storage at Swinderby. This Mosquito was then moved to St Athan for preparation for display in the RAF Museum Bomber Command display, where it was delivered in February 1992, replacing T.MkIII TW117.

* * *

Mark	B.Mk35
Identity	VP189
Country	Canada
Location	Edmonton Aviation Heritage Centre
Status	Public display

Although this aircraft no longer looks the part, it was built as B.Mk35 VP189 by Airspeed at Christchurch in 1947. It was delivered to 22 MU at Silloth for storage, and was then bought by Spartan Air Services in Canada as CF-HMQ. VP189 was ferried to Derby Aviation at Burnaston for preparation as a photo survey aircraft and then delivered to Canada. During its service with Spartan, VP189 was operated in Kenya as VP-KOM, and following retirement in 1966, it was acquired by No. 418 (Reserve) Squadron RCAF and put on display at RCAF Base Nameo in May 1973, painted to represent FB.MkVI VA114 TH-F. However, exposure to the elements and vandals resulted in the aircraft being close to scrap, but after care and some restoration work by Mr Bill Harvey, in 1993 the Alberta Aviation Museum Association offered to undertake the full static restoration of this aircraft. It was estimated that some 7,000 man hours and Can $52,000 would be required, which would include the conversion from the bomber configuration to the fighter-bomber, which included a flat windscreen, relocation of the crew entry door, and modification of the nose to incorporate the guns. The engines and propellers are now the only sign that this was once a Mosquito bomber. With the restoration completed the Mosquito was rolled out at the Edmonton Aviation Heritage Centre on 23 September 1995 as HR147 TH-Z, representing the Mosquito FB.MkVI flown by Sqn Ldr Russ Bannock RCAF (rtd), who with his navigator R. Bruce accounted for nine enemy aircraft and 19 V-1s during the Second World War. The aircraft is now preserved under cover as a permanent memorial to the aircrew of No. 418 Squadron who failed to return from active duties with the squadron.

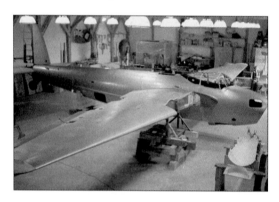

Mark	B.Mk35
Identity	VR796
Country	Canada
Location	White Rock, BC
Status	Stored, pending sale

Mosquito B.Mk35 VR796 was built by Airspeed at Christchurch in 1947 and delivered to 22MU at Silloth for storage on 15 June 1948. Unlike many of the other surviving Mk35s, it was not converted to a target tug, but sold to Spartan Air Services in Canada on 16 December 1954 as CF-HML. Before delivery to Canada, it was flown to Derby Aviation at Burnaston, where it was converted for mapping duties and delivered on 26 April 1955. On

retirement from Spartan, the aircraft was donated to No. 647 Squadron Canadian ATC, who then sold it to Don Campbell for restoration to flying condition. The aircraft was moved some 2,000 miles to British Columbia, but progress was slow, and it was sold to Ed Zalesky in 1985. Ed and his family have continued to restore and maintain VR796 to flying condition, but have run out of space and resource to continue. The rebuild is estimated to be about 85 per cent complete with the woodwork restored, and all the parts and systems available. This Mosquito has been advertised in *Trade A Plane* for US $1.2 as part of a lot including other aircraft.

* * *

Mark	PR.Mk41
Identity	A52-319
Country	Australia
Location	War Memorial Museum
Status	Public display

Mosquito A52-319 was originally built at Bankstown as an FB.Mk40 A52-210, but converted on the production line to a PR.Mk41. It was delivered to No. 2 Aircraft Depot at Richmond on 12 February 1945, following which it was flown to No. 3 Aircraft Depot for long-term storage. On 20 March 1953 it was purchased by Captain J. Woods who registered it VH-WAD as an entry in the London to Christchurch Air Race. However, the aircraft was withdrawn due to lack of finance and stored in the open at Perth. It was then believed to have been bought by an American collector, and dismantled and moved to Melbourne where it continued to deteriorate, and never left Australia. In 1979 the aircraft was acquired by the Australian War Memorial Museum, and following full restoration by Hawker de Havilland at Bankstown with the help of the War Memorial staff has been put on permanent public display since 1994, where the restoration continues at the Treloar Centre at Mitchell in Canberra.

Mark   T.Mk43
Identity   NZ2305
Country   New Zealand
Location   Museum of Transport &
             Technology, Auckland
Status   Restoration for public viewing

Built by de Havilland Australia at Bankstown as FB.Mk40 A52-19, this aircraft was modified on the production line to become T.Mk43 A52-1053. It was accepted by the RAAF on 6 August 1946 and delivered to No. 3 Aircraft Depot at Archerfield, Queensland, for storage. On 18 December it was sold to the RNZAF as NZ2305 and was flown by No. 75 Squadron from 1 April 1947 until retirement in 1952 when it was disposed of to a Marton farmer, who eventually donated NZ2305 to the Museum of Transport & Technology. Among the challenging restoration was the rejoining of the wings, undertaken by the RNZAF Museum in Christchurch.

Mark   T.Mk43
Identity   NZ2308
Country   New Zealand
Location   Auckland
Status   Rebuild to fly

Mosquito NZ2308 was initially built by de Havilland Australia at Bankstown near Sydney as FB.40 A52-20, but was completed as T.43 A52-1054 in August 1946. It was soon sold to the RNZAF and delivered to Ohakea on 10 June 1947 where it became NZ2308 coded YC-Z with No. 75 Squadron. After flying 479 hrs 35 min it was declared surplus on 30 June 1955, and sold to an orchard equipment company, finishing up derelict on a farm. The surviving metal parts were acquired by Glyn Powell in New Zealand, and he is undertaking the challenging task of rebuilding the aircraft to fly, and since the surviving woodwork was useless, he has started by constructing new fuselage moulds from timber, over which the two halves can be formed.

Mark   Bomber/PR
Identity
Country   Australia
Location   Greenock, SA
Status   Kit of parts for static rebuild by
             Lincoln Nitschke

(This listing and data was prepared with the help of Ian Thirsk.)

INDEX